BLUE MURDER
'CHELSEA TILL I DIE'

MARK WORRALL

BASED ON A TRUE STORY
Certain names and places have been changed

HEAD-HUNTER BOOKS

FIRST PUBLISHED IN FEBRUARY 2007
BY HEAD-HUNTER BOOKS

Copyright © 2007 Mark Worrell

ISBN 978-1-906085-01-8

HEAD-HUNTER BOOKS

Cover Concept : Cheeky Fella
Rear Cover Photograph : JoJo Gorman
Website Design : Amanda Sage

Printed in Great Britain by Creative Print and Design

Foreword | *by Martin King*

I've been going to Chelsea now for just over 45 years. I really have seen the highs and the lows. The highs being our F.A. Cup final replay win at Old Trafford against Leeds Utd in 1970 to our European Cup Winners triumph in Athens and then in Stockholm. To more recently our League Cup and F.A. Cup wins and in the last few seasons our back to back Premiership crowns. The lows, me being one of only fifteen thousand fans watching us play York City at home in 1975, where in that season we played the likes of Bristol Rovers, Oldham, and Notts County and finished a miserable 11th. I first went to Stamford Bridge as a, 5 year old boy with my dad and we stood at the back of 'The Shed' near the Bovril entrance. One of the first games that I remember was against Spurs in front of, nearly fifty eight thousand fans, but we lost that day 3-2, with Jimmy Greaves scoring one of our goals before he jumped ship and became one of them. That season Spurs lifted the First Division title with Sheffield Wednesday in runners-up spot with Wolves 3rd and Burnley in 4th. How times have changed? Then into the mid- sixties where I watched Venables, Bridges and Tambling followed by the likes of Osgood, Hudson, Hollins, Chopper Harris and my hero Charlie Cooke. Around this time saw the birth of the Skinhead movement and with it came, the fashion of shaved heads with the cut in partings, Harrington jackets, Jungle Greens, Levi-Sta-Pest, Ben Sherman shirts, Crombie overcoats, Pork Pie hats and Dr Martens boots. The music was Blue Beat and Ska and black and white youth mixed without prejudice. Born from this new working class culture was the football gangs or firms. Chelsea's mob in them early days was The Shed Boys, while rivals Tottenham had The Park Lane and West ham and Arsenal had their North Banks This new phenomenon quickly grew and nearly every football club across the land (except Watford) had their own firm which would defend its territory and its clubs name and honour. With all this came the evolution of faster, cheaper and a more reliable train network. Football fans could now travel to away games and reach other parts of the country now, within hours instead of days. My first away trip out of London to watch The Blues play was a trip up to the Midlands to watch us play at West Bromwich Albion. I was 13 years old and went with two mates from school. On that trip I vividly remember being one of hundreds of young Skins dressed up to the nines ready to give those Northern Monkeys a lesson in respect and fashion sense. We were giving it large and thought we were invincible. We all stuck together; there was a common bond a sense of unity. I felt a part of something. The next home game back at The Bridge I noticed lots of faces who'd been on that trip up to The Hawthorns. I didn't know their names or even where they lived, but they'd nod and I'd nod back. If you were lucky you'd get a "alright mate?" There was always a hierarchy and a pecking order within the firm but if one of the main faces like, Eccles Jesus, Premo, Prof, Babs, Hicky, or Skitzy gave as much as a nod or an hello, it made your day and lifted you up that order. You were someone now, amongst your group of friends. In the late 80s and early 90s the police carried out dawn raids on various known faces from various clubs, in a clampdown on football hooliganism. The order it seems had come from high up within the British government, and the message sent out was, that enough was enough and that the football hooligan like Trade unionists, Ship builders and Steel Workers should have war raged upon them and be wiped out, it was, we were led to believe, for the good of society and the country as whole. Many known faces on the football scene were arrested in these televised dawn raids and stood trial. A good few of them received prison sentences to match those handed out to a murderer or armed bank robber. But as time passed it came to light that some of the police officers involved in the cases had been less then honest and in getting a conviction had falsified and fabricated parts of the evidence presented at the original trial. Those in jail were released and had their sentences quashed and received huge payouts in the way of compensation. A couple of the boys headed to Thailand and opened up a bar with the bags of cash courtesy of the Met.

As I say, I've been going to Chelsea for along long time and I've met and know a lot of people and a lot of people know me. I most have nodded or even have spoken to the likes of Johnny Nipper and Chopper Lewis some where along the line. We certainly mixed in the same circles by the sounds of it. One things for sure they'd be my kind of people.

This book is dedicated to Chelsea Gate 17 and the North Surrey Mafia, real people in an unreal world.

Acknowledgements

I'd like to personally thank Martin King at Head Hunter. Dave 'hurry up' Johnstone at cfc-UK and Peter Sampson at cfc.net for their ongoing support of my literary efforts. Martin Knight … a diamond geezer. The inspirational John King. Long Way Round Pete for the helpful travel advice. Lord Dicky Milham of Chelsea. Riddler Rowan for his colourful refinement of the English language. Lucky Jamie for the daily 'one liners' … remember to stop at a winner son. On the manor: Hatchet Walters, Five Card Charlie, Richard D, Chopper L, Terry the Slice … he's Craigs brother.Brother Craig he aint heavy he's my brother, Chris the Hand, Cousin Graham, Cousin Steve, Sex Case Clive, Nipper, Growler Fowler and his best mate Animal Magic Morris. Billy the Dog, Nigel Firestarter, Little Mark, Bin Lid Bertie, Fuck Off Colin and his lad Ian, Dangerous Kev, Dave the Undertaker, Chiller Chillman. Off the manor; Sir Larry Thakkar, Sergeant Barnes and Ugly John. Mark Fernandez, Zanzibar is the best beach shack on the planet … you know that! JoJo Gorman … a proper treacle. Mum, so are you. Thank you for the music :- Pink Floyd, Count Bishops, Junior Murvin, Sex Pistols, Clash, Stranglers, X-Ray Spex, Penetration, Bananarama, Cliff Richard, Mel & Kim, Ce Ce Rogers, Maze, A Guy Called Gerald, Raze, The The, Olive, The Verve, Alex Reece, Kenny Bobien, Eric Prydz, Rui Da Silva, Ron Carroll, Masters At Work, Johnny Nash, Soul Providers, KC & The Sunshine Band. The movers and shakers; McClaren, Westwood, Strange, Sallon, Rampling, Bates, Harding and Abramovich. The Chelsea chronicles of the late legendary Ron Hockings. One Bar Regulars and denizens of Gate 17: Ossie (no relation), Young Dave, Hip Hop Dan, Big Chris you should cut down on your pork life mate and get some exercise.The lantern jawed Salisbury Rog, Lemon, Baby Gap Brian, All right Pav, Chicken Plucker, Vegas Dave and Princess Tara. The little acorns … Lewis Allen, Billy Walters, Deon Broughton, Joshua Fair, Madeline Johnson and Ben Gray. Tom Slattery, Angelo 'boom boom' LaCivita and Spanish Ken … hands across the ocean. Finally, none of this would have happened without a certain lemon squeezer called Gus Mears whose bright idea it was to form a football club called Chelsea all those years ago.Cheers mate.

www.overlandandsea.net

Prologue | *January 2005*

BACK TO ESCOBAR

'If you do what you have always done … then you'll get what you have always got.' Chopper's voice was calm, authoritative, and poised on the cusp of pretentiousness and honesty.

'Thanks for that mate … here, let me buy you another beer,' replied Nipper sarcastically, shrugging his shoulders and momentarily looking away from the heavy teak framed mirror that adorned the wall behind the bar. Whether he liked it or not he knew that there was some merit in Chopper Lewis' remark.

'Two bottles of your finest Kingfisher Mr Hernandez please,' he drawled, reaching across to accept a Wills Classic from the shack owner before refocusing his attention on the reflection of his own face in the mirror. Jaded blue eyes, a trellis of burst blood capillaries that resembled stained glass windows, were set in ominously dark loops of shadow. Evidence enough, not that it was needed, that endless days of drink and drug fuelled melancholic introspection were beginning to take their toll on his appearance.

'It's not a sin to be skint … but it's a sin to look skint', sniggered Chopper, pushing his Zippo lighter along the rough wooden surface of the bar. 'That's what Tommy Philips, God rest his soul, always used to say,' he continued, wondering how long it would take his old acquaintance to respond with some of the dazzling wit and repartee for which he was renown.

Nipper picked up the lighter and with a deft flick of the wrist lit the cigarette Mr Hernandez had given him. As he did so, he looked down and grimaced at the state of his own apparel. A grubby sweat stained wife-beater string vest and threadbare faded denim cut off jeans hung from his sinewy nut brown tanned body, and his grimy feet were encased in a well worn pair of Jesus sandals. Robinson Crusoe personified.

Good enough, he thought to himself, rubbing at the stubble on the back of his shaven head, a smile replacing the frown at the thought that his ramshackle appearance would draw little attention from anyone … particularly the snap happy tourists that congregated here at the Escobar beach shack each evening to watch the sunset.

'I'll tell you what else Tommy Philips used to say as well,' replied Nipper, turning to face Chopper and flicking cigarette ash over the washed out Stone Island T-shirt his equally dishevelled looking friend was wearing. 'He's a lovely geezer that Chopper Lewis … but he couldn't dress a salad'.

'80 roops boss,' said Mr Hernandez, interrupting the entertaining verbal small arms fire the two men were engaging in, and placing two large bottles of Kingfisher beer on the bar directly in front of Nipper. 'Will you be watching the Chelsea match up at the Cave later?' he asked, smiling as Nipper glanced at his watch and nodded before rummaging in his pocket and handing over a wrinkled 100 rupee note.

'Keep the change Mr Hernandez,' said Nipper, pausing to take a long swig of beer before continuing. 'What time is kick off?'

'6.30pm … which is 1pm back at home,' volunteered Chopper, before Mr Hernandez had a chance to reply.

'We've got half an hour,' muttered Nipper, double checking the time and walking away from the bar to the front of the shack.

'Dunno what's getting at him these days, eh Mr Hernandez,' tutted Chopper, pushing his fingers through the shock of tousled silver hair that adorned his head as he watched Nipper kick off his sandals and skip down the steps at the front of the shack that led directly onto the beach. 'He's been here a month, and he still seems as edgy as a leper contemplating another day of high winds.'

Mr Hernandez smiled at the analogy. 'Sometimes it's best not to ask,' he replied sagely, whilst trying not to laugh at Chopper's hair which, having been caught by a sudden gust of wind, resembled a grey squirrel that had leapt on him from the branch of an overhanging palm tree and was now struggling enthusiastically to retain its balance.

★ ★ ★ ★ ★

Nipper stood at the waters edge enjoying the quicksand sensation as the Arabian Sea ebbed and flowed gently over his bare feet, drawing away with it the fine grains of sand lodged between his toes. He looked up at the early evening sky, a pale blue canvas suffused with myriad mauves at its highest point, and a vague glow of orange shot through with blood red streaks at its lowest.

'Fucking beautiful … but what's the point when it's all come on top,' he sighed, watching the sun as it began to disappear over the horizon creating the illusion that it was sinking into the serene, deep blue expanse that stretched out before him.

'Remember when you were young, you shone like the sun … shine on you crazy diamond.'

Nipper picked up on the words of the Pink Floyd classic that was playing out on the expensive sound system that Mr Hernandez had recently installed at his shack. The track would be almost thirty years old now, but it stood up well against the more modern soulful funky vibes that the patrons of Escobar were accustomed to. Floyd tracks were regularly rinsed into the eclectic mixes of old and new music that guest DJ's spun on the ones and twos here when Mr Hernandez held one of his fabled 'full moon' parties.

Chopper mentioning Tommy Philips had set the windmills of Nipper's troubled mind in motion. Since his arrival in Goa just over a month ago, he'd made a reasonable fist of throwing an alcoholic, drug infused blanket over his past in the forlorn hope that it would blur and fade from memory. This however was proving difficult, and the panic attacks that blighted his more sober moments were getting worse by the day.

Tommy Philips was buried out here, as was his son Pete who had been a teenaged Nipper's best friend. Peter Philips, the original crazy diamond. That Floyd song could have been written about him, thought Nipper as he mouthed the familiar lyrics.

'Come on you target for far away laughter, come on you stranger, you legend, you martyr, and shine!'

And if Pete had been radio rental, what did that make the small, perfectly formed creature that was Tommy's daughter Holly? Nipper's love for her had been like an addictive poison, from the first lick he'd craved the next hit. She'd engulfed his body like an inhuman virus, sucking at his heart and coursing through his bloodstream with such vigour it had made his veins glow.

'Fuck it!' cursed Nipper, shaking his head. No matter how far he travelled, no matter what 'medicine' he prescribed himself, he just couldn't shake the disease. Holly Philips had been his companion, guru, confidante, sexual trapeze artist, personal shopper and drinking partner, all rolled into one size eight, little black dress wearing, coke snorting package.

They say that love is blind, but as far as Nipper was concerned it was deaf and mute as well. Together, he and Holly had created their own world. A world as separate from the real one as Narnia. The trouble was, this idyllic world had soon became hard bitten, crime ridden, drug tainted, corrupt and populated by the type of people that parents never warned their children about, because quite simply they couldn't bring themselves to believe in their existence … and that was well before they'd opened what was to become the most upfront happening club in London. Hysteria … now that place had a lot to answer for.

'Sunglasses cleaning?'

Just as his kamikaze dive into the past was about to become emotional, Nipper was distracted by the expectant, entrepreneurial attentiveness of Utpal, the young lad Mr Hernandez employed as shack gofer.

'I aint got em with me son,' he replied, grinning as he patted the boy on the head. Utpal looked crestfallen, a frown replacing the dazzling toothy smile that had previously lit up his impish face.

'Tomorrow?' he implored, putting in his pocket the cloth and small phial of cleaning fluid that he had been brandishing at Nipper.

'Okay tomorrow.'

'Promise?'

'Promise.'

'Tomorrow … tomorrow … tomorrow … sunglasses cleaning for Mr Nipper tomorrow.'

Nipper laughed as he watched Utpal whirl like a dervish in front of him before regaining his composure and approaching a young couple who, judging by the ghostly pallor of their skin, had just arrived in Goa.

Barely ten years old, Utpal wasn't a native of Goa. He was from the southern Indian state of Karnataka, and like most of the other boys employed by the shack owners along this stretch of Baga Beach, had arrived along with the rest of his family in search of work in Goa's burgeoning tourism industry.

From dawn until dusk Utpal would be at the beck and call of those people that chose to make free use of the sunloungers on the section of beach directly in front of the shack. Taking peoples food and drink orders kept him busy most of the time, whilst during the slack periods he would offer a variety of services which included the cleaning of sunglasses and shoes and the running of errands. As if this wasn't enough, and providing you were prepared to take the risk, Utpal would cut your hair for a very modest 50 rupees; included in the tariff was the 'free' removal of earwax.

Nipper had never seen anyone take Utpal up on this particular offer, although thinking about it he wondered if Chopper's interesting coiffure mightn't have been the result of an encounter with the boys scissors at some point in the not too distant past. How Utpal had happened on the novel pairing of a haircut and earwax removal was anyone's guess, and the very concept made him smile.

'Tomorrow Utpal,' shouted Nipper, waiting for the boy to acknowledge him, before he turned on his heels and strode purposefully back up the beach towards Three Toes Lane, where the Cave was located.

★ ★ ★ ★ ★

'How are we doing mate? I see it's still 0-0,' said Nipper, glancing up at the Cave's wall mounted TV screen as he carried a chair over to the table where Chopper Lewis was strategically sat on the bars alfresco red brick veranda.

The veranda backed onto Three Toes Lane and was generally at its busiest in the small hours of the morning when revellers would congregate there for one last drink or six after leaving the beachfront club Café Rambo.

'Playing well mate,' replied Chopper, chinking beer bottles with Nipper who was now sat beside him and continuing with his summary. 'The conditions are fucking awful, look at it ... pissing down with rain ... Terry's marshalling the back four well and Lamp's is looking the business in midfield. I reckon it's gonna take a mistake or a flash of genius to win this one though. 0-0 away at Liverpool ... you'd take that wouldn't you eh Nipper?'

'Depends mate, we've won all of our Christmas fixtures so far ... be nice to keep the ball rolling at Anfield though wouldn't it eh. Oooh go on Robben my son ... ooh fuck me that was close.' Nipper's response was fractured by the sight of Chelsea's live wire Dutch winger Arjen Robben latching onto a Tiago pass and rifling the ball straight at the Liverpool goalkeeper Dudek.

Nipper took a healthy swig of beer and sparked up another Wills. It was 7pm and at last his New Years Eve hangover was beginning to fade away. Averting his gaze momentarily from the TV screen, he glanced furtively up and down what was a relatively quiet Three Toes Lane .

Several taxi drivers were pitching for fares from holidaymakers who looked as weary of the walk from beach to hotel, as they were of the cries of 'come look my shop ... cheaper than Asda', which greeted them as they walked past the various emporiums that lined both sides of the narrow dusty track.

'Bollocks you cunt!' exclaimed Chopper, immediately drawing Nipper's attention back to the footballing matters at hand.

'Nah ... yer havin a bubble aintcha,' growled Nipper, in the best cockney accent he could muster as he stared up at the TV screen which was now blank.

Despite the fact that Goa was advanced enough to have its own mobile phone network and cable TV franchise, it was still susceptible to one of the most infuriating facets of third world country life ... the power cut.

'Fucking tweekers.' The whirring of an automatic camera shutter, and its accompanying flash, served to further agitate Nipper who shaded his eyes as he turned around and peered through the gathering darkness at the couple who were sat at the far end of the veranda. It was the same couple that Utpal had turned his attention to on the beach an hour or so earlier.

'Easy tiger,' breathed Chopper, looking over his shoulder at the happy pair who were giggling excitably, blissfully unaware of the effect their presence and actions were having on Nipper. 'That's exactly what they are son,' he continued, unravelling his friends colloquialism. 'Tweekers, two-weekers! Holidaymakers, not Old Bill, the paparazzi or anyone else for that matter ... you've gotta calm down mate, remember this is Goa not the Smoke.'

'That's easy for you to say mate innit,' whispered Nipper, tilting his head from side to side and frowning. 'You've been out here for nearly eight years, the filth back in Blighty have most probably closed their files on you.'

'Yeah maybe, but people know I'm here ... so I've still gotta be careful haven't I,' replied Chopper, huffily pulling a copy of the Navhind Times, Goa's English language daily newspaper, across the table. 'Ere look at this,' he continued, picking it up and flicking at the front page headline which read, *Tsunami, death-toll reaches 100,000.* 'You've had a right touch telling people you might go to Thailand if it all came on top. Loads of Brits have been killed there, and loads more are missing ... most probably including one Johnny Nipper.'

'Yes mate, I know that. It's fucking shocking that a scumbag like me should profit from misery like that.' Nipper's reply was plausibly profound, and as he continued to speak, the deepening timbre of his voice reflected the serious nature of the set of circumstances that had led to him being forced to lower his profile. 'The thing is my mug could accidentally turn up in the background of some tweekers holiday snaps, or worse still one of those poxy picture messages that people send with their camera phones ... you never know who might see em. I aint paranoid mate, but I've made my bed with dirty linen, and for the time being I'm gonna have to lie on it.'

'If you lie down with dogs ... you get fleas,' grinned Chopper, trivialising the situation and motioning the waiter to bring over another two bottles of beer.

'Yeah, you know it mate … but you aint familiar with the full story,' replied Nipper, scratching at his chest with both hands as his mood lightened. Chopper's liberal use of proverbs never ceased to amuse him, and being in his company was slowly chipping away at the rust called anxiety that had spread like a cancer under the paint of his demeanour in recent weeks.

'D'ya wanna tell me the full story then?' asked an expectant Chopper. 'I'm a good listener,' he continued, tossing the paper back onto the table and reaching out his arm to pat Nipper on the back.

Nipper looked at Chopper with a raised left eyebrow but didn't reply. Suddenly he found himself mulling over the prospect of what might become of him if he decided to play dead and keep a low profile here in Goa. If he chose to do this, what type of person would he become?

The Westerners that came to live in Goa could generally be divided into two very distinct camps. In the red corner; the emotional castaways, bruised lost souls who harboured tales of broken dreams and came seeking redemption. Nah, not me, thought Nipper.

In the blue corner; those people who, at some point during a past visit, had been redeemed and had chosen to smugly while away their dotage in this tropical paradise. Nah, they were tossers.

Of course there were some notable exceptions. The trust fund hedonists; trustafarians as they were mockingly referred to by the denizens of the red corner. These were the 'dropouts' from polite society who grew their hair, got their noses pierced and spent their days smoking dope and marvelling at how far 'daddies money' went in this old colonial outpost. Wankers!

Then there were the entrepreneurs. Bar owners, restaurateurs and shopkeepers from odd sounding places like Wivelsfield Green, Poringland, and Ashton in Makerfield. All of them arrived believing that they couldn't fail in a country where property, labour, and commodities were plentiful and cheap. The fact of the matter was that the majority of start-ups here fell foul of local laws and customs.

Ultimately they folded because the proprietors of these fledgling enterprises had forgotten the key reason why people holidayed in Goa. It was a reputable low budget holiday destination. To put it simply, there weren't enough rupee's to go around. In time, those that were successful found themselves in the blue corner … and those that failed returned home, or worse still pitched up in the red corner.

Last, and certainly by no means least, there were the genuine characters.

People like his old mate Chopper Lewis, whose life stories were the stuff of legend, often verging on being spectacularly ridiculous.

★ ★ ★ ★ ★

Nipper had first encountered Solomon 'Chopper' Lewis on the terraces at Stamford Bridge in the early 1980s. The home of Chelsea Football Club was an altogether different place in those days. Today's glacial modernity, in which over 40,000 souls regularly gathered to watch a money-no-object assemblage of multi-racial stars playing the likes of Barcelona and Bayern Munich in the Champions League, was once a ramshackle, crumbling affair whose home end, aptly named the Shed, was the stomping ground of a notorious hooligan gang called the Chelsea Head Hunters and a fertile territory for the dissemination of hard right politics.

In 1982 there was no sign of the nouveau riche, 'where were you when we were shit?' Chelsea fans, like Peter Prawn-Sandwich from Kensington, or Johnny and Joanna Come-Lately from Surbiton. Chelsea were a very ordinary Second Division side plying their trade in front of a few thousand diehards against teams like Cambridge United, Wrexham and Grimsby Town. It was under this heavy blanket of complete mediocrity that true friendships were forged amongst Blues supporters, friendships that endured right through until the present day.

That season, Chelsea suffered a humiliating 6-0 defeat away at mighty Rotherham. On his way out of the ground, Nipper, who'd arrived late for kick off and had watched proceedings from a side paddock, encountered Solly Lewis engaging in a furious verbal spat with a mounted policeman intent on barring his way back to the side-street where he'd parked the Ford Granada he'd stolen the previous evening to facilitate the journey north.

'Leave it out son,' Nipper had said, tugging on Solly's collar as the policeman went to draw his truncheon. 'Let's go round the other way ... I'll come with you mate. It aint worth getting nicked for this ... come on.'

Solly had seen sense. One hour later, having given up on trying to find their way through the dark labyrinth of muggers cul-de-sacs that surrounded Millmoor they were forging their way south in a maroon Vauxhall Viva which, unfortunately for its owner, had been left unlocked in the car park outside a working men's club where the two men had nervously tarried for a couple of lager tops.

Nipper had been impressed.

'You touch the dogs arse well,' he'd remarked, praising his newfound friend with the underworld slang for the criminal offence which the Queens Constabulary generally referred to as 'taking and driving away'.

'Chopper' was an evocative appellation, but few ever dared ask about its origins. Most assumed that because of the Chelsea connection, it was in some way related to the sobriquet Solomon Lewis shared with the clubs highest ever appearance maker, legendary hard tackling defender Ron Harris.

Tweeker girls that Solly had entertained during his sojourn in Goa assumed that he was known as Chopper because of his sexual prowess, and the allegedly fearsome size of his manhood.

Those that partied with Chopper believed the epithet had been bestowed on him because of his penchant for 'chopping out' more than just the occasional chubby white line of the old 'devils dandruff'.

The truth, however, was one step removed from behaviour that was considered law abiding by a police force, which in 1997, the time of Solomon's nickname earning misdemeanour, believed that the unruly element who had blighted England's national game for many years were well under control.

In 1997, on their way to winning the FA Cup, Chelsea had been drawn to play Wimbledon in the semi-final of the competition. The victors of this tie would play either Middlesboro, or that seasons giant killers, Third Division Chesterfield.

It had been 15 years since Solly Lewis and Nipper had first enjoyed the pleasure of each others company following the Rotherham debacle. In the seasons that followed Solly had 'sorted out' the travel arrangements for many a Chelsea away game. Despite earning the respect of his peer group, by virtue of his ability to cost- effectively get them from A to B, he'd often lamented the fact that the limelight always belonged to the terrace legends.

Scrappers like Ronny Cutlass, Duncan Disorderly, Fuck Off Colin, Topper Townsend and Belfast Billy, regularly earned the plaudits from Nipper and the rest of the boys when anecdotal war stories were being told in their old pre-match Kings Road drinker, Come the Revolution. It was there, following Chelsea's 3-0 demolition of Wimbledon at Highbury, that the conversation had focussed itself on the potential mischief to be had at Wembley with the Boro Frontline, the hooligan element of their most likely cup final opponents, Middlesboro.

The blame for the hostile rivalry between two clubs, separated geographically by a long tortuous journey along the length of the A1, could be laid at the door of the mandarins at the Lancaster Gate headquarters of the Football Association whom, in their infinite wisdom, had contrived the concept of the promotion playoff.

In 1988 Chelsea became the first and only top flight side to be relegated via the playoffs following a 2-1 aggregate defeat at the hands of promotion chasing Boro. There had been the usual run of the mill trouble at Ayresome Park in the first leg, a match which Chelsea had lost 2-0, but nothing too serious.

In the return leg at the Bridge, a Gordon Durie goal had given the majority of a crowd in excess of 40,000 some hope. The final whistle however came with the score still at 1-0, and the pot, filled to the brim with Chelsea supporters bubbling with anger and resentment, boiled over.

Belfast Billy and Duncan Disorderly had led a well orchestrated pitch invasion from the Shed terrace, whilst Fuck Off Colin and his cohorts had made an assault, via the West Stand benches, into the North Stand where the Boro fans were corralled. The violence that ensued was widely reported in the media, and the FA had bowed to government pressure eventually forcing the Chelsea chairman, Ken Bates, to close the terraces at Stamford Bridge for the first six games of the following season.

In subsequent fixtures between the two clubs, including their 1991 meeting at Wembley in the final of the much maligned Zenith Data Systems Cup, there had been disorder, and it would have been a foolish man who'd suggested that hostilities would not be renewed should the teams meet once more at the famous old stadium.

To make things even more interesting, Chesterfield had played out a thrilling 3-3 draw with Middlesboro at Old Trafford, meaning that because Boro were involved in a Coca Cola Cup Final replay the following week, Chelsea would have to wait almost a fortnight to find out the name of their Wembley opponents.

Much of the discussion at Chelsea's home game with Leicester City on the Saturday following the semi-final victory had concerned the news that had filtered south about a new firm to be reckoned with. A firm that had just made a very large blip on the hooligan radar screen. Chesterfield, a team who went by the whimsical nickname of the Spireites, and averaged gates of 3,000, was home to a lunatic fringe who had given themselves the trouser browning moniker of the Bastard Squad.

The Chesterfield Bastard Squad had given a surprised Boro Frontline a good run for their money at Old Trafford, and with plenty of time to plan a repeat performance, it was odds on that the replay, which would take place at Sheffield Wednesday's Hillsborough stadium, would also provide a platform for a lively off-field encounter. Such was the concern of the local authority, all South Yorkshire Police leave had been cancelled on April 22nd, the day of the replay.

There had been a few eyebrows raised when Solomon Lewis had suggested a 'Trojan horse' style attack on the top boys of both the

Frontline and the Bastard Squad, who according to various postings on the internet were going to meet for an early evening fracas at a Sheffield pub called the Barracks Tavern which was located on the Penistone Road. The pub had been chosen because it was far enough away from the stadium to be disregarded by police surveillance teams.

'You're a fuckin roll and butter son', Nipper had remembered Riddler Rowan saying to Solly. 'A proper nutter. You stick to thieving jam jars ... pull a stroke like that and Old Bill will feel that Moschino collar of yours good and proper ... and besides the games on a fuckin Tuesday night, it would mean playing truant from work'.

On the morning of the match, having failed to canvass any support for his incendiary idea, Solomon Lewis hotwired a Jaguar XJS that he'd found conveniently unlocked in the car-park at the Wimbledon branch of B&Q and drove north to Sheffield. Even now, Nipper could remember the unnerving phone-call he'd received at 4pm that afternoon from Solly, who having found the Barracks Arms easily enough, had set up base camp in a nearby burger bar.

'Yes mate, you know that ... I'm gonna go in there, wait till they kick it off, and then drop a can of CS gas in the middle of em. I was gonna leave it at that, but this motor I nicked outside of B&Q this morning had a lovely new set of Spear & Jackson tools in the boot.'

'What sort of tools?'

'A garden rake, a spade, a pitchfork ... and a very impressive looking axe.'

'Fuck me Solly! Riddler Rowan was right about you ... you're six enchiladas short of a fiesta, proper mum and dad. In fact you're stark raving bonkers mate. You'll either end up killing someone, or getting killed yourself.'

'Nah ... leave it out, I aint mad. Listen mate, I've gotta go and buy a gas mask, speak to ya later.'

'Yeah be lucky.'

Be lucky! ... Nipper had shaken his head in dismay. He couldn't believe that Solly would go through with his plan. If he did, he'd need more than luck. He'd need a small miracle. For a start there was the small matter of how he was going to avoid drawing attention to himself. Solly was a sharp dresser, and Nipper figured that a man wearing Gucci loafers, carrying a pitchfork, and asking for a lager top in a gas mask muffled cockney accent, would be as conspicuous as a giraffe wearing Raybans trying to gain admission to a polar bears golf club.

If the earlier phone-call had been unsettling, then the one he'd received just as he'd sat down to watch live TV coverage of the replay that evening had resulted in Nipper reaching for the skunk and the Rizla papers slightly earlier than usual.

'They was having a stand off across the bar ... just shoutin and swearin at each other, in the end I got bored and went and had a line of the old Gianluca. When I come back that's when I done it.'

'Done what?' Nipper had enquired, tutting as he'd struggled to hear Solly above the sound of sirens wailing in the background.

'First I gassed em, and then as they started panicking, I went in and gave em all a few whacks with the flat end of the axe. Spear & Jackson mate ... they're the tools to trust ... you know that.'

'You're a fuckin tool Solomon. Where the fuck are you now? It sounds like World War Three up there.'

'Hiding mate! You wouldn't Adam and Eve it, but some cunt has only gone and nicked my Jag.'

'What fuckin Jag?'

'The one I nicked this morning to get up here soppy bollocks.'

'Quality mate ... Well I'd stay hidden until after the match kicks off. Ere you didn't tell anyone you was Chels did ya?

'Course not. Whaddya think I am ... stupid?'

★ ★ ★ ★ ★

Nipper's reminiscences were curtailed by the restoration of electrical power. As the TV flickered back into life, just in time for the start of the second half of the Liverpool – Chelsea match, he suddenly felt the urge to laugh.

'Blinding, about time too ... Come on the Chels!' growled Chopper, banging the flat of his right hand down hard on the table and then clenching it into a fist. 'Oi, oi ... what are you laughing at then? ... Cheered up then have we?' he continued, as he moved his chair back into a position where he could watch the game without getting a crick in his neck.

'I was just musing over the time you metamorphosed from being plain old Solomon Lewis into the almost legendary Chopper Lewis. Fucking quality son,' chuckled Nipper, reaching for another Wills. 'Priceless ... the last home game of that season ... Leeds, I think ... yeah Leeds. The whole of the ground was chanting yer name ... *One Chopper Lewis ... there's only one Chopper Lewis.* By the time the next season had started you'd already become a storybook hero who'd given Old Bill the slip, and depending on which drinker people used, was living the good life with Ronny Biggs in Rio, selling Persian rugs in Ibiza, or running a moody bar in Thailand.'

'Persian rugs … cheeky fuckers, fancy people thinking I was a drug dealer … oooh go on Robben … look it takes three Scousers to stop him,' whooped Chopper, re-focussing his attention on the match as an inch perfect Makalele pass sent the flying Dutchman racing towards the Liverpool goal.

'He's got his own chant now Robben … fucking sweet and all,' said Nipper, pausing mid-sentence to take a long drag on the cigarette that was drooping borstal-style from the corner of his mouth.

'Well come on then,' replied an expectant Chopper.

'Do you remember the old Robin Hood theme? Y'know, *Robin Hood, Robin Hood riding through the glade* … and all that bollocks.'

'Yes mate … C'mon, c'mon then.'

'Check this out my son,' said Nipper, clearing his throat before bursting confidently into song. '*Robben's good, Robben's good … running down the wing. Robben's good, Robben's good … hear the Chelsea sing. He's got no hair, we don't fucking care … Robben's good, Robben's good Robben's good.*'

'That's fucking brilliant mate, best ever,' said Chopper shaking Nipper's hand. Three further renditions of the verse resulted in the two men attracting a puzzled audience of several stray dogs who sat at the entrance to the Cave, heads cocked quizzically to one side, listening and trying to understand before howling in what seemed like appreciative unison at the conclusion of the impromptu concert.

'I'd give Joey Cole a go, Duffer's run his legs off. Look he's knackered,' observed Nipper, pointing at the top right-hand corner of the TV screen.

Chelsea were trying at every opportunity to slow down the tempo of what had become an absorbing game and the strain of so many fixtures over a short space of time was beginning to show on some of their players. Chopper nodded at Nipper's suggestion, and then a couple of minutes later patted him on the back when Chelsea manager Jose Mourinho effected the desired substitution with just a quarter of an hour remaining on the clock.

'I reckon we can win this mate … come on Chelsea,' squawked Chopper, as the Blues won their first corner of the second half with just ten minutes left.

'Wicked corner Robben!' exclaimed Nipper, as the ball was swung in across the penalty area. 'Nice one Glen … nice one boy,' he continued, as Chelsea's young defender Glen Johnson headed the ball back from his far-post position into the path of Joe Cole who was loitering with intent on the edge of the penalty area.

'Go on Joey … FUCKING HIT IT SON!' screamed Chopper in encouragement.

'GOAL!' yelled both men simultaneously, jumping up and punching the air as the ball, precisely leathered by Cole, ricocheted off a pair of red stocking clad legs into the back of the Liverpool net.

The last few minutes of the game saw nails nervously bitten and cigarettes chain smoked, as Chelsea continued to repel Liverpool's frantic efforts to secure an equaliser.

'We've won this mate,' grimaced Nipper looking skywards, wondering if he was tempting fate as the Chelsea keeper Petr Cech pulled off an outstanding save from an unmarked Garcia's free header.

'C'mon ref … that's enough … YES!' The referee blew the final whistle as Chopper was speaking.

'Fancy a celebratory live'ner mate?'

Chopper's question was rhetorical.

'You holding then?' replied Nipper, shaking his head and sniggering at Chopper's antiquated turn of phrase.

Back in the naughty '90s 'having a live'ner', live being pronounced as if it were part of the word alive, was terrace slang for snorting a cheeky line of cocaine.

'Course I'm holding … What are you laughing at, you piss taking cunt?'

'You of course … You sound like Topper Townsend, he still calls em live'ner's.'

'Topper Townsend ha ha ha,' said Chopper, rocking back on his chair. 'That's a name to reckon with. Topper always had to 'top' everything you'd done. Been there, seen it, drank it, shagged it, and bought the fucking T-shirt … all before you. If you said you'd been to Tenerife … Topper, well he'd look you in the eye and say he'd been to Elevenerife. On my life, what a cunt! Now listen son, I don't care what you call it now … Charlie, Pram, Nikki bleedin Lauda, Gak, Flake, Percy, Shovel, Posh, Bugle, Beak, Chisel, Gian fucking Luca, Chang, Nose, Chubby, Sparkle, Spin, Disco Dust, or any one of eight South American fucking countries prefixing the words marching and powder … I've heard it all. For me, for once … and once only, I'll stick with Topper on this topic. It's a fucking live'ner … now do you want one or not?'

'Be rude not to mate.' Nipper shrugged his shoulders, giggling as he reached under the table and accepted the folded paper packet that Chopper pressed into his hand. Part of him was disappointed. One of the items on his mental check list of self improving New Years resolutions was about to be discarded on January 1st.

'Gonna give it up then were you?' said Chopper, earnestly second guessing his friend.

'Yeah. I had it pencilled in,' retorted Nipper sarcastically, patting

Chopper on the back as he got up to go to the toilet. 'Lemme see, it's half way down the first page of my list. Look, right there ... in-between giving up smoking and reading my entire back catalogue of those brilliant cfc-UK fanzines that I've brought with me.'

Cocaine was the ultimate quick fix for Nipper. A line provided him with the self confidence, comfort and pleasure he sought. It wasn't really a habit, but after one hit he was ready for more.

★ ★ ★ ★ ★

'The fucking mosquito's in that khazi, bloody nightmare,' cursed Nipper, slapping at his legs as he returned to the table.

'You taking the old Malaria tablets then my son?' enquired Chopper, motioning Nipper to keep hold of the packet of coke he was in the process of handing back to him.

'Nah mate, they make me feel sick,' replied Nipper rubbing at his nose, sniffing and shaking his head all at the same time.

'They might make you feel sick mate ... but Malaria will make you feel a fuck of a lot sicker,' was the cheerless riposte.

'Oh yeah Doc ... and I suppose you're taking em everyday eh, nah you've got so much gear flowing around your system ... if a mozzy bites you it'll probably die of an overdose ... and that's my insurance as well ha ha ... blimey this gear is livelier than anything I've had since I've been here ... yeah ... ooh nice ... fucking hell mate!' The words tumbled in freefall fashion out of Nipper's mouth faster than he could assemble them sensibly together, but he wasn't about to complain.

'I keep the best stuff for myself son,' said Chopper, standing up and patting the back pocket of his jeans. 'Right come on then, lets head back ... get freshened up and go down to the shack. Mr Hernandez is having a soiree for those Russian birds who are heading home the day after tomorrow ... one of em is gonna get lucky tonight.'

'Two of em mate.' Nipper clapped his hands and laughed as he stood up. So much for keeping a low profile he thought to himself, as his new found, chemically propelled, ebullient mood overwhelmed him.

★ ★ ★ ★ ★

The midday sun slanted through the crevices in the wooden window shutters that opened out onto the balcony of Nipper's hotel room. With the one eye he had just fractionally opened, he lazily scanned the room endeavouring as he did so to piece together the events of the previous evening.

There was no escaping the damning evidence of the noxious lifestyle he despaired about but continued to live. Laid on its side by his bed was an empty bottle of Officers Choice whisky. Next to that was an ashtray brimful of stinking cigarette ends,whose sight and smell made Nipper retched and swallow hard to contain the bile that was rising from his stomach. With his mouth desiccated by the effects of prolonged licentious drug use, the act of swallowing caused him to wince in pain and swear loudly.

'You're a fucking cunt Nipper!' he rasped, cursing himself in a voice not unlike that of the devil when it possessed the soul of the poor helpless girl Regan in the film the Exorcist. 'Oh no not that as well, for fucks sake,' he continued, opening both eyes and glancing down at his groin.

Hurriedly hauling himself out of bed, Nipper stumbled into the bathroom. 'Oops,' he said, standing stock still and bollock naked in front of the toilet. Despite showing obvious signs of ageing, the mirror tiles behind the waist high cistern were still reflective enough to confirm the precise nature of his problem.

'Two eyes looking down ... one eye looking straight back up, ha!' he said indignantly, trying to underplay the situation. As he walked back into the bedroom, Nipper likened himself to one of those priapic mythological beasts whose bronze sculptures were available to buy from many of the stalls at the local flea markets.

'Ann Widdecombe, Christine Hamilton, Ann Robinson, Condoleezza Rice, Margaret Thatcher ... er Dot Cotton ... nah she was a babe once ha ha ha,' he guffawed, conjuring up images of countless old harridans in a vain attempt to persuade the increasingly uncomfortable erection he'd woken up with to subside.

'That blokes a bloody nightmare, he gets me at it every-time,' he continued, shaking his head and muttering as he espied the source of his penile problem, a small blister pack of tablets lying on the bedside table next to a rolled up 100 rupee note.

'Fuck it ... not a whole one, shit!' Nipper picked up the pack and looked at the familiar blue coloured diamond shaped pills. Sildenafil citrate ... generic viagra. Illegally manufactured and marketed under a variety of names in India, just half of one of these 100mg tablets was all that was required to swiftly counter possible impotence brought on through an evening of prolonged alcohol and substance abuse.

The rupee equivalent of £8 could buy you a carton containing 40 tablets from any local chemist without prescription. The club scene back in the UK had been the first to embrace the rejuvenating powers of the drug, and with a street price often as high as £10 per tablet, you didn't need to be Carol Vorderman to work out the high margins to be made if you could find a way of shipping the 'blue fellas' back home in bulk.

Chopper Lewis had done the maths himself several years ago following an uplifting encounter with a liberated young Irish nurse called Rosie that he'd met at a popular local hippy hangout called the Shore Bar. Nipper recalled Chopper explaining to him over the phone how Rosie had suggested that they double drop Ecstasy and viagra, and how impressed he'd been with the results.

'It redefines the 'up' element of that whole 'Loved Up' thing mate,' he'd said. 'You could go large with these in that Hysteria club of yours, I've just gotta figure a way to get it over to you in London.'

And figure it out was exactly what Chopper did. Viagra became his livelihood. Sourcing the mighty blue diamonds was easy enough as they were readily available from any chemist in bulk and no prescription was required. Safe transit back to Nipper in London had been assured when Chopper had struck up an arrangement with a regular conquest, an air hostess called Mimi who worked for one of the charter airlines that flew the Goa route regularly. Mimi was a Hysteria raver and known to both Nipper and Holly Philips.

It was easy money all round. When the twenty odd cartons that Mimi was safely able to smuggle back to the UK on each of her return trips became insufficient to meet the enthusiastic demand, her best friend and fellow air hostess Senga became a willing accomplice.

It was all coming back to Nipper now as his powers of recollection improved with every waking minute. 'Go on mate ... have a whole one ... in fact fuck it, have a whole packet', he'd remembered Chopper saying to him as they'd partied with the Russian girls at Escobar last night. 'That Olga birds well up for it ... just make sure you are too son', he'd continued, crumbling a tablet into Chopper's vodka tonic and encouraging him to down it in one whilst he'd pushed the packet containing the three remaining tablets into the back pocket of his jeans.

'Fuck it ... yeah the Russian's,' muttered Nipper, delving into the corners of his frazzled mind. Cor, that Olga was a peanut covered in chocolate ... a proper treat. She'd definitely have got it, he thought to himself, before mentally cursing the fact that he couldn't keep his minds eye trained on the less than libidinous virtues of the women he'd thought of earlier.

'So you are vaking now yes ... Meezter e Neeper?'

'Who the fucks that?' exclaimed a startled Nipper, wheeling round and squinting as the shutters to the balcony opened and the room was suddenly bathed in brilliant sunshine.

'You av forgotten me already ... surely not beeg boy,' came the husky reply.

'Olga ... fucking hell it's you!' he gasped, the relief in his voice palpable.

'Eet is very clear zat you are pleased I am still here ees eet not Meezter e Neeper?' she breathed, the towel that she had wrapped around her body falling to the floor as she pulled the shutters closed behind her and walked towards him. Fucking lovely, he thought as he sat on the edge of the bed and marvelled at the vision of flaxen haired, golden skinned femininity that was gliding gracefully towards him.

'I make it vith you four times in ze night and steel you are unsatisfied ... you Eengleesh boys are so, how you say it? ... Hornee da da ... so horneeee,' she continued, dropping gently to her knees in front of the bed and reaching her right hand out to grasp his throbbing rod of currently uncomfortable joy.

'Ouch, Olga ... be careful ... ooohh, ahhh.'

The pain Nipper felt initially was soon replaced by spine tingling pleasure as Olga, without any need for encouragement, began to give him one of the best blow jobs of his life. Her oral devotion was well practised, and Nipper was soon in throes of an orgasm which he sincerely hoped would alleviate his problem.

★ ★ ★ ★ ★

'Right lets have a look at this ... yeah good, very good ... now go and get me a couple of bottles of Kingfisher and get yourself a cold drink.' Nipper spoke hesitantly to the boy as he checked the quality of his workmanship before nodding his approval.

'Yes Mr Nipper,' replied Utpal, his face beaming with precocious enthusiasm. 'Drinks 80 rupees, sunglasses cleaning 10 rupees ... 100 rupees altogether, you pay later.'

'Yeah Utpal ... and you can clean Mr Chopper's glasses as well when you come back since that leaves me 10 roops in credit.' Nipper shook his head and laughed as he watched the boy skip and bound his way up the beach towards the shack. Somehow he felt better today. Up until last night, Goa's ambient and calming environment had done little to remedy his depression which had deepened over the last week as the scorching personal analysis of his life, that he'd undertaken with such coruscating honesty soon after his arrival, had led him to believe that he had lost the plot slightly, and was now harvesting the unwelcome fruits of the bad seeds he had sown over the past few years.

He'd tried to fathom it out as he'd made his way down to the beach earlier that afternoon. Maybe it was something to do with the advent of the New Year ... rebirth, regeneration and all that superstitious old bollocks; maybe it was the dawning of the realisation that Chelsea might actually win the league this season; he'd have to sneak back to England to see that if it ever looked like happening wouldn't he.

Of course it was quite possible that it could just be down to last nights revelling and the frantic coupling with Olga that had followed. What a blessed release that had been. Whatever it was, Nipper suddenly felt the overwhelming urge to share his troubles with someone, and who better than Chopper, a man for whom the elusive concept of being sane had ceased to trouble him from the very day that he'd walked into the Barracks Arms in Sheffield back in 1997.

'Well lets have it then,' said Chopper, licking his cracked lips in anticipation as he spotted Utpal making his way back down the beach carrying two bottles of ice cold Kingfisher.

'Have what mate?' retorted Nipper, quizzically arching his left eyebrow.

'The full story. The love, the sex, the drugs, the deals ... start to finish. You never answered me yesterday when I asked you if you wanted to talk about it.'

'What are you, a bleedin psychic ... or some sort of trick cyclist?'

'Nah mate. I aint no mind-reader and I certainly aint no psychiatrist,' replied Chopper, waving at Utpal before continuing. 'But I've been out here long enough now though to know when someone wants to get something off their chest. It's come on top for you. I mean let's be honest mate, them panic attacks you've been getting lately are hardly about the state of secondary school education in Worcester Park now are they?'

'Yeah, yeah ... a problem aired is a problem shared and all that bollocks eh,' lamented Nipper, lighting his first Wills of the day and tossing the cigarette packet across to his friend. 'So how long have you got then eh?' he continued, coughing slightly as the harsh smoke filled his lungs.

'All the time in the world mate,' replied Chopper calmly. 'All the time in the fucking world. So come on my friend, it's time to unburden your mind.'

PART ONE

1

June 1976

THE SPICE OF LIFE

'They said that Ferguson, the Cardiff City centre forward, toe poked the ball from a good thirty yards out, and that it hit a divot before skimming off the Arsenal keeper Lewis and rolling over the line.' Pete Philips loved it, sitting in front of his friends taking the piss about this, that, and Arsenal football club in particular. 'D'ya know what?' he continued, his expletive riddled dialogue adding to the humour. 'The fucking wanker only blamed his new jersey. He said that the ball had slipped between his chest and his hands because the shirt had not been washed, and the wool was consequently non stick ... what a cunt! Yeah, 1927 what a great year.'

Danny Green and Nipper roared their approval.

'Blinding stuff ha ha,' laughed Danny, struggling to get the words out of his mouth. '1927, the only time the FA Cup has ever left England and it was all down to the Gooners and a Teflon goalies shirt. Mugs.'

★ ★ ★ ★ ★

As Nipper was listening to the story, he glanced around the bar and looked at each of his three acquaintances in turn. She was there of course, Pete's younger sister Holly. Not the red lipped, stiletto heeled vixen that you'd be familiar with today; oh no, back then she was just another fed up teenage schoolgirl with peachy skin and a glowing complexion.

A fifteen year old girl whom, through an unfortunate set of family circumstances, found herself doing her schooling in Scotland far away from the bright lights and buzz of London's West End about which her brother, two years her senior, would write to her regularly. Holly couldn't wait for the summer holidays. She didn't really know anyone in London, but this didn't matter because she was more than happy to spend her time in the company of her brother and his friends.

Nipper didn't mind, secretly he was quite smitten by her, hanging onto her every word as earlier that evening she'd vividly described her end of term train journey south.

'The rolling fields were becoming more and more parched in appearance and the rivers were running dry,' she'd said, imaginatively describing the effects of what was turning out to be a scorcher of a summer as they'd made their way out of Leicester Square tube station. The atmosphere inside the tube station had been oppressive and there had been little respite outside, the stifling heat almost mugging them into a sweaty submission as they'd made their way along Charing Cross Road.

The metaphorical bushfire that Nipper knew was burning in all their throats could only be extinguished by the ice cold lager served in the Spice of Life, and by the time they'd reached their chosen destination, the fire burning inside him was raging almost out of control. Its flames fanned by the sight and sound of Holly Philips.

The Spice of Life was a home from home. Its location at Cambridge Circus, where Shaftesbury Avenue bisects the Charing Cross Road on the fringes of Soho, had made it popular with generations of stylish youth tribes. It was in the main downstairs bar some twenty years earlier, that a flash young larrikin by the name of Tommy Philips had spent a large proportion of his wages on a regular basis, and his son Pete had every intention of keeping up the family tradition, albeit upstairs where there was a pool table and a jukebox. Here, provided you were reasonably discreet, you could get away with smoking the odd reefer and Pete Philips generally wasted little time in skinning up.

With Holly still at school, and none of the boys in regular employment, money was scarce, but there always seemed to be just enough for a night out. Mates, beer, fags, pool and music. Happy days, thought Nipper. Oh, and one last thing, as long as you had enough put by to watch the Chels on a Saturday then that was all that mattered.

'Come along, come along, come along and sing this song … were the boys in blue, Division Two … and we wont be here for long.'

Mid table, in the old second division that's where they'd finished in May … fuck it.

If Pete, Danny and Nipper had Chelsea, Holly had herself. She was going through that narcissistic pubescent girl phase. A germ free adolescent, obsessed with maintaining her petite figure, cleansing her alabaster skin and grooming her shoulder length jet black mane of hair. Holly didn't think of herself as being beautiful, but Pete was always telling her that she was a real looker, sometimes too often for her own liking.

Pete was popular enough with the girls though. His great cheekbones and intense, Western movie blue eyes made him look every inch the matinee idol. Clothes were important to Pete; he loved that early '70s skinhead look ... button down Ben Sherman shirts, off white Levi Sta-Prest trousers, and cherry red Doc Marten shoes. When he wore a jacket, it was a red Harrington. He had a blue one too, but that was saved for football matches.

Pete had inherited his appreciation of clothes from his father and if he was given half a chance he would wax lyrical about the fashions of the day. Nipper recalled him explaining how the Harrington jacket was named after Rodney Harrington a character played by Ryan O'Neal in the American TV soap Peyton Place.

A couple of years ago Holly had enraged Pete by borrowing his first Harrington and wearing it inside out to a Bay City Rollers concert. The tartan lining had made it the perfect garment to wear to see the group, and Nipper remembered Holly saying that she thought he looked like the lead singer Les McKeown, which at the time he'd taken as a great compliment.

Thankfully Rollermania had been and gone for Holly, who now revelled in playing the part of the teenage temptress. A regular Lolita that Nipper couldn't help repeatedly eyeing up as she stood there in front of him wearing a hand me down Biba dress that redefined the terms skimpy and diaphanous.

If the Philips siblings carried the torch for street fashion, then Nipper reckoned that he and Danny Green weren't too far behind. Pete could keep his Harrington's and his Sta-Prest, Nipper and Danny were into donkey jackets, and Nipper couldn't wait for the winter to arrive as Danny's dad, who worked for the Council, had promised them both one of the dark blue, thick woollen, mid length single-breasted coats each. Just to make the wait worthwhile, the jackets would have WBC (Wandsworth Borough Council) emblazoned on the back ... the real deal, fantastic!

Nipper turned his attention to Danny Green and smiled. Danny Green, what a character. He'd been the class comedian at school, which had probably prevented him from being bullied as he was short in stature and possessed a spare tyre which as Pete indelicately used to put it was 'just waiting to be pumped up'.

'*He's short, he's round, he bounces on the ground Fatboy Green, Fatboy Green,*' was a favoured chant. But everyone loved him, especially Pete, Holly and Nipper. Nipper had a Christian name, John ... but nobody called him that apart from his mother. Most people never realised that Nipper was his surname, thinking instead that it was a playground nickname originating from the Roy of the Rover's style character Nipper Lawrence, who played football for the fictional team Blackport Rovers whose comic strip adventures were chronicled in Scorcher and Tiger.

★ ★ ★ ★ ★

'So anyway Pete, what's the big deal with 1927?' asked Nipper, refocusing his mind on the discussion as he skinned up the last high number of the night. 'I mean I know the Arsenal thing is pretty funny, but what was it that Fatboy was goin on about?' he continued, mindful of the time and the fact that last orders had been called a couple of hours earlier. If his fingers and thumbs got it together with the Benson, the Rizla and the weed, then with the aid of a little concentration they would have one last smoke before it was time to leave.

'Dunno, I can't remember,' replied Pete, characteristically scratching at his forehead. 'I was talking to someone the other day about getting some speed, and we got into this like history of drugs session as you do y'know,' he continued, reaching into his pocket for some change and getting up to walk over to the jukebox. 'Well something happened in 1927... Fuck it! I know, it was Ballroom Bertie telling me one of his old stories. He was banging on about the war, and how all the pilots were buzzing around on benzedrine ...which my friends, was first synthesized in 1927. Yeah ... speed. Kings of speed ...we're gonna need some gear for the Count Bishops gig on Saturday. C'mon Jem, gissa toke on that spliff.'

Nipper lit the joint and handed it to Pete, smiling as he watched him turn around and insert 10p into the jukebox's coin mechanism. Without consulting the play-list, he programmed it to play selection 99A. Danny and Nipper nodded their approval whilst Holly shook her head as they waited for the opening bars of the song to fizz and crackle from the machines huge loudspeaker.

There wasn't much to choose from that was new or inspiring; in keeping with the current misfortunes that beset Chelsea Football Club, the music scene was dull and turgid, in fact everything in Nipper's life seemed to reflect the fact that mid '70s England was in deep recession. Unemployment was at its highest level since the Second World War and the Labour government was rapidly running out of ideas.

Nipper didn't care much for politics, but he'd heard all about Margaret Thatcher the new leader of the Conservative Party. The grocer's daughter from Grantham wanted to change things, and she'd already begun propagating ideologies that would change the very fabric of everyone's existence in the years that followed.

This was what the music scene needed ... someone or something to agitate, educate and organise things. The early '70s glam rock posturing of Bolan, Bowie and Ferry had been surpassed by the pompous 'progressive' rock meanderings of Genesis and Yes ... in short, it was fucking dreadful.

'When that train took my baby away from me. Tears in my eyes ... I could hardly see. Oh train train ... Won't you bring my baby back to me ...'

'Train Train' by the Count Bishops, was as good as it got for Nipper, Pete and Danny. They loved the group, and idolised its founder member, rhythm guitarist and occasional vocalist, the fabulously named Zenon de Fleur. Gum chewing Zenon's actual surname was Hierowsky, but his appetite for alcohol had often seen him lying sprawled out on recording studio floors. 'Look at Zen on the floor,' a sound engineer had mumbled one night. Zen on the floor, became Zenon de Fleur, and the Bishops were on their way.

The Count Bishops sat musically somewhere between London R&B scene stalwarts Dr Feelgood, and Eddie and the Hot Rods. They were the first group to release material on the seminal Chiswick record label, and their relative obscurity, coupled with the fact that Zenon had given Pete an acetate copy of the soon to be released 'Train Train' to put on the jukebox in the Spice, appealed to the music press driven pretentiousness that the boys thrived on.

On Thursday's you could guarantee that Pete would have his head buried in the latest copy of the New Musical Express, Nipper though, favoured the more direct reporting style of a music paper called Sounds. Just to make sure that nothing was overlooked, Danny would always pick up a copy of Melody Maker, although his severe dyslexia meant that he only ever looked at the pictures.

'Oh train train ... will I ever see her again?'

Nope. Holly just didn't get it. Not then, not ever. Two years later, when Zenon de Fleur died from the injuries he'd sustained in a car crash, she'd found it hard to believe that there could be such an out pouring of grief to mourn what effectively became the final nail in the coffin of the Count Bishops. A group that for the life of her, sounded like a very poor mans Status Quo.

★ ★ ★ ★ ★

The tune was still in Nipper's head as they'd got the night bus home, and it was still there as he'd crawled into bed and, not for the first time, had a long lazy wank thinking about Holly Philips. Holly Philips, in bed next to him. Her body naked and glistening with sweat; legs apart, backside pushed up in the air, rouged mouth open in anticipation ... fucking lovely ... fucking illegal. Nipper knew that whilst Pete might not mind, old man Tommy would do more than just box his ears if he found out that he'd ever laid a hand on his daughter before she'd turned sixteen.

2

ALL THE YOUNG PUNKS

'Ere have a look at this,' exclaimed Pete, holding up a shirt which had a picture of two camp looking, Stetson wearing cowboys facing each other with their trousers around their ankles and their cocks hanging out. 'Fifteen bleedin quid for a T-shirt ... you're havin a laugh aren't ya?'

Nipper shook his head and looked at the floor as the shop manageress scowled at him. She had a huge blonde beehive hairdo, and was dressed in an outfit the like of which he'd only ever seen in the fetish magazines that his Uncle Ewan kept in the shed at the bottom of his allotment. It was thrillingly transgressive sexual imagery and he felt a stirring in his seventeen year old loins.

'Come on mate, we'd better get going,' he replied eventually, regaining his composure and looking at his watch. 'It's gone 2.30, we'll miss kick off at this rate.'

Danny Green was waiting for them on the street outside, propped up against a lamppost, reading a cheap looking flyer that had just been handed to him by a tall, skinny youth with peroxide blonde hair wearing a full Nazi uniform.

'Look at this lads,' he said, holding out the piece of paper that was nothing more than a cheap photocopy. 'That Punk Rock festival you was on about Pete ... It's on Monday and Tuesday at the 100 club on Oxford Street, we'll have some of that then.'

Pete nodded and looked up and down the Kings Road, which was busier than usual for a Saturday afternoon because Chelsea were playing at home. The shop they had just been browsing in was a regular pre-match haunt. Owned by a mouthy flame-haired Teddy boy called Malcolm McLaren, and an outré clothes designer called Vivienne Westwood, the latest incarnation of the shop was called Sex and it had become a Mecca for trendsetters from various parts of the country.

Pete grinned as he acknowledged a hard-looking bloke called Welsh Chris whom along with his leather-trousered, jackbooted cohorts from the valleys, was stood outside the nearby Worlds End public house vying for the general public's attention with a group of Midlands based pretty boys in stack heeled shoes and makeup. Nearby a wedge-haired Soul boy was in deep discussion with a blue suede-shoed Ted and a couple of tonic-suited Mods. It was style eclectics at its very best, and it was fucking funny.

'Tell you what lads,' he said, as they walked briskly along Gunter Grove which took them from the Kings Road, to the Fulham Road, and the football ground. 'These are interesting times eh ... new sounds, new styles.'

Nipper and Danny nodded in agreement but said nothing as Pete continued to chatter away excitedly. 'Did I tell ya that Holly has been promised a part-time job at Sex by that bird Vivienne?'

'Your joking?' they replied in unison.

'Nah, no joke lads ... she's obviously recognised that with such a skinny frame, my little sister's got potential to become a mannequin for some of her more risqué concoctions.'

'That would be very cool,' said Nipper, pausing to light a cigarette and trying to imagine Holly similarly attired to the shop manageress. 'Maybe she could get us a good discount on some of that gear they sell in there ... I quite fancy a pair of those bondage strides.'

'Bondage strides!' exclaimed Danny, a look of incredulity creeping across his ruddy-cheeked face. 'What the fuck are they?'

'Shit-stoppers ... with the legs tied together by straps of material,' replied Nipper coolly.

Danny Green frowned. It wasn't that he didn't have an interest in looking sharp, it was more down to the plain and simple fact that his body shape just didn't meld with certain styles of garment. Drainpipe trousers, so called shit-stoppers because if you happened to lose control of your bowels you wouldn't have to worry about the resultant mess sliding down your inside leg, were out of the question.

'Won't you fall over if you try and walk in em?' he enquired, grinning as he tried to picture Nipper hopping around in his new pair of leggings. 'Nah the straps have got enough give in em for walking, but dancing and running would be a bit more difficult,' was Nipper's knowledgeable reply.

'You wouldn't have wanted to be wearin em at Carnival then would ya?' chuckled Danny, as the boys turned left into the Fulham Road and joined the throng of supporters jostling and joking with each other as they made their way to the football ground.

'And you wouldn't have worn em to Millwall the other week either,' added Pete, rummaging in his pocket to find enough change to buy a hot dog.

Nipper didn't bother replying, he knew that both points made by his friends were valid. The Notting Hill Carnival, traditionally held over the August Bank Holiday weekend, had ended up in a full scale riot. Old Bill had displayed a less than liberal attitude when it came to maintaining order amongst the spliff-smoking, Dragon stout-drinking ragamuffins who'd weaved and bobbed to the bass heavy reggae pounding from the speakers of the boom-shack-a-lack sound systems that had sprung up on every street corner of this particularly cosmopolitan area of West London.

'Police and thieves in the street … fighting each other with their guns and ammunition.' Thanks to late night Radio One DJ John Peel, Junior Murvin's high pitched falsetto reggae anthem was currently embedded somewhere deep inside the rhythm section of Nipper's brain. It hadn't quite come to guns and ammunition at Carnival, but Old Bill, and the notorious Special Patrol Group in particular, had used riot shields and truncheons to 'maintain' order. Order that had only broken down in the first place because of their heavy-handed presence, and lack of tolerance towards the Afro-Caribbean community.

Pete, Danny and Nipper had found themselves caught up in trouble at Carnival when a mallet-faced PC had challenged their presence with a few choice racist comments. There had been little point arguing their case any further when it came to the crunch, and the crunch had come when Old Bill had started wielding their truncheons indiscriminately at anyone who'd dared to voice an opinion.

Fleet of foot, the three amigos turned and ran as the blows started to rain down on their unprotected heads. That night they'd got away with a couple of bruises each, sprinting away from the ensuing row with anger and resentment towards authority building in their hearts and minds.

A new England, thought Nipper … yeah, fuck it, … Fat Boy Danny Green was right. Bondage strides might have an exalted place in the current fashion hierarchy, but they would have served him less than well at Carnival that weekend.

Pete was right as well. Chelsea's opening fixture of the current campaign had paired them away with Leyton Orient. Loads of Chels had descended on East London to witness a 1-0 victory … good enough, happy days. This had been followed by a couple of dull home games, a 1-1 draw with Notts County, and a 2-1 victory over Carlisle United … and then came Millwall away.

Cold Blow Lane, where Millwall Football Club's ground the Den could

then be found, was a name that in itself was enough to strike fear and trepidation into the souls of those visiting fans brave or foolhardy enough to
venture over to this decaying part of South East London to give vociferous
support to their team. On Saturday September 4th, Pete, Nipper and
Danny Green, along with a very healthy contingent of Blues fans had
turned up at the Den expecting to see their team maintain its unbeaten
start to the season. Chelsea lost 3-0.

To make matters worse, Millwall's hooligans, the Bushwhackers, were
intent on enhancing their reputation for aggro. Pitbull-faced dockers,
older geezers who wore surgical masks and called themselves F-Troop,
battled in and around the ground with Chelsea's butcher-aproned top
boys. They were serious blokes, with names like Harry the Dog, Mad Pat,
and Winkle. Caesars of the Millwall terraces, they authoritatively
marshalled the members of their junior ranks, who dependent on age and
pugilistic capabilities fell into a line of ascendance as part of either
Treatment or the Half Way Line.

3-0 on the pitch, and 3-0 off the pitch. Pete, Danny and Nipper had
taken a beating on their way out of the ground. Later they'd compared
pupil-dilated black eyes in a speed-fuelled evening upstairs in the Spice of
Life. Looking back, Nipper reckoned that wearing a pair of bondage
strides that day would have heralded a far worse outcome than the bruised
pride and dented ego he'd harboured as they'd shot pool and fired up the
Count Bishops on the jukebox in the upstairs bar.

★ ★ ★ ★ ★

Chelsea's team were young, most of them were in their teens or barely
out of them. It was a team that Pete, Nipper and Fatboy Green could
identify with. The Wilkins brothers; Graham and the prodigious Ray.
Marauding centre forward Steve Finnieston, and dynamic midfield
carrot top Ray Lewington. Kenny Swain and swashbuckling centre half
Stevie Wicks. The one concession to youth was the illustrious custodian
of the Chelsea goal. 'The cat', Peter Bonetti, was still as agile as ever.
They were good lads managed by early '70s Chelsea legend Eddie
McCreadie, a team with panache, flair and that typical Kings Road style
and guile.

Following that ignominious defeat at Millwall, Chelsea had bounced
back to beat Plymouth Argyle 3-2 away from home and had propelled
themselves to 5th place in the Second Division. The team had everything
to play for as they faced up to today's difficult home game against one of
the early season pace setters Bolton Wanderer's.

'We're the white wall, we're the white wall ... we're the white wall of the Shed. We're the middle, we're the middle ... we're the middle of the Shed. We're the west side, we're the west side ... we're the west side of the Shed. We're the Shed end, we're the Shed end, we're the Shed end ... Stamford Bridge.'

Fucking great, thought Nipper, joining in with the chant as he clambered up the tired, weed-encroached concrete steps that led from the Shed end turnstiles up to the top of the terrace.

Built in 1934 the south stand covered just over a fifth of the terrace area. It had originally been designed by the Club's architect, Archibald Leitch, to provide shelter for bookmakers and punters alike in the days when Stamford Bridge was also a prominent greyhound stadium. When it rained there would be a scrum of people huddled together underneath its eaves seeking shelter from inclement weather.

The angular barn-like construction, originally known as the Fulham Road End, was re-christened 'the Shed' following a supporters letter that had been printed in the Chelsea programme published for a home game against Leicester City in September 1966.

'From now on we wish the Fulham Road End to be called 'The Shed.' That is the section where the fanatics stand ... why don't more people come in the Shed and join in the singing and chanting'.

In the ten years that followed, the Shed established itself as one of the foremost 'ends' in British football, and its match-day 'Shedite' tenants had developed an unhealthy reputation for objectionable chanting and trouble. But that was all a part of it. Being Chels.

You could be a Shedite for just 80p. Mind you, having said that, it was the only place where Pete, Nipper and Danny would freely admit to being juveniles. That way it only cost them 40p to gain admission.

40p, what a fucking bargain! But Nipper was dismayed as he looked around the ground and realised that with kick off rapidly approaching, Stamford Bridge was half empty. At the opposite end of the ground, the North Stand, which was now just a bleak open terrace, was playing host to around 400 travelling Bolton fans. To the left, the West Stand seemed reasonably full, and its occupants, particularly those sat on the concrete benches adjacent to the pitch, were in full voice responding to the request from the Shed faithful to give them a song.

'We are the famous, the famous Chelsea.'

Chelsea had enjoyed fame. For a brief period, when Pete, Nipper and Danny were still in short trousers, they'd been a cavalier outfit on a par with the best teams in the land. Not any more. Mismanaged ambitions off the pitch had taken care of that. The clubs owners had decided in their infinite wisdom that the team, which in the early '70s had won the FA Cup and conquered Europe, should showcase their abilities in a stadium which befitted their achievements and future potential.

Plans were drawn up for a new 50,000 capacity stadium, and in 1973 the gargantuan East Stand was erected. Nipper shook his head as he looked to his right. Today the stand was sparsely populated. He didn't know how to read a balance sheet, but surely somebody must have been aware of the punitive cost of the rebuilding project.

Star players had been sold in a bid to stave off bankruptcy, and inevitably the club had been relegated. With Chelsea on the verge of extinction, creditors had been persuaded to give them one more season to prove their viability. After the disappointment of finishing mid-table last season, when home attendances had averaged below 19,000, it was now down to the manager, players and supporters alike to make sure that the club achieved promotion in this current campaign. A win against Bolton today was deemed essential.

'Whaddya reckon the gate is then?' asked Danny, as they made their way around the back of the Shed heading towards the Tea Bar section of the terrace, a preferred vantage point.

'About 25,000 mate,' replied Pete, clapping in unison with the rest of the crowd as the players emerged from the tunnel.

'*Ten, Nine, Eight, Seven, Six, Five, Four, Three, Two, One ...*'

Everyone turned momentarily to face the lone figure of Duncan Disorderly, clad in his trademark white butcher's apron, who was perched precariously on the white wall that ran down the centre of the covered section of the terrace.

'*Zigger zagger, zigger zagger,*' he yelled, right hand pointing skywards.

'*Oi, Oi, Oi.*' Came the reply from the massed ranks gathered around him.

The chant would have continued for some time had it not been for the intervention of several Old Bill who marched down the side of the white wall and grabbed Duncan by his legs, pulling him into their less than welcoming arms.

A minor scuffle ensued.

'*Kill, kill, kill the Bill,*' chanted the Shed, as Duncan Disorderly was bundled down the terrace and ejected from the ground. A reworking of the traditional music-hall sing-a-long, 'London Bridge is falling down' swiftly followed.

'*Harry Roberts is our friend, is our friend, is our friend. Harry Roberts is our friend he kills coppers ... Put him on the streets again, streets again, streets again. Put him on the streets again, let him kill some others.*'

Ill feeling towards Old Bill abated as the game got under way.

'You dirty northern bastards, you dirty northern bastards.'

The Shedites directed their chanting at the Bolton players rather than their supporters. The first half had been largely uneventful although Bonetti, making his 650th appearance for the Blues, had capably demonstrated that the passing years had not affected his catlike nimbleness when he'd made a fingertip save from a fierce Bolton shot on 20 minutes.

'Dirty twat ... Britton's fucked now, look at him. Poor cunt,' said Pete, pointing at Chelsea's industrious winger Ian Britton who had been pole-axed by a Bolton defender and was now lying on the grass writhing in agony.

'It's his Achilles mate ... he'll be off with that poor fucker,' observed Danny, shaking his fist in anger as they watched the unfortunate Britton get carried off the field.

'Come on Chelsea, come on Chelsea.'

'We aint gonna score now. Injury times nearly up. Twats.' Nipper's laconic impatience with Chelsea's inability to carve out a goal turned to words of encouragement as Finnieston centred the ball towards Chelsea's record signing David Hay. 'Go on Davie. Go on son ... get yer head on it ... YES!'

Pete, Nipper and Danny jumped in the air and gleefully bundled themselves, along with those around them, down the terrace.

In the second half, Chelsea continued to impose themselves on the game, with Ray Wilkins in commanding form.

'One more goal, to make it safe,' said Nipper, craning his neck to watch proceedings as Steve Wicks tapped a free kick sideways to Wilkins.

'Look their keepers well off his line,' observed Pete, as Wilkins knocked the ball on to Garry Stanley who was perfectly positioned just outside the box to try his luck with a deft chip.

'Goal ... ha ha ha.'

'2-0, 2-0, 2-0, 2-0 ... You've come all this way and you've lost ... and you've lost.'

The Shedites euphoria wasn't dampened by a last-minute Bolton consolation goal. Victory was secured, and a rabble-rousing rendition of the timeless terrace classic *'You're gonna get your fucking heads kicked in'*, ensured that the Bolton fans hid their scarves at the final whistle.

As they made their way out of the ground Pete, Nipper and Danny chattered excitedly about how they'd just witnessed the dawn of a new footballing era at Stamford Bridge. Later that night they'd discussed the dawn of this supposed new musical era which they were going to witness first hand in a couple of days. Life was interesting.

★ ★ ★ ★ ★

Holly wasn't interested in football in the slightest. The terraces were no place for her, the thuggery and braggadocio that her brother and his friends applauded and occasionally embraced reviled her. She'd been cajoled into going to a match against Notts County a couple of weeks ago, and had witnessed at first hand the sickening racial intimidation meted out to the opposing team's one black player by bullnecked, NF badge-wearing skinheads, whose seig heiling arms had been covered in a bewildering array of swastika tattoos.

'He was only a poor little skinhead, he wandered alone in the night. Now he's joined the National Front and he's found a reason to fight.'

The Stamford Bridge terraces were the perfect place for the far Right to swell their ranks, and copies of the NF's youth paper Bulldog, which ran a regular column entitled 'On the Football Front', calling upon young fans to 'join the fight for your race and nation', were being freely distributed at half time.

Holly could see that this was an orchestrated political campaign trading on frustration and political confusion, and she couldn't understand why Pete, Nipper and Danny turned a blind eye to what was going on around them. If that's what going to Chelsea was all about, then the boys could keep it. Of course it wasn't, but Holly had seen and heard enough that afternoon to make her own mind up, and it would be a full twenty years before she would be persuaded to return.

Whilst the boys were watching Chelsea triumph over Bolton, Holly had spent the afternoon sat in the living room at her father's house leafing through a week-old copy of Sounds and musing over how long she could continue to feign the mysterious illness that had prevented her from returning to school in Scotland. Her infatuation with all things thin had helped her cause, and Tommy Philips had been guided by the family doctor who'd suggested that Holly might be anorexic and that being away at boarding school might make matters worse.

Flicking through the pages, she'd paused when she saw the face of someone she recognised who'd been working in the clothes shop on the Kings Road that Pete had taken her to earlier in the summer. She'd taken the offer of a job at Sex with a pinch of salt. The people who owned and frequented the shop appeared mentally unstable, and it was only Pete's constant reminding that made her rethink the possibilities, especially now she'd made her determined little mind up not to return to school.

Glen ... Glen Matlock, that was it. Here he was, pictured with a sneering, disaffected, Dickensian-looking character and a couple of beery-faced young hooligans who looked more like they should be standing on the terraces chanting cod shit along with Pete, Nipper, Danny, and the rest of the Chelsea louts rather than making popular music.

Except it wasn't popular music. The article was about a group called the Sex Pistols, and Glen Matlock was their bassist. Fucking hell … the Sex Pistols! A couple of months previously the group had gone into a studio and recorded seven songs on a four track machine, among them 'Anarchy in the UK' and 'Pretty Vacant'. Holly had heard them on the John Peel show, there was definitely something about the energy of the music that made a connection with her in a way that the drone of the Count Bishops never had.

Holly read and re-read the article, and then turned to the back of the paper to check out the concert listings. They were on the bill at the Punk Rock Festival that was taking place … fucking hell, the day after tomorrow. Holly went into the kitchen, opened the fridge and grinned as she saw the large bottle of Dandelion & Burdock, the fizzy brown liquid contents of which provided her with all the daily nourishment she felt she needed.

As she opened the bottle, she wondered if Pete knew about the concert but had chosen not to tell her. Holding it to her lips, she also wondered if Vivienne Westwood would remember who she was if she paid a return visit to Sex. Gulping down several mouthfuls of Dandelion & Burdock made her eyes water and the accompanying sugar rush made her feel giddy. But there was something else also, the buzzy expectation that something exciting was about to happen in her life.

★ ★ ★ ★ ★

'Where's Nipper?' Holly enquired, stepping out of the queue and looking expectantly at the two exits to Tottenham Court Road tube station which she could see clearly.

'Don't worry doll face, he'll be here,' replied Pete, brushing his right hand down the front of the scraggily knitted blue and black mohair jumper he was wearing.

'You wanna be careful mate,' said Danny, offering Pete a cigarette. 'That jumper looks like it'll go up in flames if someone taps it with a lit fag end,' he continued, trying to prevent himself from laughing at Pete's garb.

'Bollocks! It says on the label that it's flame retardant. Bleedin should be as well it cost me a week's wages,' smirked Pete, putting the cigarette behind his left ear.

'How can it have cost you a week's wages? You aint got a fuckin job.'

'Well if I had a job, it would've cost a week's wages.'

'You nicked it didn't ya.'

'Might've done.'

'You could've nicked something for me, I feel proper dressed down … look at all these cunts in their whips, leathers and chains.

'I would've … honest, but I couldn't find anything in your size you fat cunt.'

At this point Danny lunged at Pete, dragging him to the floor and giving him a couple of playful slaps across the face.

'Oi … pack it in you two,' snarled Holly, tugging at the collar of Danny Green's distressed Fred Perry shirt.

'The lot of you can pack it in or you can forget coming in here.' The voice was raw and abrasive. It had a menacing edge to it that immediately drew Pete, Danny and Holly's attention.

It's owner, a skinhead elegantly dressed in a Persil white button down shirt, with regulation red braces holding up jeans which finished high above the ankle to reveal a pair of ox blood-polished Doc Marten boots, didn't look like the sort of person who would make the same request twice.

'Up the Chels, eh mate,' said Pete, catching sight of the familiar rampant lion, Chelsea FC's club crest, which was tattooed on the right side of the skinheads neck.

'Not tonight lads … I'm working,' came the reply. The skinhead winked at Pete, nodded at Danny and blew a kiss at Holly, before jerking his chin out and strutting purposefully back to the entrance door to the 100 Club.

'Fascist wanker!' snarled Holly, thrusting an unladylike two fingered salute in the direction of skinhead before helping her brother to his feet.

'Shut it sis … don't you know who that is?' whispered Pete, finally lighting the cigarette that Danny had given him.

'Duncan Disorderly … leader of the Shed,' interjected Danny with an air of reverence.

'Duncan Disorderly … leader of the Shed,' sneered Holly, in a whining voice. 'What a pair of pricks you two are,' she continued, tugging at the zip that she'd stitched into the diagonally slashed, tie dyed, and now barely recognisable Biba top she always loved to wear.

'Oi oi. Here he is!' exclaimed Pete.

Nipper's timely arrival diffused the situation, and Holly's anger soon dissipated as they paid their £1.50 entrance fee and made their way down the dimly lit, beer sticky stairs into the club.

The expectant atmosphere had an extra edge to it as soon as Pete, Nipper and Danny had snorted their first couple of lines of the nostril reddening amphetamine sulphate Nipper had procured for a very competitive £6 a gram from a mutton chopped, Chelsea supporting dealer known as Riddler who peddled his wares from the boot of the black taxi cab he drove around London town.

As she looked at the competitively attired punk rockers gathering at the front and to the sides of the stage, Holly became enthralled by the feeling of exclusivity and insurrection.

'The Mortlake mob … fucking weird bloke he is, that Vic Godard. I didn't know he was in a group,' spluttered a surprised looking Pete, beer spilling from his mouth as the first band, Subway Sect, took to the stage.

'He wasn't until the other week,' said Danny casually. 'Malcolm McLaren was in the bog when I was in there just now. He was saying how he paid for 'em to rehearse all this past week, because he needed a roster of groups for the festival to make it look like more of an event.'

'Fucking rubbish,' shouted Nipper above the discordant twang and Bowie style oik oik vocals.

'The Count Bishops would blow this lot off stage,' sniffed Pete. 'They're miserable, look at the way they're dressed … boring.'

Danny Green didn't volunteer an opinion. He was too mesmerised by everything else that was going on, and besides that the sulphate was quickening his pulse and making him want to move.

Meanwhile, Holly just stood still. She continued to stand still during the performance of the next group to take the stage, Siouxsie and the Banshees.

'She looks amazing,' said Pete, looking at the groups swastika armbanded singer.

'Fucking scary more like,' replied Nipper, finishing the contents of his pint and wondering if he had enough money in his pocket to buy them all another drink.

'Spontaneity innit,' said Pete, gesturing Nipper to get another round in. 'They only formed at the weekend. That bloke on the drums, John … he hangs around McLaren's shop … calls himself Sid Vicious now.'

Having crucified 'Knocking On Heaven's Door', the group then assaulted 'The Lord's Prayer' at which point Pete, Nipper and Danny made their way to the bar.

Holly remained transfixed.

The next band, the Clash, could actually play their instruments with a fair degree of proficiency.

'*Black or white, turn it on. Face the new religion … Everyone's sitting round watching television. London's burning with boredom now … London's burning dial 99999.*'

The brothel creeper booted singer had some decent lyrics, and the groups trebly guitar sound was infectious enough to drag the boys away from the bar and back to the stage area where they found Holly grooving away in a manner that got Nipper thinking again. Thinking about his virginity, and how he'd like to lose it. Lose it to his best friends sylph like sister, whose gyrating body, severe attitude, and rising hemline was beginning to play serious havoc with his hormones.

'Quality!' exclaimed Danny as the Clash finished their short, electrically charged set. 'They are fucking quality!'

'Not as good as the Bishops,' replied Nipper, hurriedly dabbing some bitter tasting sulphate powder onto his tongue as Pete held the wrap open for him.

By the time the Sex Pistols took to the stage, the club was a sweaty, heaving mass of bodies. Necks craning, shoulders being leant on, as the people at the back of the room tried to get a better view of what was going on at the front.

'Anarchy for the UK … it's coming sometime and maybe …'

What was going on at the front was an unparalleled display of visceral energy, as the crowd, Pete, Nipper, Danny and Holly included, responded to the group's untamed aggression with a frenzied display of un-choreographed dancing. Except it wasn't dancing. People were jumping up and down, spitting and slamming into one another with varying degrees of force.

'Better than the Count Bishops,' yelled Holly at Nipper, as she charged at him, grabbing him by the waist, bundling him to the floor and kissing him fully on the mouth.

'Yeah. Better than the Bishops,' replied Nipper moments later as he staggered to his feet and watched Holly, already up and away, push herself right to the front of the stage. 'Better than fucking anything!'

The phenomenon that was Punk Rock had arrived, and things would never be quite the same again … especially for Holly and Nipper.

3

June 1977

GOD SAVE THE QUEEN

'I'm telling you sis, the Chels are back … make no mistake,' said Pete, taking off his leather motorcycle jacket and handing it to Holly before sitting down.

Holly loved the smell of the jacket, and in particular the feel of the hide. Pete had bought it from Lewis Leather's in Great Portland Street just before Christmas with his first wage packet and, come rain or shine, he'd hardly been seen out of it since. The respective bass players with the Clash, the Stranglers and the Pistols; Paul Simonon, Jean Jacques Burnel and Sid Vicious, who'd replaced Glen Matlock, were all good looking boys who favoured the classic, cross over zipped, motorcycle jacket.

The 'Lewis' had become a punk fashion icon, and Pete, with his jet-black dyed hair and tall skinny frame swathed in the latest lines from McLaren's shop Sex, which had been re-launched as Seditionaries, looked like he was a model for the scene.

'Bloody hell Pete, it's June … the season finished weeks ago, and all you can go on about is fucking Chelsea. Can't we talk about something else … like the Pistols gig on the river tomorrow night?' Holly shook her head and sighed, resigned to the fact that until either Nipper or Danny arrived at the Spice, she would have to listen to Pete enthusing once more about his favourite football team.

Chelsea had won promotion back to the First Division, finishing second behind Wolves. The team had remained unbeaten at home all season, and their last couple of matches at the Bridge had attracted crowds of over 40,000.

'Sorry sis,' replied Pete smiling. 'But I was just reading in the Standard about Eddie McCreadie being involved in a stormy negotiation over his new contract with Brian Mears the Chairman ... I hope it gets sorted out cos Eddie's the man to lead the team next season, has to be,' he continued, ignoring his sisters plea to change the subject.

'Ahh ... thank God!' exclaimed an increasingly irate looking Holly, as she saw the familiar figures of Nipper and Danny enter the bar.

'Oi, Oi ... drinks then?' said Nipper, rolling back his head and winking at Holly whilst giving the thumbs-up to Pete which was immediately reciprocated.

Holly smiled. Since their playful clinch on the floor of the 100 Club, she'd stolen a few precious kisses from Nipper ... but nothing more. Sixteen now, she was growing impatient. Tiring of Nipper's immaturity, but conscious of the fact that she desired him with an incandescent passion, she was a lady in waiting. And whilst she waited, Nipper watched. He was almost ready to make his move, but the timing had to be right.

'Boring you is he?' said Danny, blustering across the room to where Holly and Pete were sat in his own inimitable style. A style that thanks to Holly, had gradually embraced elements of the current street fashion. His weight was always going to be a problem, but the wrap around black sunglasses and white muslin shirt that had the word CHAOS stencilled across its front, gave him an edgy urban cool.

'You're not kidding,' replied Holly, running the index finger of her right hand along her perfectly tweezered eyebrows.

'Ere Pete, did ya see the piece about Eddie Mc in the paper?' said Danny, picking up a stool and placing it by the table where Pete and Holly were sat.

'Oh for fucks sake ... that's enough!' Holly stood up and glared at Pete and Danny, before making her way over to the jukebox which Nipper was hunched over examining the weeks latest additions.

'What's that all about then ... PMT?' asked a startled looking Danny.

'Nah mate ... too much talk about Chelsea, you know what she's like.'

'She should know better than moan about the Chels.'

'Yeah ... she should. You know that.'

Danny Green took a long drink from his pint glass and belched loudly. An act which caused Holly further consternation.

'Pig!' she yelled from across the room, as the opening vibrato bass line of the Stranglers track 'Peaches', which had just been released that day, growled from the jukebox's speakers.

'Great selection,' said Danny, clenching his fist and looking over at Nipper before continuing his discourse with Pete.

'You know the best thing about last season?' said Pete, leaning across the table and helping himself to one of Danny's Benson's. 'Getting promotion. Yeah, that was great ... nah, the best thing right ... was the fact that Spurs got relegated the day we went up at Wolves.

'Yeah, I agree,' replied Danny, rapping his hands on the table in time with the musical beat. 'Remember, it was those bastards that put us down back in '75,' he continued, before adjourning the conversation in favour of singing along with the jukebox.

'Is she trying to get out of that clitoris? Liberation for women, that's what I preach. Preacher man. Walking on the beaches, looking at the peaches.'

Holly looked over and rolled her heavily made up eyes skywards. She liked the look of the Stranglers, but their misogynistic attitude to women, so often reflected in their lyrics left her feeling cold. And besides that, everyone knew they weren't real punks. They were just a decent pub rock band who'd been plying their trade for a couple of years, and were in the right place at the right time to jump on the punk bandwagon.

Holly had willingly immersed herself in the burgeoning punk culture. In December, Vivienne Westwood and Malcolm McLaren had given the shop at 430 Kings Road a complete facelift. Sex had become Seditionaries. 'Clothes for heroes' was the new enticing strap line, and when the shop re-opened, Holly Philips found herself working full time behind the counter.

In six months she'd transformed herself from a demure, ever so pretty, girly-girly schoolgirl, into an assertive, articulate, agent provocateur. The long black hair had been replaced with a purple tinged spikey crop. Make-up was applied skilfully. Lipstick, rouge, mascara and eyeliner, were combined to create what became the classic, gothic shock-horror B-movie, female punk look.

Punk galvanised a moribund scene, and Holly found herself at the epicentre of the earthquake it created. Through working at Seditionaries, she knew who was happening, what was happening, and most of all where it was happening. As much as she liked what the guys were doing, it was the women who fired her imagination.

Siouxsie and the Banshees had learnt to play their instruments, and Holly loved to watch them play live at the Vortex in Soho. The groups manager, Nils Stevenson, had a punk stall at Beaufort Market which was near enough to Seditionaries for Holly to be able to wander over there on her occasional fag breaks and update herself on what was going on outside the elitist McLaren emporium.

At the market, she'd befriended a strikingly pretty, tooth brace wearing girl of mixed race, called Marion Elliot. Several years older than Holly, Marion had a cocky infectious enthusiasm for all things punk. By day she ran a clothes stall at the market, and by night, under her nome-de-punk, Poly Styrene, she fronted a band called X-Ray Spex.

Unusually for punk, the group also featured a female saxophonist, Laura Logic, who gave them a unique sound. Pete had likened this sound to Gerry Rafferty's 'Baker Street' being played at 78rpm through a cement mixer. Poly's stage presence and caterwauling vocals made them another great live draw for Holly, who would spend many an evening at the nearby Man in the Moon pub, where the band had a residency.

'Oh Bondage ... Up Yours!' was Poly's cry for liberation from the human bondage of material life. The female anger and defiance to be found in the lyrics, struck a resonant chord with Holly, who suddenly found herself analysing the meaning of songs in the same way that her brother did.

She was searching for a song that she could say ... 'Yeah! That's me!' Something she could shriek along to with complete conviction, and finally she found it. In January, Pete, Nipper and Danny had encouraged her to join them at the Roxy in Covent Garden. Generation X were playing. Holly had been reluctant to attend as she'd found their music too formula ridden, and their lead singer Billy Idol had, in her opinion, an ego far too big for his natty winkle picker boots.

The boys weren't interested in the support band, a group of wannabes from the north east called Penetration.

'Geordie's! What the fuck do they know about punk?' Pete had said, as they propped themselves up at one end of the bar.

The conversation soon drifted into a north vs south debate, which all too predictably for Holly soon shifted its focus from music and fashion to football.

'Boring tossers,' Holly had muttered to herself, as she'd meandered over to the stage and waited for Penetration to make an audio-visual impression on her.

The group were competent, and their singer, a girl called Pauline Murray, was sassy enough to draw the boys away from the bar to join Holly near the front of the stage. Then it happened. The perfect song. Holly's song. A bludgeoning descending bass riff, leading to a set of decipherable idealistic lyrics that summed up the way that Holly felt about the world she'd left behind and the people who were in it.

'Don't tell me what to do. Its my life I'll take it, I'll chance it. Don't dictate, don't dictate, don't dictate, dictate to me.'

'That's it ... that's it,' proclaimed Holly. 'That's what it's all about for me, that's why I'm a punk.'

Penetration's debut single, 'Don't dictate', was eventually released later in the year, and Holly was right at the very front of what was sadly a short queue to buy it.

★ ★ ★ ★ ★

'Come on hurry up, the boat's leaving at 6.30,' said Holly, tugging at Pete's arm as they crossed the road and made their way hurriedly along the Embankment to Charing Cross Pier.

'Bloody Hell sis, hold on,' replied Pete, pulling up and reaching in his pockets for his cigarettes and matches. 'They wont leave with out us will they,' he continued, pausing to light up before jogging after his sister.

'Danny and Nipper might wait,' said Holly breathlessly. 'But the boat won't.'

June 7th was the night of the Queens Silver Jubilee. The country had been gripped by patriotic fervour, and the Union Jack garbed inhabitants of every other red white and blue bunting festooned street were revelling at parties being held to celebrate 25 years of Queen Elizabeth's sovereignty.

Malcolm McLaren and Virgin, the Sex Pistols latest record company, had other ideas. Their plan was to hijack the occasion to promote the Pistols new record, 'God Save the Queen', and they'd hired a pleasure boat, aptly named the Queen Elizabeth. The boat would cruise the River Thames and the group were to perform in front of a select group of fans, music journalists, and record company executives.

The single was already an unprecedented success. Spirited along on a magic carpet of hype, media revulsion and anarchy, 'God Save the Queen,' with its controversial lyrics and infectious guitar riff had already sold 150,000 copies by the time of the concert. The Sex Pistols were no longer part of the 'next big thing'. They were the 'big thing'.

'God save the Queen ... the fascist regime.'

Fucking right as well, thought Holly to herself as the lyrics tripped through her mind. *'There is no future in England's dreaming ... No future for you, no future for me.'*

She wondered if Johnny Rotten knew the full impact of his savagely penned tirade.

'Ha! Look at that,' exclaimed Holly, her lyrical analysis concluding abruptly as she pointed at the huge streamer which was fluttering from a flagpole on the pier. 'QUEEN ELIZABETH WELCOMES THE SEX PISTOLS, fantastic!'

'Come on you two,' yelled Nipper, beckoning Holly and Pete onto the boat which was ready to depart.

* * * * *

'When are they gonna play?' asked Nipper, handing the wrap of sulphate to Holly and motioning her in the direction of the toilet.

'Dunno. Soon I expect,' she replied, ignoring Nipper's suggestion that

she use the toilet and brazenly opening the sulphate wrap at the bar.
'They've unfurled a banner down the side of the boat advertising the new
single,' she continuing, pausing only to dab some of the bitter off-white
powder onto the tip of her tongue. 'Yeuch … disgusting.' Holly grimaced,
as she reached for her fourth vodka and tonic of the evening.

'Bit two bobish aint it,' said Nipper rubbing his runny nose.

'What the speed?' replied Holly.

'No. The fact that the bar is refusing to serve doubles.'

'Probably worried about what us nasty punk rockers might do if we
drink too much.'

Holly handed the wrap back to Nipper, grabbed him by the hand, and
led him back 'upstairs' where a congregation of familiar faces were
gathered, posing, preening, and checking each other out.

The stiff breeze had an unseasonable chill to it and Holly was glad that
she'd chosen to wear a thick mohair jumper over heavy duty leather
trousers. Nipper looked up at the clouds gathering in the darkening sky
and pulled Holly towards him.

'Look at the lights on Chelsea Bridge eh,' he whispered, his arms encircling Holly's waist as he stood behind her. 'Fucking nice that aint it.'

'You say the most romantic things Nipper,' she replied, reaching
behind and squeezing hard at his crotch.

'Ouch … fucking hell Holly, what's that all about,' he winced, letting go
of her and doubling up in ball aching pain.

'Ha! You'll find out later,' she replied, pointing at the police motor
launch that had been trailing in the wake of the Queen Elizabeth since
she'd altered course at Battersea and began cruising back upstream.

As the Houses of Parliament came into view a volley of feedback
heralded the arrival of the group on 'stage'.

'C'mon, let's get in there,' said Nipper, joining in the scrum to get to the
raised covered area at the back of the boat where venomous looking lead
singer Johnny Rotten was grappling with his microphone stand. Guitarist
Steve Jones snarled as he cranked out the opening power chords to
'Anarchy in the UK' and the pent up excitement of the audience was
suddenly unleashed in a spectacular display of pogo dancing.

Holly could feel her pulse racing as the combined effects of amphetamine sulphate, alcohol, and seeing the Pistols at their filthy and ferocious
finest took effect.

Suddenly, gripped by claustrophobic paranoia, she pushed and jostled
her way through the seething mass of people and made her way to the side
of the boat.

'Better here … better here,' she gasped, gripping the safety rails and gulping in several lungfuls of fresh air before turning her attentions to the gig once more. Despite the sound problems and the novice plunkety plunk plunking   of bass player Sid Vicious, the Pistols were at their manic, adrenalin rush inducing best.

'And we don't caaaaaare,' sneered Rotten, spitting out the words to Holly's personal Pistols favourite, 'Pretty Vacant'.

She could see Pete, Nipper and Danny, their distant head's bobbing in the crowd in unison with the beat. She could also see that one police motor launch escort had become two, and that they seemed to be escorting the Queen Elisabeth back to dock.

'No Fun' was drilled out cacophonously whilst Holly repeatedly fingered a V sign at the police officers on the landing stage who were waiting to board the boat. As the boat docked, the captain switched off the power plunging everything into darkness. The bemused audience stood still, looking up at Johnny Rotten who was continuing to scream *'no fun'* repeatedly, whilst drummer Paul Cook maintained a perfect rhythm with his cymbal, snare and bass drum beat.

'C'mon, lets get the fuck off here … I feel sick,' said Holly, snatching at Nipper's hand as he stumbled towards her.

'What about Pete and Danny?' replied Nipper, shaking his head as the police began to order everyone off the boat.

'They'll be ok. C'mon, it's only 10.30. Lets go to the Spice. I need a sit down drink.' Holly tugged at Nipper's fingers like an insistent child would tug at a parents hand on hearing the ding-a-ling bell ring of an ice cream van drawing up outside their house.

Pete and Danny didn't make it to the Spice of Life. Unfortunately for them, they were among a group of people arrested by the police and carted off to Bow Street Police Station. News of their predicament reached the pub at around 11.30 sparking Nipper and Holly into immediate action. In a matter of minutes, they had walked the short distance to Bow street and made a number of impassioned pleas for Pete and Danny's release. Pleas which had fallen on deaf, unsympathetic, heard it all before, ears.

'There's fuck all we can do then is there?' said Holly, in a semi-provocative manner to the middle-aged desk sergeant.

'No there isn't,' glowered the ruddy-cheeked jobs-worth. 'And I suggest you curb your tongue young madam … unless you want to join them,' he continued, his patience with Holly rapidly expiring.

Holly opened her mouth and lasciviously drew her tongue across her top lip causing the sergeant to blush.

'Locked up for "using insulting words likely to cause a breach of the peace" … it's hardly anarchy is it,' she brayed, spoiling for a fight.

'Right that's enough,' said Nipper, taking control of the situation. 'Come on Holly you can stay at my place,' he said, bundling her out of the station before the sergeant had chance to respond.

'You're so masterful Nipper,' chuckled Holly as Nipper flagged down a black cab. 'Stay at your place … ha ha ha. I bet you had all this planned.'

★ ★ ★ ★ ★

Holly was pressed up against the kitchen wall in Nipper's flat. The room was dimly lit by a naked low wattage light bulb that flickered as it threw eerie shadows across the cobwebbed ceiling. Her open eyes were intense and intent, darkening as her pupils dilated.

Nipper was kissing her with an urgency that she had never previously experienced. As he did so, she knew that the intoxicating merry go round of fancying and frisson that had existed between them for so long was about to be consummated. Nipper unbuttoned Holly's leather trousers and forced his hand inside, pushing the moist gusset of her panties hard against her crotch. He pulled away, turning her round and pushing her across the kitchen sink counter. Behind her now, he bit into the nape of her neck causing her to yelp with pain.

'Ouch! … you bastard. Come on, come on,' growled Holly gutturally, in a manner not in keeping with her tender years and sexual inexperience. Her shoulders tensed as she helped Nipper wrestle her leathers and panties down to her knees at which point he lifted his foot and used it to push them down to her ankles.

'I want you Holly,' breathed Nipper heavily, his right hand grasping at her sex. 'I've always wanted you,' he continued, crudely pushing his fingers inside her.

'Take me then,' she moaned, feeling herself let go, fumbling behind herself as she worked loose the clasp on Nipper's belt and pulled at the zipper on his Levis.

Nipper dropped his jeans to his ankles. Skin on skin, Holly could feel his previously constrained erection against the bare skin of her buttocks. Putting his left arm across the small of her back, he pushed her down onto the counter, roughly kicking her legs apart at the same time.

'Fuck me Nipper, fuck me now.' Holly's plea was desperate. After all those years of pent up schoolgirl frustration, of wondering how it would feel … her curiosity and desire were now about to be sated.

'Oh … oh my God!' she squealed, bucking her hips as Nipper entered her.

'Oh my God … oh my God!' The repetition of the phrase, timed with Nipper's clockwork thrusting motion soon brought her to the verge of orgasm.

'Harder … Oh my God … arggh!' Holly's body convulsed as she climaxed, her hands flailing as she tried to grip the windowsill in front of her.

The onset of Holly's orgasm brought Nipper to his own point of no return. 'God save the fucking Queen!' he groaned, pulling out of her and finishing himself off by hand, his issue splattering across the inside of her creamy white thighs.

4

December 1979

A NEW AGE OF ROMANCE

'Where does all the time go?' said Holly to herself, breathing out the words onto the shop front window and tracing Nipper's name into the condensation that had formed immediately on the cold glass surface.

In the summer Covent Garden was full of tourists, harmless drunks, stalls selling scented candles, and people who sprayed themselves gold and stood motionless on boxes for a living. On a wet, miserable, winters day like today, it was deserted. The cobbled streets outside were soaking up the hammering rain with an insatiable thirst, visibly quelling any desire that people may have had to venture out and do that last bit of Christmas shopping.

When Holly had time to herself she would reminisce. It was December 1979, punk rock had come and all but gone. Pink Floyd were at the top of the charts with 'Another Brick in the Wall' and the Iron Lady, Margaret Thatcher, had made number 10 Downing Street her home. Nipper's mighty Blues, after an all too brief sojourn in Division One, were once again battling to get out of Division Two. Tonight they were playing away at Queens Park Rangers, at least Nipper didn't have too far to travel. Division Two … Shrewsbury Town, Wrexham, Bristol Rovers, Swansea City. Why bother? Holly shrugged her shoulders and bent down to switch the radio on.

'London calling to the faraway towns …'

Appropriate enough. The Clash's new single 'London Calling', fantastic, but sounding terribly tinny on a transistor radio.

'London calling, yes I was there too … and you know what they said, some of it was true.'

Holly frowned as she switched the radio off again.

'Ahh punk rock … yeah, I was there too,' she sighed, looking around the empty shop it was her paid duty to clean. Punk, the yellow headed pimple on the countenance of humanity, had been exploded in a pus like shower of glory by the thumb and forefinger of mass publicity. The Pistols were no more, Sid Vicious was dead, and the Clash were well on their way to becoming a stadium rock band.

Holly shook her head. Eventually she'd seen right through the rampant commercialism and plastic anarchy that, in her opinion, Malcolm McLaren had selfishly promoted to line his own pockets. Six months working at Seditionaries had been enough to convince her to return to school and complete her studies.

She was no rebel, and neither were Pete, Nipper or Danny. They were musical youths with stylistic flair and a smattering of pseudo-obnoxious teenage attitude who'd ridden the crest of the punk rock wave for eighteen brilliant months.

Holly traced a heart next to Nipper's name and smiled. Unlike Pete and Danny, Nipper had grown up. He exuded a new sensitive masculinity that appealed much more to her than the machismo streaks of football terrace brutality that were simmering away under the surface of his skin that he thought she knew nothing about.

The sound of a pianist tinkling the ivories in the bar next door, singing a song whose lyrics harked backed to a romantic age photographed in sepia, made Holly wonder if punk rock would carry any sort of long term legacy. Punk had borne a number of bastard children, a new wave of would be heroes surfing on a sea of aural possibilities.

But for Holly, the fashion that harnessed itself to these new groups was as murky drab and grey as the weather outside. She'd felt like a bystander, looking on disinterestedly as Punk metamorphosed into New Wave spawning critically acclaimed groups such as Joy Division, Echo and the Bunnymen and the Fall.

New Wave wasn't for her and nor was the Mod revival that Pete, Nipper and Danny had been flirting with. The Jam, who had started life as a punk group, were the adopted champions of the scene. The Chords, the Purple Hearts and Secret Affair could manage a few decent tunes between them, but Holly was no revivalist, she was already into something colourful and new.

There was however one notable exception to her veto of all things Mod. Her love of the film Quadrophenia, which by now she'd seen several times. The film, based on original Mod pioneers the Who's album of the same name, was the story of a pill popping, scooter riding, parka wearing herbert called Jimmy Cooper, portrayed by an up and coming young actor called Phil Daniels.

'He's a Chelsea fan that geezer … goes all the time, stands right near us in the Shed', Nipper had said, pointing at the silver screen with monotonous regularity every time 'Jimmy' rode across it on his multi-mirrored Vespa Gran Sportique.

Holly's fascination with Quadrophenia stemmed from the fact that her parents had been part of the original Mod scene. A scene that her father Tommy, who also rode a GS scooter, would recall with lachrymose fondness whenever the opportunity arose.

'Your mother Lexie was a spirited woman', he'd say, finishing off another round of answers to questions about her childhood that Holly was always eager to pose.

★ ★ ★ ★ ★

Alexandra Murdoch was the youngest of six children. Lexie, as she was known, hailed originally from Crail, a small fishing village on the east coast of Scotland. A bright inquisitive girl with a zest for life, she grown up in a tightly knit, deeply religious community where a woman's place was most definitely in the home.

Lexie rebelled. At the age of sixteen the bright lights of Edinburgh beckoned, but the lights weren't bright enough and she'd soon returned home. London, that's where she wanted to be. The streets were paved with gold in London, everybody knew that.

As luck would have it, Marjorie Gorman an old family friend who lived in London, had returned to Crail to visit a sick relative. Whilst there, she'd called in on the Murdoch's. Marjorie, a prim and proper spinster, managed a charitable trust close to King Cross station. Over tea, she'd told the Murdoch's about life in London, and about the work she did helping the poor and needy who lived rough on the streets. It was rewarding but difficult work, made harder by the fact that few people were prepared to offer their services voluntarily. What the trust needed was some younger volunteers, people with energy, vitality and commitment. Lexie couldn't believe her luck.

Marjorie Gorman lived above the charity's small office in Camley Street, just behind Kings Cross Station. Lexie cleverly played the game. After an eyebrow raising discussion during which her motives were questioned by all concerned, it was finally agreed that in return for board and lodgings she would work for the charity in a fundraising capacity for a trial period of three months.

Marjorie was shrewd enough to realise that with careful tuition Lexie could become an invaluable fundraising asset. The wink of an eye and a surreptitious smile was often all that was needed to part the businessmen who lunched in the café's and restaurants of Soho from the loose change that rattled around in their trouser pockets. Lexie excelled, and her position was made permanent.

She was so impressed with her young protégés endeavours, that when Lexie had courteously enquired if it was okay to go on a date with a nice young man who'd asked her out whilst she'd been having lunch in a coffee shop on Carnaby Street, she'd approved wholeheartedly.

Tommy Philips was as taken with Lexie Murdoch's flowing black mane, wasp waist and thick Scottish vowels, as she was with his tailored suits, navy cut cigarettesand sharp one liners. It was love at first sight.

Tommy Philips lived nearby in Camden Town, which made it easy for him to frequent Camley Street. He was there most evenings, and at the weekends he would often stay overnight. Marjorie Gorman didn't mind, in fact most of the time Marjorie Gorman didn't know. Her fondness for gin would render her unconscious long before Tommy and Lexie arrived home from a Saturday night out dancing at the Crawdaddy, or one of the many Beat clubs that had sprung up in the West End.

The way Holly had been told the story, it transpired that some six months after she'd met Tommy, Lexie had written home to explain to her own mother how love's young dream had unexpectedly blossomed into pregnancy. Understandably her father Jack had been singularly unimpressed.

Jack Murdoch had travelled to London the next day. The first that Tommy Philips knew about his prospective father in law's arrival in the Capital was being on the receiving end of a Jack Murdoch left upper cut and right hook; punches that had knocked him to the ground with pugilistic efficiency.

Tommy got to his feet and apologised. It was the sensible thing to do. He understood Jack Murdoch's anger. He'd have done the same thing. He explained his love for Lexie, and his plans for their future together. Jack Murdoch, disappointed as he was, admired the young mans vigour. He too had once found himself in a similar position.

It was Marjorie Gorman, rather than Tommy Philips, who'd been held responsible for the shame Lexie had brought on the family, and her name was not on the guest list when invitations to a hastily convened wedding were posted out.

Three months after the wedding, Lexie gave birth to a boy who was christened Peter. Tommy moved the three of them into his grandmother's old council house in Eversholt Street. Two years later Holly was born.

Holly and Pete were pretty comfortable as children. As a kid, Holly couldn't remember there being too many cross words between her mother and father. During the school holidays Lexie would always take her children up to Scotland for a month, and Tommy would join them for a week in July.

In the summer of 1972, Lexie began suffering from severe headaches. Tommy eventually persuaded her to visit the family doctor who was sufficiently concerned to ask for a second opinion on the findings of his initial analysis.

His diagnosis of a brain tumour had been correct. Unfortunately, the tumour had spread so aggressively that by the time Lexie was admitted to hospital it was deemed inoperable. Lexie Philips died on August 31st 1972. In keeping with family tradition, her body was returned to Crail and buried in the Murdoch family plot at the Collegiate Church of St.Mary.

Holly was inconsolable. Tommy, struggling to come to terms with his own grief, was finding it difficult enough to cope and it was agreed that it would be in Holly's best interests for her to remain in Scotland for the time being, whilst he returned to London with Pete.

★ ★ ★ ★ ★

'Oi, oi … come on doll face, open up.'

Holly brushed the tears from the corners of her eyes, a smile quickly replacing the crumpled frown on her face as she recognised the familiar voice.

'I'll be right there,' she replied, scraping her hair back with her fingers, and fashioning it into a tight bun which sat proudly on the top of her head, likening her to a priggish school teacher.

Holly unlocked and opened the door, flinging her arms around Nipper as he entered the shop.

'What's the matter Hol's?' asked Nipper, holding Holly close and looking over her shoulder at the time on his watch.

'Ahhh nothing,' she sighed. 'I was just thinking about mum and dad, you know that eh. Well it just makes me sad sometimes,' she continued, stifling a sob and pushing Nipper far enough away to enable her to kiss him on the lips.

'Do you have to go to the game tonight?' she whispered in his ear, squeezing his groin with her right hand as she did so.

'Does Riddler Rowan rhyme Vincent Price with ice?' he replied, dropping his hands down her back to grope her buttocks.

'Yeah … very funny,' retorted Holly, tightening her grip on Nipper's inside leg. 'But it's Tuesday night Nip … you know we always go to the

Blitz on Tuesday nights,' she pleaded, knowing all the while that she was wasting her time trying to dissuade him from attending the match.

'I'll come along after the game, it's only over in the Bush. Oww! Come on doll face … let go of me pods, yer hurting,' winced Nipper, heaving a sigh of relief as Holly eventually relaxed her grip.

'Oh yeah … and what you gonna wear then? she sneered, pulling herself away from him and eying his rain sodden attire. 'Steve wont let you in the club if you aint made an effort.'

'Listen doll face,' came the reply, in a fey Welsh accent. 'If you think I'm going down Loftus Road dressed up as Robin fucking Hood just so I can get past Steve Strange on the door at the Blitz later, you've got another thing coming.'

'Well you'll just have to go home and get changed after the game,' replied Holly curtly, an impish smile lighting up her face. 'You know Steve guards the club door like St. Peter guards the gates to heaven,'

'Yeah … yeah, I know.' Nipper shook his head. 'Look, it's six-o-clock. I have to go … I'll see you later.'

Nipper kissed Holly on the forehead, slapping her backside playfully before opening the shop door.

'Course you will Nip,' she replied, winking at him and blowing a Marilyn Monroe style kiss. 'Oh and don't come dressed as Robin Hood,' she called after him, 'you did that last week.'

Nipper failed to acknowledge Holly's last point, and she giggled as she watched him skip down the street, dodging in and out of doorways as he tried to avoid the worst of the swirling rain.

'Robin Hood … Chelsea Football Club, bloody big kid!' Holly closed the shop door. Six-o-clock, she thought to herself. Only four hours to get ready.

Holly's appetite for fashion was razor sharp. Like many others, she'd rather have died than fall behind in the race to be hip. Her desire to remain a part of the trend setting crowd that had been the vanguard of the London punk scene had not gone unnoticed by Nipper who had realised that there was money to be made from tapping into the 'next big thing'.

★ ★ ★ ★ ★

The 'next big thing' and its devotees, had yet to be christened. Holly, like most of the shakers on the punk scene, had been a fan of David Bowie and Roxy Music. David Bowie's chameleon like persona, innovative musical style, prodigious output and slightly ambiguous sexual orientation, had given him a certain kudos with the London 'in crowd' who'd begun to congregate in increasing numbers on Tuesday nights at a decrepit club in the heart of Soho called Billy's.

Holly loved its sleaze appeal, and in particular the stylish extravagance of the outfits worn by its patrons who were drawn from the usual glitzy collective of art students, hairdressers and fashion designers.

She had also paid more than passing attention to how the club night had been originated. Billy's was a gay night held weekly in the confines of a notorious club called the Gargoyle, on Meard Street. Tuesday nights being Tuesday nights, customers were thin on the ground. The concept of an external promoter filling a venue with his own punters was new to clubland, and Holly had been very impressed when ex punk Steve Strange, who'd been a part of Welsh Chris' Kings Road entourage, and his business partner Rusty Egan had persuaded the owner of the Gargoyle to do just that.

For a share of the takings, Steve and Rusty promised they could fill Billy's with the bright young things that had lurked in the shadows of the now defunct Soho club Louise's. The Gargoyle was re-launched as Gossips, and the nascent scene continued to flourish right up until the day that Steve Strange and the clubs owner had a furious disagreement over finances.

Just when it seemed like the party would end before it had really begun, Steve and Rusty found a new venue. A wine bar in Great Queen Street, Covent Garden, called the Blitz. They struck up the same Tuesday night arrangement they'd had at Billy's with the owner of the Blitz, and before long this new club night was at the heart of everything that was deemed fashionable in London.

The a-la-mode appeal of Blitz was enhanced by the fact it had its own house band, a group of young lads from Islington who went by the name of Spandau Ballet. Although they had yet to play a proper concert, many of the regulars, Holly and Nipper included, had seen the group rehearse. They had the right image and the right sound, and Holly reckoned it would only be a matter of time before they had a recording contract.

She could see that there was a living to be made from serious creativity and effort. People like Steve Strange and Rusty Egan were easily able to front out their ambitions, and it was the same with the clothes designers, some of whom had shops in and around Covent Garden and Soho. These were the people Holly and Nipper would see in the clubs. Young people like them, but with money in their pockets to finance a decent lifestyle.

What was even more interesting to Holly, was that the fact that the more successful ventures were underpinned by a variety of straight acting business people who were operating, almost transparently, in the background. This infrastructure was, not surprisingly, made up predominantly by ethnic immigrants and Jewish business people. Holly knew that if she ever came up with a credible idea, she would need to try and tap this resource.

Her mind was brimful of ideas and concepts. The 'next big thing', if only she could figure out what that was going to be. Holly was confident that through watching how people like Malcolm McLaren and Steve Strange operated, she had enough of a blueprint to ensure any business venture she entered into would stand a true chance of success.

★ ★ ★ ★ ★

'It's just like a fancy dress party,' explained Nipper to Pete and Danny as they queued to get into Loftus Road to watch the match.

'It all sounds a bit queer to me,' replied Danny, tilting his pork pie hat in an attempt to prevent the rain from running down the back of his neck.

'Men in tights and makeup, fuck that.' Pete added with a grin, taking a drag from one of a never ending stream of cigarettes.

'It aint that bad,' said Nipper defensively. 'There's always some sniff floating around, and that Rusty Egan plays some decent music which me and Holly like.'

'Rusty Egan … what, Rusty Egan who plays in the Rich Kids with Glen Matlock? enquired Danny, blowing at the drips of rain which were running down the bridge of his nose.

'Played mate … played,' replied Nipper knowledgably. 'Yeah! He plays a bit of Bowie, Roxy, and electronica like Kraftwerk, as well as the usual disco stuff. Y'know Chic and all that.'

'DISCO!' exclaimed Pete in a mocking falsetto voice.

'Yeah! Disco you cunt!' replied Nipper abrasively.

Pete was starting to wind him up again. In the past year or so his best friend had become too opinionated, too smug, and too dependent on drugs for his liking. Tonight, like most nights, he looked ill. The 'some girls gonna be lucky tonight' ace face had a ghostly cadaverous pallor. Pete, with his hollowed cheeks, yellowed teeth, gaunt frame, and bad attitude was maturing rapidly into a seedy looking, toxic bachelor.

'Fancy doing some drugs?' Nipper shook his head, recalling Pete's now all to common call to action whenever they would meet up at a gig, or to go to watch the Chels. The trouble was, Pete wasn't doing drugs, they were doing him.

Nipper had fallen out with Pete a couple of times mainly over money and a couple of times over Holly. He had a reasonably well-paid job working as a courier for a photographic agency in Soho. The job paid weekly, and he was always flush and flash in the Spice of Life on a Friday night. A bit of whiz and a spliff made a Friday night for most people in Nipper's world, but it wasn't enough for Pete who had progressed from chasing the occasional dragon, to skin popping.

Heroin had been glamorised by Pete's punk hero Sid Vicious. Despite Sid's self destruction and untimely death the previous year, Pete still held him in high esteem and a heroin habit coupled with the kitsch, wasted youth lifestyle that went with it he considered to be the epitome of cool.

Wasted youth … cool! Bollocks to that! thought Nipper.

Holly had summed Pete up easily enough. 'He's pretty vacant, just like the Pistols song', she'd grumbled, after an afternoon of garbled conversation with her brother at their fathers birthday drink the previous month.

'There's no point in asking you'll get no reply, oh just remember I don't decide. I've got no reason it's all too much … you'll always find us out to lunch'.

Nipper didn't understand heroin. For him it was a hippy drug. Who wants to be out of control? Fuck that! He'd seen people strung out on it. Such a short buzz, hours on the nod, and then the sickness. Tolerance was quick, the gear was relatively cheap and available, and overdoses were frequent.

Tommy Philips was doing his best to straighten his son out, putting up with Pete's nausea, vomiting, cramps, sweating and vicious mood swings, when most parents would have called the police or the welfare, or simply just given up. The methadone treatment was supposedly working, Pete hadn't been using for that long, and Tommy said that he was sorting him out with doses of just 20mg a day.

* * * * *

'You're a touchy fucker aincha,' said Pete, prodding Nipper in the ribs and motioning him through the turnstiles. 'You wanna be a little less critical and a bit more rock and roll. You might enjoy life more.'

'Rock and roll!' scowled Pete, 'I'm rock and roll enough. You mate, you fucking stupid smack head. You're just gonna wind up with a rock and roll death. You wont be happy unless you're found dead at the bottom of a swimming pool, strapped into the seat of some flash motor with a bottle of bubbly in yer hand. Or maybe found lying face down in a pool of yer own vomit with a needle sticking out of yer arm.'

'Or shot dead by a transvestite, like Marvin Gaye was,' interjected Danny Green, trying to defuse the situation with humour.

'That was his dad, you fat cunt,' chuckled Nipper as they made their way onto the terraces.

'Are you saying my dad's a cross dresser you twat?' asked Pete, grinning from ear to ear as he looked around to see who was and wasn't at the game tonight.

'Whaddya mean?' asked Danny, pointing out the familiar faces of Fuck Off Colin, Duncan Disorderly and Riddler Rowan.

'Marvin Gaye was shot dead by his dad ... who just happened to be an occasional transvestite as well as a fundamentalist preacher,' answered Pete, his attention being drawn to the game which had now kicked off. 'Come on the Chels.'

'Nipper's a transvestite ... ooh go on Johnny B, luverly ball my son.' Danny Green's flow was interrupted by some fantastic one touch football by Chelsea which had the travelling support applauding loudly.

'I aint a transvestite.'

'You wear tights and lipstick when you go to the Blitz.'

'That's me outfit you twat! Robin Hood mate, I go dressed as Robin Hood ... he wore tights because it was the fashion at the time.'

'Bollocks! What about the lipstick? Robin Hood never wore lipstick did he. You're Stoke on bleedin Trent I reckon.'

'Fuck off! I'm not bent ... Oh come on Chelsea, for fucks sake.'

'Come on you yellows ... come on you yellows.' The roar was deafening. Despite this being an away match for Chelsea, playing in their change strip of yellow shirts and blue shorts, almost half of Rangers' biggest crowd of the season were there to cheer on the visitors.

'Oh you fucking cunt! ... Bollocks!' Nipper buried his face in his hands as Clive Allen struck a wicked free kick from the edge of the box that sailed past Chelsea's often erratic Yugoslav goalkeeper Petar Borota into the back of the net.

'The cat would've caught that,' said Pete, sniffing the back of his hand and watching as a large space opened up in Loft. The end where the home supporters gathered had been infiltrated by a couple of hundred Chelsea boys who rapidly muted the goal celebrations of those around them.

'Chelsea aggro, Chelsea aggro ... hello, hello.'

'Imagine what a cunt you'd look like if you was having a ruck dressed as Robin Hood,' said Danny Green, looking on intently as Old Bill did their best to restore order.

'Watch the game ... watch the game,' said Nipper as Tommy Langley shimmied past a couple of Rangers defenders before turning to shoot at goal. 'Go on my son ... YES!'

'1-1, that'll do ... take us back to the top of the table on goal difference if everything else stays the same ... right who fancies a pie and a Bovril?' said Danny applauding at the referees half time whistle and rubbing his stomach.

'Do all the blokes at the Blitz wear tights Nipper?' smirked Pete, putting his arm around Danny Green as they made their way to the refreshment kiosk. 'Cos if they did,' he continued, not waiting for a reply to his question, 'Fatboy 'ere could go as Henry the Eighth.'

'At least it's stopped raining now eh,' said Pete as play restarted with Chelsea attacking towards the goal they were facing.

'The pitch is heavy though ... mind you look at Chopper go, not bad for an old un,' said Nipper, as Ron 'chopper' Harris showed some excellent close control of the ball before laying it off to Ian Britton.

'Johnny B wants it ... give ... give ... Yes GOAL!' Danny Green threw the remains of his pie in the air as John Bumstead latched onto Britton's through ball and slotted it coolly under the body of Rangers' keeper Chris Woods.

'Jingle bells, jingle bells, jingle all the way ... oh what fun it is to sing when the Chelsea win away.' The seasonal chant reverberated around the confines of Loftus Road, and despite intense Rangers pressure, it looked like Chelsea were going to hang on for a great victory.

'Out, out ... keep it out Chels. How long left Nipper?' enquired an ever fidgety Pete, chewing at the nicotine stained fingernails of his right hand.

'A couple of minutes mate,' replied Nipper, looking at his watch and then at Pete, wondering if his friend was tense because of the way the game was poised, or because he was craving his next dose of methadone.

'Oh you cunt ... you are fucking joking!' exclaimed Danny Green, dropping to his knees in anguish as Clive Allen scored with a spectacular overhead volley to level the game at 2-2.

'What a pisser,' said Pete as the referee blew for full time with honours even.

'Right I'm off,' announced Nipper, patting his two friends on the back before pushing his way through the crowd towards the exit gate.

'Oi Nipper! ... Nipper stop.' shouted Danny, waving his left arm frantically in the air.

'What?' said Nipper, turning his head back to see what Fatboy wanted.

'You've forgot this mate,' continued Danny, a broad grin etched on his chubby face.

'What is it?' enquired an irate looking Nipper, struggling to keep on his feet as the crowd surged towards the exit.

'Your lipstick, you fucking puff,' hollered Pete, cupping his hands around his mouth so that everyone could hear.

'Wankers!' replied Nipper, laughing as he turned in haste and scurried out of the stadium.

* * * * *

Holly had been sitting in the Finborough Arms waiting for Nipper to get back from work for what felt like an eternity. Locking herself out of the flat they shared in nearby Ifield Road hadn't been the best move she could have made, especially after such a heavy night at the Blitz. The last place she wanted to be was sitting in a pub on her own, but her choices had been limited. Standing outside in the rain wasn't an option, going back into London would have been a right royal pain in the arse, and sitting in the laundrette next door, with a bearded wino and a couple of nerdy looking students for company would have been too unnerving.

The Finborough was a smokey, dimly lit establishment frequented mainly by local residents and thespians who congregated there when plays were performed at the pubs in-house theatre. Even though the Finborough was a stones throw from the flat, Holly had only ventured inside once previously, and that had been to buy a packet of cigarettes. Nipper referred to it as a 'match-day drinker', a place where he and his Chelsea cronies would meet before and after games to chew the football fat and wash it down with a glass or six of lager.

Holly toyed with the packet of Benson's on the table in front of her, contemplating whether or not to smoke yet another cigarette just for the hell of it. Having lived with Nipper for a few months she was finally getting to understand his psyche, and the way he engineered maximum results with minimal effort in almost every area of his life. He was fanciable and charismatic. He had nerve, verve, and a sharp line in self salesmanship that women found irresistible; together she thought they could make a formidable partnership.

It had been her own father that had made the suggestion that she should maybe look at moving out. 'Just for a short while, until I get soppy bollocks Pete here sorted out', he'd said, referring to the Herculean task of getting her brother off the heroin.

'Why don't you move in with Nipper?', he'd suggested. Why not indeed? Nipper hadn't been averse to the idea, in fact he'd positively welcomed it. Holly Philips was his drink on a stick, a doll faced lolly to lick. She epitomised femininity without ever looking girly. She had ambition, know how, and knew how to talk to people; personality traits which Nipper found magnetically sexy.

110 Ifield Road, described by the letting agent as a 'fully furnished, bijou, pied-a-terre residence for the modern couple', was a short walk from Earls Court tube station. It was also close to Stamford Bridge, something that Nipper had regarded as an extra bonus. It was the first place they'd looked at together.

The flat was immaculate. Minimalist furniture, stripped pine floors, large tropical plants potted in ornate, oriental earthenware and framed Japanese and Chinese water colours hanging on walls that were painted in neutral pastel shades. The decision was unanimous and swift. Holly and Nipper were now an item.

Holly smiled as she thought about their blossoming relationship. Picking up the packet of Benson's, she slowly put a cigarette to her mouth, scanning the room as she did so. She'd already noticed the man stood at the bar who kept constantly raising his eyes from the pages of the Evening Standard he was reading to look over in her direction.

Holly had a sixth sense when it came to men; they were all dirty old bastards with one thing on their mind. Checking her out, mentally undressing her, and then going home to wank themselves off. Filthy cunts!

Out of the corner of her eye she could see he was about forty, give or take a couple of years. He was smartly dressed in an expensive looking navy pinstriped suit and white open necked shirt. Dark and handsome, with a square jaw and a brooding presence, he had the look of a man who could make a girl go weak at the knees.

It was still relatively early; Holly had left a note for Nipper under the doorknocker telling him where she was. He never usually got home before seven, but she'd hoped that if he was as fatigued as she was then he might be home earlier.

Holly smoked the Benson to the filter before stubbing it out and finishing her drink. She knew the man at the bar was trying to make some sort of move on her, and was just waiting for his opening line, which she'd already convinced herself would be along the lines of, 'on a night like this, what's a pretty girl like you doing all alone?'

Holly got up and ordered another shot of Southern Comfort, and as she reached into her pocket and placed a handful of loose change on the bar, the man looked over and informed the barman that he'd pay for it. Instinctively, she tipped her head back and frowned, forcing a smile as she resigned herself to having to deal diplomatically with the potentially embarrassing situation she felt sure would now ensue.

'I'm sorry to bother you my dear,' said the man warmly. 'I hope you don't think that in buying you a drink I am trying to make a pass at you.' The cut glass English enunciation took Holly by surprise. 'It's … it's just that you look very familiar,' he continued hesitantly, as if sensing that she might suspect he had an ulterior motive. 'I've been trying to place your face but I can't, and … and it's really starting to annoy me.'

Holly looked him directly in the eyes. He was handsome, handsome enough to remember, but she was convinced that she'd never seen him prior to this meeting.

'Listen mate,' she replied sardonically, 'I'm waiting for my boyfriend, I don't know who you are, but … well thanks for the drink. I'm not interested … do you get my my drift.'

Holly felt slightly nervous as she sipped at her drink and lit another Benson before continuing her justification. 'Look, I've only lived around here for a few months, and I don't hang out or work around here, so I can't see how you would recognise me.'

Uninvited, the man pulled over a chair and sat down next to Holly. He took his wallet from his jacket, opened it and removed a business card which he placed on the table in front of her. The company name, Global Fashions, was embossed in blue ink and adjacent to it was a silver crescent moon logo. The man's name was Steve Bruno, and his job title, Managing Director.

Holly looked up and smiled at him. 'Very impressive, but I've never heard of you or your company.' Glimpsing outside the window as she spoke, she'd noticed that the rain had finally stopped. She'd give Nipper another ten minutes and then take a walk up to Earls Court.

'Look, I spend a lot of time in and around the London fashion markets, I'm sure I've seen you at one or all of them … Kensington or maybe Camden?' persisted Mr Bruno, narrowing the field with his line of enquiry that aroused Holly's curiosity sufficiently enough to warrant a question of her own.

'Er maybe, so anyway what do you do?' she asked, sitting back in her chair and pushing her fingers through her hair.

Bruno looked visibly relieved at Holly's apparent change of mood as he sparked up a foul smelling continental cigarette.

'So I'm right eh?' he said, exhaling acrid blue smoke as he spoke. 'Maybe I have seen you around … it must be Kensington … that scarf on your coat there that's from Trixie Fowler's stall isn't it?'

Holly's eyes widened as she picked up the scarf and nodded. 'Very impressive Mr Bruno … Global Fashions eh, what's that all about then? You aint some sort of trading standards company are you?'

Bruno looked at Holly, nicotine yellowed teeth bared, dark eyes narrowing. 'Listen love, don't be so suspicious. I'm a business man working primarily in the import and export of haute couture. I also own the freehold of three shops in Covent Garden, and pay the leases on several stalls and a couple of shops, including Trixie Fowler's, at Kensington Market … that's just the tip of the Global Fashions iceberg.'

'Listen mate, do yourself a favour and don't call me love … ALL RIGHT! … ouch!' Holly, agitated as she was with Steve Bruno's condescending demeanour knew a meal ticket when she saw one, and prevented herself from blurting out anything derogatory by biting on her bottom lip. Here was the sort of man who might own the key to the door she wanted opening. An apology was in order.

Regaining her composure, Holly pouted her lips and touched them with the index finger of her right hand. 'Sorry for being such an obnoxious cow,' she sighed, 'but the weather's shit, and I've locked myself out of my flat.'

Bruno winked at her and smiled. 'That's okay. All I said was that I recognised your face from somewhere you know … plus the scarf thing. I wasn't trying it on darling, anyway you're not my type.'

Holly looked at Bruno and wondered exactly what his type might be, but decided to stick to a less personal topic of conversation. 'That's okay mate. Tell you what Mr Steve Bruno,' she said enthusiastically. 'Why don't you buy me another Southern Comfort and tell me about your business. It sounds very interesting. I love fashion … especially Trixie Fowler's stuff, she's great.'

Holly lightened up as her natural female inquisitiveness came to the fore. So Bruno leased Trixie Fowler's shop back to her. Holly was only on nodding terms with the woman. Trixie was a friend of Jamie Black, one of Nipper's old punk mates from the Roxy, and she was certain that the baby she always had with her was his, but she'd always forgot to ask Nipper to confirm her assumption one way or another.

Trixie's shop, Heroes, redefined avant-garde. Heroes, was well known by everyone into what was soon to be christened the 'New Romantic' scene. It was also somewhere to hangout and get noticed.

When you walked into Heroes, you felt like you were somewhere special. The flooring was kicked in hardwood, and the fittings made of polished steel. It had the ambience of an expensive designer boutique, but the clothes, a mix of modern art school couture and Italian retro, were affordable to most. The exclusivity came with the cut. Only catwalk clothes-horses could wear Trixie's creations with confidence, and waif-like Holly was a regular customer.

'Southern Comfort, there you go. So anyway what's your name then? You do have one don't you?' Bruno placed the glass on the table and Holly smiled coyly at him, offering her hand to shake and then pulling it away and thumbing her nose like a cheeky five year old.

'Holly … Holly Philips,' she replied, a mischievous grin lighting up her face.

Steve Bruno looked aghast! But with pleasantries exchanged, he willingly provided answers as Holly set about probing his involvement with Trixie and seeking an understanding of the precise nature of the Global Fashions business model.

Bruno explained that he had access to a number of well known and up and coming clothes designers lines that addressed specific markets. His business success had come from an intrinsic ability to put match the right people with the right creations and locate them in a place where maximum sales potential could be realised. In the same way that a precocious child would listen to the wise words of an elderly relative, Holly sat spellbound as she listened to the mans life story.

He was clearly older than he looked, having started trading as Global Fashions from a small room above John Stephen's boutique on Carnaby Street in the early '60s. John Stephen's. Yeah! She was sure her dad Tommy had mentioned the place on one of his occasional trips down his own personal memory lane of Mod. Bruno then mentioned that he'd also run a stall on Kensington Market in the early '70s, 'next to those awfully nice rock and roll Queen boys before they were famous', he'd added camply.

Holly, a sucker for a name, was becoming intoxicated. Not only by the several Southern Comfort's she'd drunk on an empty stomach, but also by the potential leg up that she felt sure her new acquaintance could offer her. 'Just the tip of the iceberg' eh. She wondered about the other pies that he might have his porky little digits in, and just how tasty they might be, but she resisted the urge to ask more questions, remaining content with the information he was imparting.

It was only when he finally explained how he had made the mistake of trying to continue to front a business based on young fashion ideals, when he himself was getting woefully out of touch and old, that Holly spoke up.

'Things are moving so fast now, you need young hungry people to make things happen,' she said knowledgably. 'To get the right type of customer in your shop Mr Bruno, you need to create desire. That's what I learnt when I worked at Malcolm McLaren's shop, and that's what Trixie Fowler is good at. You've gotta align the rhythm with the threads.'

Steve Bruno looked impressed.

'Very well put young lady,' he said, looking at his watch and tutting as he did so.

'I've got some idea's,' replied Holly confidently. 'Perhaps you'd let me share them with you some time, I can see you have to leave now.'

'Great idea,' said Bruno genuinely. 'You've got my number, use it.'

Holly smiled and congratulated herself on curbing her impetuousness. Whilst she had ambition, she lacked ideas. She wanted to talk to Nipper about Steve Bruno. What she needed, … no, what they needed, was a plan.

Just before 7pm Steve Bruno bade Holly farewell, kissing her hand as he got up to leave.

'Yes!' crowed Holly jubilantly, clenching her right fist as the door swung shut behind him. 'Fucking yes!'

5

THE REPUTATION OF THE CLUB

'Goddess on the mountain top ... burning like a silver flame ... the summit of beauty and love ... and Venus was her name.'

Holly was sat in the passenger seat of Trixie Fowler's VW Beetle. Even though it had just gone 11pm, the traffic was still sluggish as they headed into the West End after another frantic days trading at Kensington Market.

'Maybe we should've got the tube,' said Trixie, shaking her leonine blonde mane of hair so it rippled over her shoulders and hid the spaghetti straps of her low cut dress.

'Maybe,' replied Holly, pausing to moisten the gummed strip of a king-size Rizla paper in which she'd evened up a heady mix of Sensimillia and Old Holborn. 'But then we wouldn't be able smoke this,' she continued, holding up the spliff she'd finished rolling. 'Or listen to this,' she concluded, reaching for the volume control of the Beetle's stereo, whose speakers were being tested to the limit by Bananarama's dancefloor rework of the Swinging Blue Jeans classic, 'Venus'.

'She's got it ... yeah baby she's got it ... I'm your Venus ... I'm your fire ... at your desire.'

Holly lit the spliff, drawing its potent smoke down deep into her lungs.

'This is seriously good shit,' she said, exhaling and tilting her head back onto the well worn headrest of her seat. 'You know the name Sensimillia is derived from the Spanish words *sin semilla*, which mean 'without seed' ... when the female marijuana plant is prevented from being fertilized, it grows full of resin which was intended to make seeds.'

'Yeah, yeah ... get you. David Bellamy,' interrupted Trixie brusquely. 'Spare me the botany lecture and give us a toke ... I'm gagging for it,' she continued, laughing as she rapped her fingers on the top of the steering wheel in time with the music.

'Sorry darling,' apologised Holly, as she took another long drag on the spliff before handing it over and winding down her window. 'It's Nipper, he's a proper bore when it comes to drugs. He has to know everything about them before he takes them into his system.'

Holly smiled as she felt herself being cerebrally elevated by the almost instantaneous mellow herbal high that smoking Sensi bestowed upon her. Life was good. Life was very good indeed. With Steve Bruno's help, she'd been able to secure a renewable six month lease on an upstairs unit in the main part of Kensington Market.

Modelled on Trixie Fowler's, Heroes emporium. Holly had come up with Babelicious ... clubwear for glamour girls. The style of the stock transmuted itself as the fashions changed. Extravagant New Romantic designs had given way to understated, pared down, retro styled hot-pants and mini-skirts. The dividing line between clubwear and beachwear had become negligible, and Babelicious became the in-place for happening London girls to get themselves kitted out in the shimmeringly sexy clothes that would get them noticed on dancefloors at home and abroad.

In the midst of the Thatcherite era, young people were heading to holiday hotspots in their droves. This was the era of the Yuppie, everyone was on the make, and everyone was on the take. The club scene was a thriving, steaming hot mishmash of hip hop, break-beat, disco, electronic funk, speed and sweat. Perfect for Holly's clothes, and perfect for Holly.

★ ★ ★ ★ ★

Whilst Holly measured her progress against the commercial success of Babelicious, Nipper's life was still entwined with the fortunes of Chelsea Football Club. Back in 1980, New Romantic Nipper's eyeliner had been tear streaked as Chelsea, under the stewardship of Geoff Hurst, had thrown away the chance of promotion in the final couple of weeks of that season.

In 1984, after five years of trying, which included a couple of flirtations with relegation to the Third Division, the avoidance of bankruptcy through the Club's acquisition by tough talking dairy farmer and Captain Birdseye look-alike Ken Bates, and yet another change of manager, Chelsea had returned to the First Division, pipping Sheffield Wednesday to the Second Division championship on goal difference.

'We're proud of you, we're proud of you ... we're proud of you Chelsea,' had been the chant from the thousands of Blues fans who had journeyed across London to witness their teams return to the big time. A 1-1 draw with Arsenal, in a game that had kicked off at 11-30am, had been the outcome. Chelsea, challenging for a place in Europe, finished a credible sixth that first season back in the top flight.

Off the pitch, unruly elements of Chelsea's support had also been making a name for themselves. The violent exploits of the Chelsea Head-Hunters, whose ranks included bruisers like Fuck Off Colin, Duncan Disorderly and Belfast Billy, were widely reported by the red tops and broadsheets alike.

The Harrington, Sta-Prest, Fred Perry, boots and braces, skinhead style of the '70s, had gradually been replaced by an altogether more sophisticated casual look. Tommy Philips loved a game of golf, and Pete hadn't failed to notice how smart his dad looked when he went off to play a round. Once a Mod, always a Mod.

Pete adopted the style. A nice v necked Pringle sweater worn over a Lyle & Scott roll neck set the ball rolling. Within months, teams the length and breadth of the country had their own designer label laden firms of Casual hooligans, who were as proud of their attire as they were of their fighting prowess.

The Shed, perhaps the most critical terrace catwalk of them all, was home to several Casual mobs. Pete, Nipper and Danny were an integral part of the Tea Bar Casuals who took their name directly from the section of the Shed terrace were they stood. Unsurprisingly, the focal point of this part of the terrace was a dilapidated tea bar which served a variety of over-expensive, stewed drinks that tasted like they had been made with boiled rainwater.

Money, nothing to be ashamed of. Thatcher had seen to that. If you've got it, flaunt it. Wearing expensive designer labels was the most immediate way of making a visible statement, and once again the terraces were the perfect stage for the proud preening peacocks who followed football to strut their stuff. For many, the Tea Bar Casuals included, the violence was incidental.

Supporters of the big London clubs would argue that they held sway in the fashion stakes, but light fingered Liverpool fans returning home from European sorties wearing the latest Chemise Lacoste polo shirts, Sergio Tacchini tracksuit bottoms, and Diadora Borg Elite trainers saw it differently.

Inside the football grounds, rival supporters were kept apart by fences. Outside the grounds, lawlessness prevailed. Wearing a Jimmy Connors Cerruti tracksuit over a pair of Adidas Forest Hills, the ones with the three gold stripes down the side, made even the most unfit of Casuals believe they were fleet enough of foot to evade arrest.

Unlike the skinheads of yesteryear, easily identified by their uniform, the Casuals could ease up from a chase in any given high street and melt into the background. Weapons, what weapons? The Stanley knife had a fearsome reputation, but a knife was a knife, and only the most psychopathic of hooligans would risk their liberty by carrying a blade. What better way to top off your brand new smart casual image than with a nice bit of chunky gold tomfoolery. Yeah, jewellery! A belcher chain necklace and a nice heavy gold sovereign ring completed the look for many a Casual.

In the early '80s, man hour after man hour was spent by doctors and nurses in A&E departments of hospitals to the north, south, east and west of the country, suturing facial wounds inflicted by fists whose fingers were be-ringed with ancient gold coins of the realm.

As Chelsea embarked on their second season in the First Division the team, now managed by John Hollins, were playing on a pitch that Ken Bates had seen fit to completely surround with a high fence. If the height of the fence proved to be an insufficient deterrent to those miscreants who sought to scale it in order to get at opposing fans, old Batesey had planned to pass an electric current through it just for good measure.

Stamford Bridge was also equipped with closed circuit television that enabled the police to take film and photographs of any persons involved in disorder. A football league announcement had stated that CCTV was there to improve crowd safety and to help the police by providing evidence that could be used in the courts. In turn, the police were given the power to deal with any person who involved himself in disorder or committed a criminal offence. This could mean arrest and prosecution for the alleged wrongdoer.

The Heysel tragedy in Brussels highlighted to the world what had become known as the English disease. UEFA authorities decided that the most effective way to prevent its most virulent strain, football hooliganism, from infecting the rest of Europe, would be to invoke an immediate ban on our clubs competing abroad.

Margaret Thatcher stated that good behaviour at football must be based on three points. 'Persuasion, prevention, and punishment'. Ken Bates suggested that if the serious law breakers could be regularly identified and properly punished, and by this he meant locked up, then football could once again claim its place as the worlds greatest sport.

'Bollocks!', was the general consensus of the hooligan fraternity.

When the new season had started, it had been business as usual.

'Well you've got to haven't you babe, the reputation of the club is at stake', had been Nipper's reply to Holly, when she'd quizzed him about his arrest following a scuffle between the TBC and Luton Town's MIG (men in gear) at an away match in September.

'When Pates went up to lift the Members' Cup we were there, we were there.'

On March 23rd Chelsea triumphed at Wembley. Having defeated Portsmouth, Charlton, West Brom, and Oxford along the way, Chelsea beat Manchester City 5-4 in the inaugural final of the now defunct Full Members' Cup.

4th in the First Division, Chelsea were confounding their critics. But not for long. The following Saturday, Easter weekend, West Ham visited Stamford Bridge and won

4-0. During the course of a post match fracas at Victoria Station with the East London clubs notorious ICF (Inter City Firm) and the police, Nipper had picked up a litter bin and hurled it across the concourse at an advancing line of Old Bill. He'd been arrested and charged with causing an affray and wilful damage.

On Easter Monday, Nipper and the rest of the TBC were out in full force at Loftus Road to witness QPR wallop Chelsea 6-0. In the rhyming slang world of Riddler Rowan, the great god of football was having a 'tin bath', a proper laugh.

Ten goals conceded without reply in the space of four days. The glorious unpredictability of following Chelsea Football Club was testing the patience of many supporters. Nipper's view was that the slump in form had a lot to do with the recent dreadful knee injury sustained the week before the Members' Cup Final by regular goalkeeper Eddie Niedzwiecki.

Almost 30,000 were at Stamford Bridge to witness the West Ham debacle, the next home game against Ipswich a week later was played in front of just 13,000. The TBC were there, but it was to be the last time they would visit the ground that season.

* * * * *

'Chim chimernee, chim chimernee, chim chim cheroo ... we hate those bastards in claret and blue,' sang Nipper as he'd sat in the bath the night before Chelsea were due to play West Ham at Upton Park in a rearranged midweek fixture.

Holly laughed at the lyrics. Not quite what Walt Disney would've had in mind for Julie Andrews and Dick van Dyke to sing in his film adaptation of the P.L. Travers classic children's book, Mary Poppins.

'It's gonna go off tomorrow night with the chimney sweeps, and when it does we're gonna have a pop at Old Bill ... fucking liberty takers, I aint forgotten what happened to me on Easter Saturday', he'd offered, by way of an explanation for what the TBC had planned for the following evening.

There wasn't much Holly could do to dissuade Nipper. If the truth be told, she didn't give a shit. They still had that love thing going on between them. Nipper had his job, and she had Babelicious. Babelicious was her consuming passion, she was making money, she had new friends, and most of all she was having fun. So if Nipper and her brother wanted to jump on the District Line to play Cowboys and Indians across the capital with their overgrown schoolboy friends, stupid nicknames and all, then that was their business. It was a bloke thing and they could all fuck off.

With hindsight she might have asked a few more questions when Nipper told her that Fatboy Green was going to drive the TBC down to Plymouth immediately after the West Ham game in his white transit van. They would take the roll-on-roll-off ferry from Plymouth to Santander in northern Spain. The plan was to take a bit of time out on the Cornisa Cantabrica before heading south to Madrid, from there they would make for the port of Denia. Depending on cash flow they would then either take a ferry direct to Ibiza, or get some work in nearby Benidorm to pay for the passage.

For the past two years, always at the end of the football season, Holly, Nipper, Pete, Trixie and some of the others had been spending up to a month on the Balearic island of Ibiza. The place had a laid back hippy feel to it, and a soothing vibe which eased the stress of life in London. But that was always at the end of the season, not with quite a few fixtures still remaining. Holly was puzzled.

★ ★ ★ ★ ★

'When I was a little bitty boy, my grandmama bought me a cute little toy. A Chelsea fan on a piece of string ... she taught me to kick its fucking head in ... fucking head in, fucking head in ... she taught me to kick its fucking head in.'

'Listen to them poxy Hammers fans,' said Chiller, turning up the collar of his Aquascutum raincoat. 'Chuck Berry wouldn't be too enamoured with that version of 'My Ding A Ling' now would he eh?' he continued, shaking his head and pushing Danny Green away from him so that he didn't accidentally tread on his brand new Giorgio Armani brogues.

'Not half catalogue man,' replied Danny, laughing as he looked over his shoulder at Chiller, whose lean wiry physique was clad in vestments that would have cost most people a months wages.

Jack Chillman, otherwise known as Chiller, was a relative newcomer when it came to watching Chelsea. Now a confirmed Tea Bar Casual, who undeniably took his clothes very seriously, Chiller had first met Pete, Nipper and Danny at Newport Pagnell services on the M1.

Attired in a navy blue and red trimmed Kappa sweater, Ellesse tracksuit bottoms, and Adidas Trim Trab trainers, Chiller had looked the part, and they'd automatically assumed that he was a Chelsea fan travelling back from watching the teams 2-1 away defeat at Grimsby Town.

'Oi mate did you get that jumper from Stuarts on the Uxbridge Road?' Pete had enquired, as they'd queued to buy tea and sandwiches whilst waiting for Solly Lewis to organise a 'replacement' car for the stolen BMW they'd been heading home in which had inconsiderately been burning oil for the last fifty odd miles.

'Yeah, you know that', had been the reply.

During the label riddled conversation that ensued, it transpired that Jack Chillman, a clothes and music obsessed bricklayer from the Surrey commuter belt town of Dorking, supplemented his income with a spot of male modelling. He was returning to London from Leeds where he'd been involved in a photo shoot for a new range of gym equipment.

Chiller, whose grandfather was Jamaican, had inherited a love of Caribbean music. Reggae, soca, ska, calypso, gospel, jazz and soul, you name it, he was into it. Influenced by his older brother Max, a skanking, QPR supporting Rude Boy, Chiller would take the train up to London with him on match days. Max would go to the game, and Jack, who had no interest in football, would spend the afternoon moseying down the Uxbridge Road checking out the latest dub plates and twelve inch imports at Websters Record Shack in Shepherds Bush Market, before finally winding up at Stuarts, where he'd spend the rest of his weeks wages on the latest Gabicci zip up top or Adidas Shell Toe trainers.

'Mate, I cant believe you dress like that and aint never been to a game. You should see it when we go away. Brilliant buzz. Funnily enough, we're playing Leeds United away next Saturday, you should come, its gonna be one hell of a day'. Pete had tempted Chiller, explaining the bitter rivalry that existed between the two clubs, and exaggerating the quintessentially unique mob handed thrill to be had from swaggering down the street of some nondescript town, defacing its walls with aerosol graffiti, smashing up phone boxes, baiting Old Bill, chatting up shop girls, swearing at the locals and cheering on the Chels.

Chiller bought Pete's sales pitch and made the trip to Leeds United. He'd revelled in the hostile atmosphere, been riveted by the match, a classic 3-3 draw, and subsequently sampled the delights of the Shed the following weekend when hardly anyone turned up to see the Blues beat Blackburn. Chelsea avoided relegation to the old Third Division by the skin of their teeth that season, and the reggae boy was hooked.

★ ★ ★ ★ ★

'*Ne ne ne ne, ne ne ne ne, Spackman,*' chanted the Chelsea supporters in an entertaining bastardisation of the Batman theme, as gritty midfielder Nigel Spackman saluted them. It was his equaliser that had put Chelsea back on track after West Ham had taken the lead. The Blues were good value for the 2-1 victory, and the result left them in fourth place, just one point behind Man Utd with a couple of games in hand.

'Pat Nevin scoring the winner with a header, unbelievable!' said Pete to Solly Lewis as they applauded the victorious Chelsea players from the pitch.

'Yeah but it was a great cross from Kerry, wasn't it,' replied Solly, looking down the terrace and giving the thumbs up to Nipper who, along with Riddler Rowan, was high fiving Eggy Barnes, the newest member of the TBC.

On the Wednesday morning following his Easter Saturday arrest at Victoria Station, Nipper had been pacing up and down the steps outside Horseferry Road Magistrates Court. Chain smoking away the time before his scheduled 10am appearance before the Beak, he'd wondered what the SP would be this time. Old Bill, the judiciary, and the media in general were taking a much dimmer view of terrace related violence, and some stiff sentences had already started to be handed down.

A custodial sentence was the last thing Nipper wanted on his CV right now. A smacked wrist, a night in the cells, and a fine was one thing, but a trip down Du Cane Road to Wormwood Scrubs nick was an altogether different proposition.

In court, Nipper was polite and apologetic. He'd accepted the veiled threats of a custodial sentence from the magistrate and considered it a result that he had got away with a very reasonable £80 fine and 250 hours community service. It would be a bit of a bastard having to do the community service on Saturday afternoons next season, but fuck it he still had his liberty.

With his freedom assured, and over an hour to go until the pubs opened, Nipper had decided to while away the time sitting at the back of the court observing his fellow miscreants being dealt with. He'd watched and listened intently as the next defendant, a wedge haired, carrot topped, broad shouldered man wearing a very natty Chevignon jacket took the stand.

Edward Egbert Barnes, a roofer from Earlsfield in South West London. Nipper recognised him, but couldn't be sure if he was Chelsea or not. Egbert though. Fuck me! You'd wanna keep that one quiet from your mates, he'd thought to himself, stifling a laugh as the arresting officer described how he had initially seen Barnes urinating into a milk bottle in the toilets at Victoria Station.

The arrest had been effected because the copper, who'd been in plain clothes, believed that the bottle and its contents were going to be thrown at a group of youths nearby who were being escorted out of the station by his colleagues. Barnes had resisted arrest, and the copper had been covered in piss as both men had tumbled down the stairs onto the main station concourse during the scuffle that ensued.

The magistrate had asked Barnes to account for his actions, and Nipper had been suitably impressed by the novel explanation given. Barnes stated that he'd continuously forgotten during the course of the previous week that he had been asked by his doctor to provide a urine sample which was required to check if he had a kidney infection; his memory had been jogged when he'd seen the bottle on the window ledge in the toilet. He hadn't seen the officer display his warrant card, he'd simply thought he was a chancer who was trying to mug him.

It was a plausible, well articulated rationalization of events, and the magistrate, taking into account the fact that Barnes had no previous convictions, gave him an unconditional discharge. Talk about taking the piss. Whoever he supported, Nipper wanted to buy Edward Egbert Barnes a pint.

★ ★ ★ ★ ★

'Do the filth ... come on lets have it,' yelled Riddler Rowan, flicking his right wrist and opening out the fearsome telescopic truncheon he had just drawn from the inside pocket of the lightweight Burberry mac he was wearing.

Pete, Nipper, Fatboy Green, Chiller, Eggy Barnes, Solly Lewis and Riddler Rowan were fronting six mounted police officers and two dog handlers who were barring their entrance to Pragel Street, one of the many blind alleys that fed off the Barking Road, the main thoroughfare that bypassed West Ham's Boleyn Ground.

As the mounted police officers advanced, riot sticks at the ready, Pete, Eggy Barnes and Chiller reached into their pockets grabbing fistfuls of the glass marbles they had kept carefully concealed, ready for this eventuality.

'Wankers!' they screamed in unison, hurling a shower of marbles along the street and standing back momentarily to watch as the panicked horses reared up, neighing in blinkered bemused terror before throwing their riders to the floor. It was an apocalyptic sight, a modern day medieval joust, floodlit by streetlamps and watched by a curious crowd of local residents, mainly Bengali immigrants, who had gathered a safe distance away at the far end of the street.

'Watch the dogs … watch the dogs,' bellowed Fatboy as they dodged past a snarling Alsatian, a split second before its handler allowed it to run onto its long leash.

'That's for Notting Hill you fascist cunts,' bellowed Pete. 'I aint forgotten,' he snarled, lashing out with his right foot as one of the grounded policemen tried to grab his legs.

'Toe to toe with Old Bill, that's how I like it,' growled Nipper, thrusting a clenched fist in the face of the officer who was trying to wrestle him to the floor. 'The van … get to the van,' he yelled to the others, watching the bloody nosed policeman slump unconscious to the pavement before charging after Chiller and Eggy Barnes who were already halfway up Pragel Street.

'In, in. Get in now!' screamed Pete, opening the rear doors of Fatboy Green's transit van, which under heavy revs was being expertly restrained by Solly Lewis' intuitive use of its clutch, accelerator and handbrake.

'Oi, oi, oi … watch the threads,' said Chiller, as Eggy Barnes bundled him into the back of the van before hauling himself inside.

'Where's Riddler?' panted Nipper, lighting up a Benson and wishing he didn't smoke.

'Fuck it, he must be still out there,' wheezed Fatboy, new beads of sweat forming on his forehead as soon as he wiped the old ones away.

Police reinforcements had arrived in the form of a burly, ruddy cheeked, flat footed Sergeant and a younger brat faced Constable who was out to make a name for himself.

'Stand exactly where you are, and drop the fucking weapon, you Chelsea cunt! You're nicked.'

The outlook didn't look good for Riddler Rowan who had eased up to a breathless walk some 100 metres or so from where the van was parked.

'What did you call me?' he asked with mocking politeness as he turned around to face the younger of the two policemen who had by now caught up with him.

'A Chelsea cunt!' came the cocksure reply.

'You know what son?' said Riddler, shaking his head and quickly reviewing his options. 'You're like the man who just got off the bus.'

'How's that then?' asked the copper, reaching for his radio.

'You're not on,' replied Riddler Rowan, arching his left eyebrow and slapping his adversary fully across the face with the open palm of his hand before turning and running after Fatboy's transit van which had just cruised slowly past him.

'Well done grandpa, my fucking hero,' said Nipper, reaching out to pull a smiling Riddler into the back of the van. 'Okay ... all in. Right amigos, as the shepherd said to his sheep ... lets get the flock outta here.' Nipper spat the words out triumphantly as he closed the transit van doors.

Solly Lewis dipped the clutch and released the handbrake. Like a scalded cat, the transit van bolted down Pragel Street, Solly full throttling a right turn into the Barking Road. Screeching tyres, burning rubber, blue flashing lights, sirens, the Tea Bar Casuals' adrenalin pumping as the getaway was made.

'All for one, and one for fucking all,' said Pete, clapping his hands in time with the opening bars of the tune warbling from vans stereo.

'Got myself a cryin' talkin' sleepin' walkin' livin' doll. I gotta do my best to please her just cos she's a livin' doll ...'

Fatboy turned the vans radio up and everyone joined in with the '6os pop classic that Cliff Richard had taken back to the top of the charts with the help of TVs 'Young Ones.'

Solly eased the van into a side street off Prince Regent Road. He'd clipped false number plates over the real ones, and they needed to be removed. It was a clever decoy thought Nipper. Fucking clever. The false number plates would confuse Old Bill good and proper. He imagined the lairy young copper that Riddler had slapped, squawking information at some dork on the other end of his radio, waiting impatiently for a reply, then cursing loudly when told that the police national computer had accurately matched the number he'd quoted with a maroon Bentley registered to some geezer called Charles Windsor who resided at Buckingham Palace, London SW1.

★ ★ ★ ★ ★

'I fucking love you doll face, more than I love myself. You behave yourself while I'm away ... Oh and Pete sends his love'. The answer machine message Nipper had left Holly just prior to boarding the ferry to Spain was plain and simple. She'd played it back a couple of times, smiling as she thought about the sex they'd enjoyed on their last night together. A smile that had soon been replaced with a scowl, as she'd sat down with a welcome cup of coffee and picked up a copy of the London Evening Standard.

'Two stabbed in soccer street riot', screamed the headline. Jim Gallagher's report went on to describe how two soccer fans had been stabbed, and eighteen others injured, as gangs of thugs had waged a series of running battles before and after last night's game between West Ham and Chelsea. Five people, including a policeman, had been detained at Newham General Hospital after the fighting in Barking Road. It said the two stab victims were 'stable'. The match had also been marred by fighting inside the ground which had halted play for two minutes. There had been a total of nineteen arrests.

Holly thought back to what Nipper had said to her about upholding 'the reputation of the club'. But if this was his way of doing it, then she wanted no part of it. What was the point anyway? It wasn't as if the Tea Bar Casuals were on the payroll of some public limited hooligan company. If there was no money in it, where was the sense in risking a stiff fine, or worse still a custodial sentence? Nipper had already been to court twice this season, surely he wouldn't get away so lightly if he were to be apprehended again.

★ ★ ★ ★ ★

'Holly … Holly, have some of this.' Trixie snapped Holly out of her daydream with a click of her fingers.

'Sorry, just thinking about that prick of a boyfriend of mine,' she replied, gratefully accepting the spliff and marvelling as she watched her friend manoeuvre the Beetle into a tight parking spot outside the gated entrance to the park in the middle of Soho Square.

'Dunno why you're so into him,' said Trixie, checking her makeup in the rear view mirror and blowing herself a kiss. 'Loads of blokes fancy you, you're well horny … and you've got a great business. You could do a lot better for yourself, you know that.'

'Maybe, baby. But I get what I want from him, and I've got my freedom.'

'You sure about that?' asked Trixie, dropping her left shoulder and placing her right hand on Holly's thigh.

'Sure about what?' enquired Holly, tingling with unexpected pleasure as her friend gently squeezed her leg.

'About Nipper being what you want?'

Trixie rolled her jade green eyes and smiled suggestively. 'Nah, don't answer that,' she continued, climbing out of the car before Holly had a chance to say anything. As they made their way out of the square, down Sutton Row and out onto the brightly lit pavement of Charing Cross

Road, Holly wondered if Trixie Fowler had been making a pass at her. She laughed as she remembered thinking that Trixie was the mother of the baby she'd often seen her with when she'd first shopped at Heroes. The child turned out to be her niece, and Jamie Black, who she'd supposed was her lover, was in fact a distant relative.

The street was alive with people queuing to get into both the Astoria and Busby's, where old New Romantic impresario Philip Sallon hosted his fabled Mud Club. Any lingering thoughts that Holly harboured about what Trixie had said were soon forgotten as they entered Busby's, descended the stairs, and entered the basement room of the split level club.

'Blinding!' said Trixie, grabbing Holly's hand and leading her through the sweaty seething mass of boys, girls, and everything in between, who were gyrating to DJ Tasty Tim's diverse selection of music. He played everything you needed for a big night out. Schoolgirl '70s disco, Motown, Glam Rock, trashy TV themes like 'Rupert the Bear', a bit of Punk, some soul, and some obscure stuff that nobody ever recognised, but that everybody still danced too, just because they could.

Absolutely fucking blinding, thought Holly to herself. I've got one, two, three, four, five ... senses working overtime.

★ ★ ★ ★ ★

The Metropolitan Police had paid several visits to the flat in Ifield Road. They were keen to interview Nipper about a 'very serious matter' but initially wouldn't divulge what the nature of the 'matter' was to Holly. At the third time of endeavouring to ascertain his whereabouts, Holly was informed that the police were acting on intelligence that a group of British hooligans, a unified firm comprising thugs from London, Leeds, and Manchester, had travelled to the USA where they had arranged to have a 'straightener' with their German counterparts.

England were playing West Germany in a world cup warm up tournament. Nipper had never shown much interest in international football, but Chelsea striker Kerry Dixon was in the England squad for that tournament, and all of a sudden Holly began to wonder exactly where Nipper, Pete, Danny, and the rest of the TBC boys might be. She'd spoken briefly on the phone to both her boyfriend and her brother since their departure, but at that time had had no reason to question their location.

'He's in Spain, I'm sure of it', she'd informed the police. 'If he gets in touch, I'll let you know'.

The concern Holly fostered about the TBC's whereabouts evaporated one fine summers morning when not one, but two letters arrived from Spain. They were from Nipper.

18th June 1986

Dearest Doll Face,

As you can see from the postmark we haven't got any further than Santander. Remember I told you about that mouthy bloke Stevie from Deptford we met on the ferry? Well he was being straight down the line with us about his dad having that building contract over here and we have got six weeks worth of work labouring on one of his sites. It's a low-rise office block right in the middle of town and we carry on like those clowns in that telly programme Half Weeder, however it's fucking spelt, Sane Pet. We are staying at this hotel called the Colon. Terrific name isn't it. It's like Faulty Towers, but its clean, cheap and only a ten-minute walk to the site.

The geezer we're working for is called Barry Barlow, Beery to his mates. He knows Steve Bruno and quite a few other faces besides. Stevie's a fucking nuisance though, he keeps banging on about being a Cockney Red, and he always seems to have a cold. Pete has christened him Sniffler.

It's hard work but we are out in the sun all day and the old San Miguel's go down a right treat in the evening when we head up to this place Plaza Canadio or something like that. We are all being well behaved because it's good money. Honest. No one speaks English here anyway so the boys have had zero luck with the local girls although Fatboy got his wire pulled by this toothless old whore down by the docks the other week, he's a fucking animal.

We are all enjoying the World Cup and will probably stay here until it finishes before heading down to Ibiza.

I will try and call you on Friday at the market.

Love you always,

Nipper XXX

★ ★ ★ ★ ★

23rd June !986

Doll faced babe,

What a load of shite! That bastard Maradona really stitched us up last night. I don't suppose you watched it. Beery let us watch the game at his hotel in town, it was great he subbed all the beers. It was his way of saying thanks, just a shame about the game. England are shit though, but at the end of the day none of us really give a fuck. The funny thing is we haven't gotten into one ruck out here. People just mind their own business. The Spanish and African blokes on the site are shit scared of Beery in case he sacks em and because we are English they just leave us alone

We have had a day off today and are spending it on the beach, the weather's fantastic. I have got hold of some lovely gear and me, Riddler and Fatboy are just sitting here soaking up the sun. Pete, Eggy, Chiller and Solomon Lewis have gone into town to meet some American girls who are on an exchange programme with the local college.

This has worked out better than we could ever have thought and Beery says that we can have regular work when we get back home if we want it. Its gotta be better than what I'm doin at the moment. He's got a contract coming up for some warehouse re-developments in the Docklands.

I can't wait to get to Ibiza I just want to chill out for a few weeks. I know you said you weren't going to come but maybe you should think about it. Just get your flight I've got plenty of potatoes to look after you with when you get out. We are going to drive straight to Denia without stopping and take the transit over. I've spoken to that bloke Carlos who we met at the Rock last year and he says that we can stay at Rita's guest house again for a couple of weeks as she's not that busy. I hope that business of yours is still doing the bollocks, call you when I reach the beach. I miss your salty taste.

Nipper XXX

★ ★ ★ ★ ★

Holly wasn't too troubled by the fact that England were on their way home having been cheated by the so called 'hand of God', she had other things to worry about. An ovarian cyst put paid to any ideas she might have had about maybe joining Nipper and the boys in Ibiza. It was a problem she'd kept to herself. Nipper wouldn't understand, so what was the point in telling him.

The last time she'd spoken to him on the phone, he'd been more concerned about Chelsea's fixtures for the forthcoming season despite knowing that he'd been spending every Saturday until the following Easter running errands for little old ladies, or whatever it was that his Community Service Order would involve.

As the summer drew to a close, Holly received two intriguing postcards from Pete. By the time she'd finished reading them, she was already planning ahead to next year.

Postcard One: A black and white photo of Ibiza's old fort.

Sis,
It's a bit different here this year. You should have come out like Nipper

wanted you to, because you would have noticed it as well. The others are just on the piss every night trying to pull dodgy scrubbers, either that or smoking themselves daft on Playa d'en Bossa during the day. That DJ Alfredo geezer is playing some interesting stuff, all 12-inch singles by the Bunnymen, the Cure, and New Order that's been re-recorded so you can dance to it. Mind you I can't get along with the likes of Go West and Wham. I've been at Pacha and they play a lot of that American stuff you like, Steve Hurley and a few other things I don't recognise. Quite a few of the locals are getting well into it. It never really kicks off till most of our lot have dropped down drunk and been ushered home by the Civil Guard. I get pretty tired with the heat cos of my old problems so I've almost stopped drinking, well apart from water. I'm going to Amnesia tomorrow, enough said. Hope you are okay, Nipper really loves you by the way, and soooo do I.

Pete x x x x

* * * * *

Postcard Two: A colour photo depicting a beautiful sunset at Cala Xarraca.

Sis,

I'm writing before I go to sleep, I've just got back from Amnesia it's by San Raf on the road from San Antonio to the old town, you know it? Yeah. Thing is cos it's open air, it's wicked in the morning as the sun comes up. No Brits come here at all, some lovely girls though, you should see the designs of the clothes they wear. I will try and find out where they get them. They all seem to have a lot of money and are obviously doing a bit of gear. The music is the same as at Pacha but it's got a much more Balearic feel to it. There's something else going on that's pushing the vibe, dunno what it is, but everyone's really free and easy. No attitude. Love you loads little sister. Dunno where Nipper is today, they all played football back in the town … must've got drunk after.

See ya in a coupla weeks luv ya.

Pete x x x

6

ECSTASY

Pete had a real gleam in his eye. A new zeal for life. Holly thought that he'd looked fantastic when he'd returned from Ibiza last year. Healthy, tanned, fit, and give or take the odd bit of puff, clean. She'd been a bit surprised when he and Trixie Fowler had started dating, everyone had. But it had been Trixie that had noticed Pete's artistic flair, and she'd been the one who'd encouraged him to design some love themed motifs that had subsequently found their way onto T-shirts sold at both Heroes and Babelicious.

Nipper hadn't gone back to his old courier job. He and Eggy Barnes had started working for Barlow Construction. As a roofer, Eggy was on serious money. Nipper though was content with labouring and forging a reputation with Beery Barlow as someone who could get all manner of things done when they needed doing, and with the minimum of fuss. Just small errands. A package delivered here, somebody picked up there. Half the time, Nipper only did them to wind Sniffler Barlow up. He knew, that Beery knew that his own son was, to put not too fine a point on it, a loud-mouthed liability.

Nipper's Community Service Order had served its purpose. Unable to attend matches taking place on a Saturday, he'd managed just five visits to Stamford Bridge. Four of these games, Coventry City, York City, Oxford United, and Southampton had attracted crowds of less than 12,000. The other match, a New Years Day 3-1 derby victory over QPR, had only pulled 21,000 fans through the turnstiles.

'Hollins must go, Hollins must go,' had been an audible chant from the Chelsea faithful on more than one occasion during the course of a season that had seen the Chelsea manager preside over a team playing up to its

reputation of only being able to raise its game against its fiercest rivals.

Away victories against Spurs and Manchester United were insufficient compensation for the ignominy of conceding six goals at home to Nottingham Forest and the embarrassing cup defeats at the hands of lowly York and Cardiff.

The Manchester United game had been played on a Sunday early on in the season, and it had been the only away match that had been attended by a full complement of Tea Bar Casuals. Kerry Dixon had obliged with the only goal of a scrappy game, but it had been enough to send the travelling Blues fans home happy.

'A load of fucking bollocks, 14th place aint good enough', had been Riddler's consensual observation when the season had been reviewed by the TBC gathered at Plough Lane on May 12th to watch their heroes get hammered 4-1 by Wimbledon. It was a testimonial match for the Dons long serving midfielder Wally Downes. Meaningless for the TBC, just a convenient excuse to get lashed on Eggy Barnes' always hospitable manor.

'Fuck it lads, we'll be in Ibiza this time next month,' said Nipper several hours later, as they'd concluded the post mortem on the season in the Corner Pin public house.

'I'll drink to that,' replied Pete enthusiastically. 'It's gonna be one hell of a hot summer out there. I can feel it in my bones,' he continued, draining his pint and banging the glass down hard on the table. 'Ibiza here we come.'

* * * * *

Holly had organised the flights so that everyone would travel out together. Trixies's assistant Phoebe had been entrusted to manage Heroes and Babelicious in their absence, and Steve Bruno would be hovering in the background to take care of any commercial problems should they arise.

Pete, Trixie, Nipper and Holly were going to be away for at least a month.Eggy Barnes and his girlfriend Rebs had planned to stay for three weeks, whilst singletons Riddler Rowan, Fatboy Green, Chiller and Solly Lewis were on a two week package holiday.

The single lads were booked into a B&B in San Antonio, and the couples at the Casa Rita guesthouse located nearby at Cala Bassa. Casa Rita, with its sky blue shutters, pastel tiles, and whitewashed stone façade was perched on a rocky headland that jutted out into the cobalt blue Mediterranean Sea. The adjacent cove with its golden sandy beach was easily accessible, as was the terrace at the Es Parral restaurant where people would gather in the evening to enjoy a drink and a smoke, absorbing themselves in the scenic thrill of another perfect Ibiza sunset.

Holly, Trixie and Rebs had been surprised at how willing their boyfriends had been to join them in embracing the chilled out bohemian beach lifestyle that they hankered after back in London. Talking about it was one thing, but putting it into practice, when the rest of their friends were jaunting around the bars of San An every night getting drunk and debauched was another, but they managed, and there were no complaints.

Lifes a beach, was the theme of the holiday … for the first week anyway. Cala Bassa, because it was on their doorstep, was an obvious daytime location. Cala Mola, which was to be found by walking round the headland, was another, whilst Playa d'en Bossa, Bora Bora to the locals, a couple of miles south of Ibiza Town, was the place they headed for when they wanted to smoke something a little more enlightening than the weed they could buy at Es Parral.

At Bora Bora, the conversation would flow freely as the three couples indulged themselves in the herbal wares pedalled by the local gypsies. Pete and Nipper would reminisce about the old days, sharing a laugh and a joke with the others, mainly at the expense of Fatboy Green who wasn't around to defend his honour.

'Fuck me Nipper,' said Pete, sniggering as another Fatboy story sprung to mind. 'Remember we were in the Gunter Arms on the Fulham Road playing pool? I … I think we were going to watch the Lurkers and the Drones play down at the Swan on the Broadway.'

'Yeah, must've been late '77,' added Nipper, nodding in approval and encouraging the others to listen. 'Go on son … tell it straight, tell it dead straight.'

'Well Danny Green walked into the bar just as Nipper here was lining up to pot the black for the funeral shot wipe out,' elaborated Pete, as those who'd heard the tale told a thousand times before began to laugh.

'So anyway, I'm sat there pouring a light ale carefully into my glass, and I hear this whistling … 'Go Buddy Go' by the Stranglers, Fatboy Green's favourite tune. Now you all know Fatboy well enough to know he aint a dedicated follower of fashion, but doll face here was working at McLaren's shop, and she'd decided that pork life loving Daniel Green needed a makeover.'

'Standing on the outside, looking in. Wishing that little chicky was with him. I said go buddy, go buddy, go buddy, go buddy, go go go.'

'Suddenly there he was … da da! Mousey brown hair bleached blonde, wearing a retina blasting lime green dyed denim jacket over a UK Subs T shirt and a pair of black shit stopping bondage strides which finished a full four inches above his ankles. His meaty little trotters were tucked into pink, orange and white striped Slade socks and encased in a pair of blue suede shoes that had a three inch crepe sole. I thought my drink had been spiked with LSD, on my fucking life I tell ya.'

'I find that hard to believe,' said Eggy, 'I reckon you must've put Holly up to it, he's quite a reserved character in all fairness.'

'Reserved,' cooed Nipper, 'you've seen him when we've been at the football, he's anything but reserved.'

'Exactly,' agreed Pete, motioning Trixie to roll another spliff. 'He aint reserved, he's fat.'

'What about that brass in Wimbledon,' said Nipper, 'that's a good story.'

'What brass?' enquired Eggy, putting his arm around Rebs who was frowning slightly.

'Yeah, what brass?' asked Holly, indignantly. 'Even I haven't been privy to this particular yarn.'

Pete lit the spliff that Trixie had expertly built and took a couple of long drags, holding the smoke in his lungs until his eyes began to water before exhaling and commencing the story.

'Yeah so Fatboy right, well he used to collect those cards that the brassy birds put in telephone kiosks in town. He'd phone 'em all up when he was drunk. He had one woman in particular that he kept going on about 'cos she had a Geordie accent and he thought it was quality. When he phoned this tart up, he'd always ask what she looked like, and what she did, and how much it all cost … y'know, her services. He'd most probably be putting one down the sink when he listened to her reply, the dirty fucker.'

'So what did she say?' asked the three girls simultaneously.

'I'm slim, blonde and busty pet,' replied Nipper, mustering his best Tyneside female brogue. 'Now a massage with relief, that'll be £20. A massage with French, that'll be £25. A topless massage with completion of your choice, that's £30. A massage with full sex, is £35. You'll have to wear a condom, and no, before you ask, I don't kiss … have you got any questions pet, or do you just want the address?'

'Very convincing,' giggled Rebs. 'I bet he asked her questions just to keep her talking didn't he,' she continued, her inborn female curiosity repelling her initial disgust at the scenario.

'Just one Rebs.'

'Go on then.'

'"Any anal?" that's what he'd ask.'

'Anal?'

'Yeah, you know, anal sex. A gentle stroll up Bourneville Boulevard. Well Fatboy just loved the way her Geordie burr came across when he got the reply "sorry luv, no anal". She must've been thick not to realise it was him phoning her up every week. Mind you, he did vary it. Sometimes he'd ask if she did spanking, or maybe bondage. She did everything, everything apart from anal. It was funny though, we never believed him until we rang her up from Beery's office … he's got one of those speaker phones. We all listened in, fucking quality it was, waiting for her to say … "sorry luv … no anal" and then he'd hang up like a naughty kid. Fatboy fucking loved it when we'd go up to Newcastle or Sunderland to watch the Blues … he'd hang out of the window shouting "any anal?" every time he saw a fit bird. Priceless … the silly fucking salad dodger. I wonder if he's found out what 'any anal' is in Spanish.

'Quien lo quiere por el culo?' proclaimed Rebs triumphantly. 'Who wants it in the ass?'

'Eggy you'll have some of that wont you,' chortled Nipper, 'is that why you're going out with her?'

'No you don't understand,' pleaded Rebs.

'Oh yes we do,' said Pete, 'we'll call you Strap On from now on eh, ha ha.'

'Oi Rebs don't tell em our darkest secret eh will ya,' said Eggy, pursing his lips effeminately.

'Hey Rebs, you'll have to tell me how you do it later,' said Trixie, slapping Pete across his backside, 'it sounds like fun.'

'You can leave me right out,' said Pete, allowing Trixie to haul him to his feet. 'Right come on you lot lets get back to Casa Rita, we'll be back too late to go out at a reasonable time tonight otherwise.'

★ ★ ★ ★ ★

On the way back from Bora Bora, Trixie had suggested that it would be a good idea for everyone, the boys staying over in San Antonio included, to have a big night out together.

It was early evening by the time they'd returned to Casa Rita. Pete telephoned the boys hotel, leaving a message for Fatboy instructing him to round up the troops and bring them over to Es Parral where they could have a few civilised drinks together on the terrace whilst deciding which club to go to.

Back in their room, Nipper and Holly, pleasantly stoned, flopped onto the large comfortable bed and were soon lullabyed to sleep by the soothing sound of the waves breaking on the nearby shore.

'Take or leave us, only please believe us, we aint ever gonna be respectable. Like us, hate us, but you'll never change us, We aint ever gonna be respectable.'

Nipper awoke with a start and looked at his watch. He'd only been asleep for 30 minutes, but it felt like longer.

'Mel & Kim, for fucks sake! I don't know how Pete puts up with that cheesy crap Trixie listens too,' he grumbled, banging on the bedroom wall before rolling onto his side and embracing Holly who was wide awake and moving her body in time with the music.

In the bedroom next door, Trixie responded to Nipper's protest by turning the volume up so loud that the partition wall began to vibrate.

'Fascination, is our sensation. We like to put ourselves on the line. Recreation is our destination, so don't wait up for us tonight,' sang Holly, reaching down to Nipper's crotch and giving it a teasing grope.

'Not you as well,' said Nipper, feeling his balls tighten and his cock stiffen.

'Why not?' asked Holly, her hand reaching inside Nipper's board shorts to massage his responsively erect penis.

'Because … ooh.'

'Because what?'

Nipper gave up complaining and lay there, clenching the muscles in his buttocks as Holly rapidly wanked him to the brink of orgasm.

'Don't stop.'

'What's it worth?' said Holly mischievously, pausing to delay the inevitable for a brief moment.

'Whatever you want … oh oh … ouch,' gasped Nipper, as Holly finished him off with several vigorous strokes, nuzzling into the nape of his neck and biting his earlobe as he came.

'Whatever I want eh … heh, heh, heh,' cackled Holly, jumping off the bed and clapping her hands. 'Well now let me have a think about that while I get ready.'

★ ★ ★ ★ ★

'Where's Nipper?' enquired Holly, as her arrival at the terrace bar was greeted by a rapturous round of applause from Pete, Fatboy, Eggy, Riddler, Chiller and Solly Lewis who were upstanding and appreciative of the effort she had put into her appearance. Trixie and Rebs, who'd been greeted in similar fashion, nodded their approval.

'He's over there talking to that couple,' replied Pete, casting an admiring eye over his sister, whose poker-straight jet black hair had been combed into a side parting. Poised, sculpted and incredibly thin, Holly was wearing a plain white figure hugging Trixie Fowler frock that accentuated her golden tan and guaranteed she would turn heads wherever she went that evening.

'Who are they?'

'Dunno.'

'The pie and mash geezer wearing Claire Rayner's, that's Davy Truelove,' interjected Riddler, 'dunno who the sort with him is though, his treacle most probably.'

'Sorry to be a bore but could you translate Peter please,' asked Holly of her brother, in the plumiest accent she could muster.

'Pie and mash … flash, Claire Rayner's … trainers, sort … girl, treacle … treacle tart, sweetheart,' said Pete, grinning and patting Riddler Rowan on the back.

Fatboy Green nodded and laughed, Riddler's cockney rhyming slang was a whole language in itself. He was one of life's diamond geezers. Wild-haired and handsome, Riddler had an engagingly restless demeanour which endeared him to the girls and made him cracking company for the lads.

'Davy Truelove eh,' said Riddler, as Nipper joined them at the bar. 'What's he doing here?'

'He's on holiday with his bird Trudy, but you'll never guess who's villa he's staying at,' replied Nipper, his pretty boy face wreathed in cigarette smoke.

'Whose?'

'Beery fucking Barlow!'

Holly immediately realised that this was one of those blokey situations where the men collectively raised their eyebrows, nodded appreciatively and exclaimed 'bollocks', 'leave off' or 'fuck me', whilst the women shrugged their shoulders.

'Excuse my girlie ignorance, but who's Davy Truelove?' asked Holly, dipping her index finger into the glass of Southern Comfort that Chiller had just handed her.

'Davy Truelove played on the left side of midfield for Fulham and England,' replied Pete, 'gifted he was, broke his leg in the cup final against West Ham and never played again, poor bastard.'

'How does he know Beery then?'

'Beery knows everyone,' said Nipper dismissively. 'Right, who fancies getting on it tonight?'

Everyone with the exception of Pete indicated their agreement.

'Okay. Well Davy and Trudy are going over to Pacha at about midnight,' whispered Nipper, glancing at the time on his watch.

'Apparently there are these new pills called Ecstasy which are doing the rounds, it's meant to be different gear. A bit pricey though at 5000 pesetas a tablet. They tried it the other night and said it's really amazing.'

'Sounds interesting,' said Pete, scratching his chin thoughtfully, 'and can he sort us out?'

'Yeah! He's told me where we can pick some up, fancy it then Pete?'

'Maybe, well it aint like skin popping and I am on holiday.'

Holly frowned but said nothing. Pete had conquered his heroin dependence, but he addictive nature of his personality remained. As a friend, Nipper should have known better than actively encouraging Pete to take drugs.

★ ★ ★ ★ ★

They took a couple of taxis over to Ibiza Town pulling up near the club in Avenida Ocho de Agosto. Nipper walked over to talk to a guy sat in a red jeep parked a couple of hundred yards down the street and then came back to tell everyone to go into the club, he would see them there in ten minutes or so. Holly had collected the money for the pills and gave it to Nipper. She smiled as she watched him walk confidently back towards the jeep, slowly but surely Nipper was maturing very nicely into the type of man she needed him to be.

Pacha was quite busy. Capable of holding several thousand people, it was bigger than any of the clubs that the girls frequented in London, and there was a vibrant energetic buzz about the place that caught Holly's attention immediately.

'Top club Hols,' said Trixie, distracting Holly from her thoughts.

'Yeah, definitely,' replied Holly, who'd been doing a rapid piece of mental arithmetic. 'All these people, paying all this money. We could do this y'know.'

'Nah, not me my sweet black eyed pea, I'll stick to what I'm good at.'

'You should be a bit more ambitious girl.'

'I do okay.'

'Yeah, well whatever. It's worth thinking about eh.'

Holly was sidetracked by the sight of someone she thought she knew who had just walked past her heading to the toilets.

'I'm sure that was Layla Goss,' she said, craning her neck to try and get a better view.

'Layla Goss. Who's she?' asked Rebs, smiling at a couple of tanned, well muscled, cocktail waiters who were working behind the bar they'd walked over to.

'Her lesbian fantasy,' replied Trixie, brushing her index finger across Holly's cheek and blowing a kiss at her.

'Seriously?'

'She's a girl who runs a stall at the San Carlos hippy market,' said Holly, arching her left eyebrow contemptuously at Trixie Fowler.

'I didn't know you were into girls Hols,' said Rebs, putting her arm around Holly's waist.

'Leave off, I'm not,' replied Holly, gripping Rebs' wrist and digging in her nails at the same time.

'Ouch! I'm only joking,' said Rebs, wincing in pain as she retracted her arm.

'Yeah, well its not funny,' said Holly sourly, 'and you can stop grinning too Trixie, we cant all be like you.'

Holly imagined her two friends having one of those 'the reality hurts' conversations about her behind her back. The only problem was, there was more than a shred of truth in Trixie Fowler's observation. Layla Goss, who was the most beautiful girl she'd ever seen in her life, had become a regular participant in Holly's hazy spliff induced sexual fantasies, something she hadn't shared with Nipper, or Trixie for that matter.

Layla was a goddess whose rake like physique, bronzed body, honed muscles, shorn sun-bleached hair and faultless dress sense, Holly thought should be gracing the catwalks of Paris and Milan, rather than the dusty tracks of Ibiza. She had an air of mystery and intrigue that captured her imagination. There had to be more to Layla than selling tie-dyed clothing and incense, Holly was sure of it.

Everything about her was cool, from the Persol wrap around sunglasses, to the embroidered denim dungarees and espadrilles. Holly would admire her from the Las Dalias bar, never having the courage to strike up a meaningful conversation during the days she'd visited the market. She'd often hoped to catch a glimpse of her in the evenings, but never had, so she simply got by on meaningless chit-chat like 'how much is this?', or 'where did that come from?'.

Holly, who'd come over all painfully shy in her presence, only knew she was called Layla because Pedro, the owner of Las Dalias, had caught her looking wistfully in her direction one Wednesday morning. He'd told Holly her name, and that she was English. He'd also told her that she'd lived on the island for seven or eight years over in Santa Eularia. There was a guy, but Pedro didn't know too much about him although he was sure her man was also English, a soldier maybe. Yeah, something like that.

★ ★ ★ ★ ★

'Look babe, Nipper's back,' said Trixie, tugging at Holly's arm and pointing at the bar.

'Great, let me see if he's come up with the goods,' replied Holly, thoughts of Layla dispersing quickly as her pulse quickened at the sight of her boyfriend who had spotted her and given her a knowing wink and the thumbs up as she'd walked across to meet him.

Nipper pushed Holly against the wall adjacent to the bar and kissed her fervently, at the same time pulling her right hand behind her back and placing what felt like a small stone in her hand.

'There you go doll face, for you and the girls ... Davy say's just do the one to start with, he reckons it takes an hour or so to get the effect. He said to make sure you drink some water ... go on then run along.' As he finished speaking, Nipper slapped Holly's arse. She reciprocated by slapped him fairly hard across the face before kissing him fully on the lips and walking away, beckoning Trixie and Rebs towards the toilets as she did so.

The pills were wrapped in silver kitchen foil. There were six of them. They were a chalky white in colour, had a dove stamped on one side and a scored radial line on the other vaguely resembling them to Anadin.

'Right then girls, let's see what all the fuss is about,' said Rebs putting a pill in her mouth and knocking it back with a slug of Perrier.

'Yeah, I'm so up for it,' said Holly, winking suggestively at Trixie as she swallowed one pill and pushed the other into the cup of her bra for safe-keeping.

'I really love this tune girls,' said Trixie, wiggling her hips and clicking the fingers of her right hand above her head as they sashayed out of the toilets and onto the dancefloor.

'Someday ... we'll live as one family, in perfect harmony. Someday ... if we all pull together, we will all be free.'

The Ce Ce Rogers track 'Someday', with its deep gospel flavoured vocal, had been playing out on Radio Ibiza all week. Now though, it's infernally catchy piano riff was thumping through the clubs sound system, inviting people to dance. Holly looked around, everyone including Fatboy Green was moving to the music.

'Nothing's happening Nipper ... nothing's happening,' she mouthed, dancing across to her boyfriend with an open expression on her face.

'Where there's a flower, there's the sun and the rain. Oh it's wonderful they're both one and the same. Joy and pain, are like sunshine and rain ...'

Nipper smiled back at her, the DJ rather than selecting the tunes was blending the music seamlessly from one track to the next, the effect was mesmerising.

As Holly sang along with the old Maze track 'Joy And Pain', she began to feel unbalanced and giddy.

'Joy and pain are like sunshine and rain, joy and pain....'

Perspiration, palpitations, eyelids flickering ... Holly didn't feel right. Out of control ... lights, shapes and people morphed with the sound into a hallucinogenic cacophony of spirals and zigzags that sent her spinning off the dancefloor in the direction of the toilets. She just made it to a cubicle, panicking as she pushed the door shut behind her and locked it.

'F F Fucking hell,' she whimpered, as her bowels loosened. 'What the fuck is this sh sh shit?' she continued, rocking her head back as her teeth chattered uncontrollably. Holly closed her eyes and felt a pulsating wavelike rush course up her spine. The rush came again, nauseous, she resisted the urge to vomit. Each breaking wave was accompanied by intensely pleasurable sensation that was orgasmic in its intensity. Sitting upright, she opened her eyes and began to regulate her breathing.

Holly licked her lips and felt a dryness in her throat, swallowing several times in an attempt to bring some moisture into her mouth. 'Fucking mental doll face,' she muttered, clenching her teeth and grinning as she pulled herself together and things began to come into focus.

'Fade away and radiate,' she sang, as the intensity of the rushes slowly ubsided and with it the nauseous feeling. Edgy uneasiness and blind panic were replaced by a feeling of euphoria that Holly suddenly felt she had to share with everyone. This was like unlike anything else she had ever experienced. Ecstasy, the pleasure principle, this was it ... this was definitely it.

'You know that,' she mumbled, as she opened the cubicle door and saw the welcome form of Trixie Fowler stood hands on hips gazing on her own reflection in the mirror above the washbasins. The expression on her face was a mixture of surprise and disbelief.

'Hey Holly ... look at me!' exclaimed Trixie, widening her eyes and pushing her hands through her hair, 'I feel fantastic!'

'Yeah! Me too. I thought it was gonna be bad at first ... but mmm. You got a fag?' Holly was trying to keep on top of the undulating sensations that were forcing her to shift her body. She could feel herself moving her lips, pursing them almost as she waited for Trixie to reply.

'Rebs has them,' replied Trixie, clicking her tongue against the roof of her mouth and dancing in front of the mirror as she applied and then reapplied her lipstick.

'Come on let's go and dance,' said Holly, grabbing her friend by the hand and pushing the toilet door open.

Out in the main room the music was really pumping and Holly felt herself merging with its physicality. She could see Rebs and Eggy Barnes embracing and mouthing the words 'I love you' to one another. Nipper was stood statue still, legs apart, hands raised above his thrown back head. He looked for all the world like a rock star demigod. Lights, camera, action! All the world's a stage.

Fatboy Green, Chiller and Riddler Rowan were busy pulling faces, smiling and shaking hands with each other. Holly felt a sense of intense communion as she walked over to them, hugging each one in turn.

'Yeah! Nice one Hols,' said Chiller, pointing at Nipper, whose arms were now outstretched. 'Look over there, Nipper … the new messiah! I fucking love that bloke.'

★ ★ ★ ★ ★

'Can you feel it,' shouted Holly, who was directly in front of Nipper dancing to Rhythim is Rhythim's stunning track 'Nude Photo'. 'Pete told me they spelt Rhythim wrong on purpose,' she cooed, as her feet tapped the floor in time with the hi-hat beat, while her body grooved along with the tunes sub-aquatic bassline.

'Yeah, doll face yeah,' said Nipper, opening his eyes and smiling. 'It's like listening to liquid electricity,' he continued, reaching out to pull Holly towards him.

'This is fantastic … imagine if we could bottle this feeling up and take it home, imagine that.' Holly closed her eyes as she mouthed the words at Nipper who reached out and pulled her close, passion and desire, right out there on the dancefloor. Opening her eyes, she looked up at Nipper, face flushed with a new love sensation. She could have sworn she'd never seen him looking so handsome.

'I fucking love you babe.'

'No … I fucking love you.'

'No … really. I really honestly do love you.'

'Yeah, my beautiful doll face … I really love you.'

On a plateau of ecstasy, they kissed and danced emotively, conscious of the music, unconscious to the space and time continuum.

'C'mon, lets get a drink, I'm thirsty,' said Holly, shivering slightly and grasping Nipper's arm with a clammy hand. 'What time is it?'

'3am doll face, we've been dancing for nearly two hours.'

'Look there's Pete … PETE!'

Pete was sweating profusely and gurning like a toothless old man as he shimmied over and threw his arms around both of them.

'Fucking brilliant eh sis, eh Nips.'

'Not half mate.'

'Yeah brother … fucking brilliant, but its wearing off.'

'Wearing off … then have another. I did an hour ago … look at me I'm fucking flying,' said Pete, breaking away from the group hug and spinning like a hip hop dancer out into the middle of the floor.

'He's off his tits, look at him,' said Nipper, reaching into his pocket and putting another pill into his mouth.

'Yeah, and I wanna get right back to where I was an hour ago,' replied Holly as she reached into her bra, found her second E, and followed suit.

'Crunch it, you'll come back up quicker,' said Nipper knowledgably, 'euch that tastes shit,' he continued, grimacing as the pill powdered in his mouth.

'Listen to you, pill head … fucking hell, shit, you're right.'

Nipper laughed as Holly screwed her face up and retched at the pills bitter essence. He was still laughing as she spotted Rebs and Trixie and ran to the bar where they were stood, grabbing at Trixie's Fanta and gargling the soft drink until she was satisfied that the pill was completely dissolved.

'Sorted!' she exclaimed, after swallowing the mixture in her mouth.

'Yeah, you're sorted all right,' said Nipper, who'd walked across to the bar.

'You're a top man,' proclaimed Trixie, reaching out to pull him towards her.

'Yeah … top, top man, thanks for sorting this out,' agreed Rebs, joining in what was now an orgiastic looking four-way hug.

Nipper couldn't remember if he'd ever felt this good before. Top man eh, he thought to himself, grinning as he extricated himself from the clutching attentions of the three women and made a beeline for Eggy Barnes, who was deep in conversation with Davy Truelove in a darkened alcove at the far end of the bar.

★ ★ ★ ★ ★

Holly felt her eyes flicker as she scanned the club. Pacha was packed now, all the beautiful people were here, everybody dancing, everybody smiling. Surely the whole club couldn't be on this vibe she thought to herself, straightening her body as she started to come back up on her second E.

'Oh my G G God!' she stammered to herself, pushing open the toilet door. 'Layla,' she muttered, catching her breath and trying to maintain her composure.

Layla Goss was preening her short spiky hair in front of the mirror.

Leaning over the sink she widened her eyes and pouted her lips suggestively before turning round to face Holly who was stood transfixed like a
hypnotists subject waiting for a click of the fingers to invite her back into
the room.

'Look … look … you have them too. Look   … look in the mirror,'
rasped Layla throatily.

Holly shook her head and shuddered as she felt the now familiar E
sensation inwardly convulse her senses. She couldn't believe how black
Layla's dilated pupils made her eyes look. Dark intense pools filled with
mystery, the coals that stoked the fires of hell. Holly averted her gaze and
looked closely in the mirror at her own reflection.

'You've got that 1000 yard stare, yeah you know that,' said Layla,
smiling as she held out her hands, 'I'm Layla, who are you?'

'Holly, my names Holly.'

'I've seen you before, last year maybe?'

'Yeah, maybe,' said Holly, gaining confidence as she held Layla's
hands. 'Don't you have a stall over at the San Carlos hippy market?'

'Yes I do, and you must come and visit me tomorrow,' replied Layla,
'sorry but I have to go and meet somebody now.'

'Manana then,' said Holly, resisting the urge to embrace Layla.

'Yes, tomorrow.'

Holly clapped her hands as the door closed behind Layla and whooped
with joy.

★ ★ ★ ★ ★

'What exactly is this gear Davy?' asked Nipper, who was finding it difficult to keep still as he lit another cigarette.

'Ecstasy … yeah right, lemme tell ya,' replied Davy Truelove, reaching
into the breast pocket of the cheesecloth shirt he was wearing. 'But first
have a bit of gum, chewing helps you stay focussed, stops you grinding yer
teeth, knoworrimean.'

'Good idea,' said Eggy Barnes, who'd cautiously moderated his intake
of E to just a cheeky half of a pill and had already identified lockjaw as one
of its less than pleasurable side effects.

'Nice one Davy,' said Nipper, unwrapping two sheaths of gum and
putting them in his mouth, 'that's better, a bit of moisture, yeah well carry
on.'

'Methylene … Dioxy … Methyl … Amphetamine,' said Davy, deliberately drawing out the chemical name for the drug, 'MDMA. Ecstasy …
this is gonna change everything back home lads, trust me.'

'Your not kidding Davy,' said Eggy, looking across the dancefloor at the gyrating forms of Rebs, Trixie and Holly, 'how come we aint seen this before?'

'Well unless you go to gay clubs you probably won't have seen it back home, but it's been around for a while.'

'How long?' asked Nipper, still finding it hard to concentrate on the conversation as the urge to dance became almost overwhelming.

'Years mate, the usual thing y'know. The Yanks synthesise the stuff, try it out as this, that or the other, and then some fucking West Coast hippy gets hold of it and blows his mind. He then blows a few of his mates minds as well, before the moral minority find out and have it banned.'

'Banned at home too?'

'Yep, since 1977.'

'That was a good year,' laughed Nipper, 'if we'd had this in 1976, punk would never have happened.'

'Yeah, and I'd never have played First Division football.'

'And I'd never have got involved in any trouble on the terraces,' offered Eggy, scratching his chin as he contemplated how different the world might have been if E had been the drug of choice in the mid '70s.

'Listen Davy,' said Nipper, soft shoe shuffling from one foot to the other, 'can we have a serious chat about this tomorrow when we're less mangled, maybe we could do some work together back home.'

Eggy Barnes nodded in agreement.

'Yes lads,' replied Davy, high fiving Nipper and Eggy in turn. 'I expect we could, now why don't you two fuck off and pay a bit of attention to those lovely birds of yours before some greasy spic does.'

★ ★ ★ ★ ★

They eventually left the club at 5am and decided to head back to Cala Bassa to watch the sunrise and have a smoke. Nipper's head was buzzing. If he hadn't known any better, he could have sworn there was a solitary mosquito flying around inside his skull, the high pitched tinnutis-like whine between his ears was tempered by the fact that he couldn't get that Ce Ce Rogers tune out of his head.

'If we could just open our eyes, we could make this world a paradise ... Someday, we'll live as one family in perfect harmony.'

'Bloody hell Nipper, that tune!' exclaimed Holly, as she picked up on the words Nipper was singing, 'it was going round my head too.'

'Someday ... Someday ... la la la.'

'It must be the E. Mental!'

'Let's go back to Casa Rita,' purred Holly, nuzzling up to Nipper as the taxi they were in pulled into the car park at Es Parral. 'I'd rather have a smoke on our own babe.'

'Good enough,' said Nipper, running his hand up the inside of Holly's thigh. 'Gracias senor, here'll do.' The taxi juddered to a halt in a cloud of dust, its chain smoking driver licking his lips as he turned around and got a flash of Holly's crotch.

'You see something you like senor?' said Holly in a fair to middling Spanish accent, pouting at the driver and cupping her breasts.

'I am a sorry miss … eet ees hard eh not to treat myself.'

'I bet it is eh,' replied Holly curtly. 'Pay this slimy muppet Nipper, before I lose my temper.'

'Yeah, yeah … what happened to that loved up vibe?'

'Oh that's still here,' replied Holly opening the taxi door, 'don't you worry about that.'

'I love you.'

'Yeah, I love you too.'

'We've gotta do this again tomorrow.'

'Not half.'

'You'll get hold of Davy Truelove then?'

'Yeah, don't worry, I'll get hold of Davy Truelove all right.'

★ ★ ★ ★ ★

Nipper woke up just after 4pm the following afternoon feeling physically and emotionally drained. Holly, who hadn't slept, had made her way down to Es Parral earlier in the afternoon, eventually dozing off in a hammock slung between two palm trees, her dead beat eyes hidden behind the dark lenses of an old pair of Wayfarers.

'La la la la la,' hummed Nipper, putting his fingers in his ears as he tried to distract himself. 'That fucking 'Someday' tune is in my head again,' he grunted, reaching across the bed to answer the phone whose offensively loud ringing had finally managed to take the imaginary needle off the imaginary record.

It was Davy Truelove calling to inform Nipper that he had to attend to some urgent business on the mainland with Beery Barlow. Nipper replaced the handset in the cradle and laid back on the bed staring up at the ceiling fan whose strobe like whirring and metronome clickety-click soon had him in flashback mode.

'Someday … someday la la la.'

The phone rang again. It was Holly.

'Yeah, listen doll face, Davy aint about, he's had to go to Barcelona,' explained Nipper, visualising the disappointment he could hear in his girl-friends voice, but surprised by her reply.

'Seriously? Okay, well if you two are happy to do that, then no-one's gonna complain, least of all me.' Nipper was impressed. Holly was volunteering to chase gear.

'Oh yeah, Layla. Right, well be careful yeah.' He couldn't remember much about the Layla discussion. Birds eh, yeah you know that one. Yeah of course you do, he thought to himself, as Holly explained how she would get Trixie to run her over to Las Dalias on the back of her scooter.

'Yeah, well be lucky. Love you doll face.' Nipper grinned as he finished the conversation, a catalyst for him to drag his weary bones off the bed and into the shower. 'Top girl, that Holly Philips, top girl.'

★ ★ ★ ★ ★

'My dad would be well impressed,' shouted pillion riding Holly, her arms tightly encircling her Trixie's waist as her friend guided the scooter at some speed up the grit and gravel covered steep lane that led away from Casa Rita.

'Did you ever ride with him?' replied Trixie, opening the throttle as they reached the top of the hill.

'No. Why?' asked Holly, catching her breath as she marvelled at the vista.

'Didn't think so, you're squeezing the life outta me. Don't worry you wont fall off.'

Holly laughed and relaxed a little, but not much. When cars passed, Trixie pushed the scooter perilously close to the great rusty slabs of rock that traced the roadside. It was an exhilarating but controlled ride. By the time they arrived at Las Dalias twenty minutes later, the only thing Holly was concerned about was quenching the raging thirst that had pursued her all day.

Pedro was sat at one end of the bar nursing a glass of red wine and leafing through a tatty copy of the Spanish daily newspaper, El Pais. He smiled when he saw the two women, flattering them about their natural English beauty, telling them they were wasted on the lager swilling football hooligans of their homeland. If only he knew the truth, thought Holly as she gulped down a large glass of iced water. Maybe he did, what if he did? Who cared? She had one thing on her mind, and one thing only, E.

'Gracias for the water Pedro,' said Holly, annoyed with herself for feeling so irritable, 'come on Trix, let's go and find Layla.'

★ ★ ★ ★ ★

'Hi Layla, remember me from last night?' said Holly bashfully, removing her sunglasses as she spoke.

Of course I do big eyes,' replied Layla, who was sitting cross legged on a wicker mat inside her stall. 'How are you doing today?' she continued, rising to her feet to greet Holly with a kiss on each cheek.

'Not bad, this is my friend Trixie by the way.'

As Layla shook Trixie's hand, Holly couldn't stop herself from staring at her. Hedonism hadn't ravaged her beauty, if anything, with her deep tan and close cropped sun-streaked hair, she was a vision of healthy A-List celebrity glamour.

'It's a bit late to be coming up here, was there something that you wanted?' asked Layla. Her manner of speaking suggested to Holly that she knew exactly why they had come to see her, and that she was used to being asked the question that they had in mind.

Sensing her friends slight unease with the situation, Trixie decided to take the direct approach. 'We wondered if you might know someone who could sort us out with some pills.'

'No problem,' replied Layla with a knowing smile, 'go over to the yellow tent over on the far side of the market. The guy there selling flowers is called Geraldo. Tell him you are a friend of Layla and that you need some Doves. He will sort you out, but you will need to buy some flowers from him.'

'Thanks Layla,' said Holly gratefully, 'we owe you. Are you going to Pacha tonight?'

'No no … you must come to Amnesia tonight … it will be really cool in there. Here take these vouchers you will be able to get in free with these. Go now, Geraldo will be leaving soon. So I'll expect to see you later then eh?'

Holly and Trixie looked at each other squarely in the eyes before both replying 'yes' simultaneously. They found Geraldo easily enough and whispered the magic words. Geraldo smiled at both of them; he asked them how they'd found it, and when they'd told him he'd smiled again, taking their money and telling them that he would be at the market again on Wednesday. They bought a colourful bouquet of flowers, Trixie's careful selection, and took them back to Layla who smiled at them and blew Holly a kiss.

It was no real surprise to Holly to find the full complement of their friends eagerly awaiting their return to Es Parral. A joyful reception greeted their positive response to the question, 'Sorted?'

They arrived at Amnesia just after midnight. Layla was nowhere to be seen. Out on the floor dancing, Nipper recognised that it was easier to anticipate the way E took you once you had tried it a couple of times. He'd already learned to gauge that initial rush and now was just getting used to going with it. 'Plateauing', that's what Davy Truelove called it, 'plateauing' … getting on the level.

Holly felt at one with the music. Chewing gum instead of grinding her teeth, ebbing and flowing, watching what was going on around her. Pete was animated, throwing star shapes, name checking the tunes and mouthing them out to Trixie. Chiller spent the entire evening paying attention to what the DJ was doing in his booth. Eggy Barnes and Rebs, without a care in the world, were gyrating their hips pornographically. Riddler Rowan, Solomon Lewis and Fatboy Green were making a point of introducing themselves to every group of single females in the club.

★ ★ ★ ★ ★

'It's a shame the nights ended so early,' said Nipper, glancing at his watch as he opened the door to their hotel bedroom and courteously allowed Holly to enter first.

'Yeah,' replied Holly, turning to kiss Nipper fully on the mouth.

'It doesn't have to.'

'How's that then?'

Nipper reached into his pocket and pulled out an E. 'Look I only did the one bean last night. I saved this one, fancy doing half each and getting loved up?'

Nipper bit the pill in half and they crunched their respective doses, chasing away the bitter taste with some ice cold Fanta from the fridge. They lay on the bed naked in a lovers embrace. Waiting, expectant, sensing, knowing that they were not going to be disappointed.

Coming up again on the E, Nipper felt that Holly was everything. Everything was centred on her and not on him. As they stroked each others skin, it felt electric. It seemed as if all their nerve endings had quadrupled in sensitivity, and when they kissed the pleasurable feelings intensified their sexuality in a way that neither of them had ever experienced before.

They spent what seemed like an eternity moving around the bed taking pleasure in each others bodies, acknowledging each others needs. This was so different to the games they played at home, this felt like making love should do; this was more than just a fuck. The sheer sensuality of it all made Holly melt as they continued to caress and hold each other. Embraced like this, she felt a newfound empathy for Nipper. Spiritual love, true love, and the strangest thing of all was the fact that he felt exactly the same way.

'I love you Nipper … I really do.'

'I love you too babe. You are the most precious thing in my life.'

As the warm fuzzy feeling began to dissipate Nipper fell into a semi-conscious dreamlike state. He dreamt he lived in land inhabited by large blue birds, where the sea was the brightest emerald green you could ever imagine, where golden apples grew on purple trees. Just one bite of a golden apple gave you the ability to fly. Holly dreamt too, and when they awoke they shared their experiences. It was as if E had opened up a whole new channel of communication for both of them.

★ ★ ★ ★ ★

On the Tuesday of the following week, Holly had taken a taxi to Las Dalias on her own. Layla had been conspicuous by her absence for the past few nights, and Holly had become concerned about her welfare. It was a concern she hadn't shared with Nipper or any of her friends, but something wavering between feminine intuition and the need to satisfy her own curiosity had spurred her into action.

With the exception of a couple of skinny dogs lying in the shade and a small boy chasing a wheel with a stick, Las Dalias was deserted. The air was dusty and hot, and Holly was just about to give up her quest in favour of returning to Es Parral for a tropical cocktail when Geraldo emerged from the shadows.

'Hola Holly,' he said, smiling languidly and tutting as he shook is head. 'I'm sorry, I have nothing of interest for you today. I will be at a club called Nightlife in San Antonio tonight, if you want to come and see me there, then maybe we can do some business.'

'Actually, I was looking for Layla,' replied Holly, a frown forming on her face at the thought that Geraldo viewed her as some sort of 'couldn't give a shit' pill rat.

'Layla … sick with fever, she is at home … do you know where she lives?'

Holly nodded. 'Yes, she lives in Santa Eularia … but I don't know where exactly. I'd like to visit her though … is she very sick?'

Geraldo looked directly at Holly, his eyes squinting in the bright sunshine. 'It is Malaria, she has attacks every year. She travelled during the monsoons in India, Goa I think, yes. She would be glad of the company I am thinking … yes.'

'How do I get there?'

'Find the street called Calle San Jose in Santa Eularia, there you will find there a restaurant called the Orange Tree. Layla, she lives in an apartment in the building across the road, it has a blue door ... you will find it easily.'

'Malaria eh! That's serious shit, shouldn't she be in a hospital?'

'No, no. Really she is okay. The fever, it lasts for one week, she rests and then she is fine. She is a strong woman ... she has great power ... you understand this yes?'

Holly didn't quite follow what Geraldo meant by 'power', but she nodded at him all the same. 'Yes, yes she is a strong woman. Thanks for letting me know, I will take a taxi and visit her now while it's still early.'

The first thing Holly had noticed about Santa Eularia was how unspoilt it appeared. No sign here of tourism leaving its unwelcome mark, she'd thought to herself initially, surveying the scene as the taxi driver had driven slowly along the seafront. The pebbly beach was quiet and natural, here there were no sunbeds or umbrellas for rent. By contrast, the marina was bustling with life. Fishermen unloading their early morning catch, porters scurrying to and fro ferrying luggage to expensive looking yachts moored in the harbour, excited children clambering aboard ancient sailing dinghies whose seaworthiness might be put to the test by anything other than the most tranquil of seas.

'Here senora, the Orange Tree,' said the driver hoarsely, finally finding the restaurant after traversing the back streets of the town for a meter clicking few minutes.

'Gracias, wait here one moment please,' replied Holly, opening the taxis' door and pausing to revel in the sound of the birdsong that greeted her arrival. There was a light fresh breeze, and the smell of mimosa in the air captivated her senses momentarily as she donned her sunglasses to shield her eyes from the dazzling rays of sunshine beaming down from the cloudless, brochure blue sky.

'Paradise,' she said to herself as she looked across the road from the Orange Tree and saw the blue door that Geraldo had described earlier.

'Hey, Holly ... up here.'

Recognising the voice immediately, Holly looked up and saw Layla waving at her. 'Hi ... Hi, Hi,' she stammered. 'Listen I hope you don't mind, er well Geraldo told me you were unwell so I thought I'd come and find you, see if you need anything.'

'Ah, that's nice,' replied Layla sincerely. 'Come up to the first floor, I will meet you there.'

Although Layla looked tired and drawn, she was still strikingly beautiful. The enigmatic Mona Lisa smile was still there, playing across her face in a manner that sent a shiver down Holly's spine. The apartment was exactly as she'd expected it to be. A tasteful blend of rustic Spanish furniture, rugs, ornaments and paintings, offset with a few subtle modern touches.

'I've been expecting you,' said Layla, motioning Holly to sit down after pleasantries had been exchanged.

'Really?' replied a genuinely surprised Holly, nervously fidgeting with the charm bracelet on her right wrist.

'Yeah, really.'

'Why?'

'I Just had a feeling, that's all. Nothing sinister, no need to be suspicious.'

There was a calmness in the way that Layla spoke which immediately put Holly at ease giving her an innate confidence and a platform on which to build a discussion. Holly talked of her childhood, about the soul-destroying loss of her mother, about her brothers drug addiction, about her emotionally taciturn father, about her thriving business, and finally about her bond with Nipper.

There was a soothing therapeutic timbre to Layla's voice as she explained her own quest for inner peace, a peace that she had found here in Ibiza. There were many parallels in their lives which fascinated Holly, what intrigued her most however, was the relationship Layla shared with her husband Del, a former soldier and veteran of numerous conflicts, whose civilian life she shrouded in a cloak of convenient anonymity.

Holly was unaware of the time passing, she wanted to stay and talk forever. Here at last was a woman with whom she could identify, someone who might listen and understand.

'We all have existential pain, but the pain we cant explain is the pain of being cut off from ourselves,' said Layla profoundly, pointing at the clock on the wall. 'And if you don't get yourself back to Es Parral, you will be cut off from your friends for the rest of the night,' she continued, laughing as Holly sat back in her chair with a bemused look on her face.

'Yeah, and when the pupil is willing to learn ... the teacher will appear,' replied Holly, folding her arms tightly across her chest as she stood up.

'You know that Holly Philips.'

'Yeah, I know that now.'

'I'll be your guardian angel.'

'Yeah, I know that too.'

* * * * *

For the remainder of the holiday, Nipper and Holly ended up avoiding the larger clubs preferred by their friends, opting instead to spend their nights in the more intimate confines of the club Geraldo had recommended, Nightlife. Everyone they encountered in that club was on E. The vibe was incredible. No attitude, just happy shiny people tuning into the music and into each other.

Through taking Ecstasy together, Nipper and Holly had visibly rediscovered their love for each other. The drug intensified their emotions, their state of being. They had never been in love with anyone other than themselves, but over the past year their love had become tarnished. Tarnished in the way many relationships become tainted by a lack of effort, jealousy and insecurity.

During the course of their almost daily discussions, Holly had explained to Layla how E had changed everything in her world. How it had re-built and strengthened the bridge of love, and how being on an E didn't make you feel love, it quite simply took away the inhibitions and fears that you might be feeling which then allowed love to manifest itself in a myriad of ways.

When Holly wafted the romantic Laylaesque scent of her new E influenced philosophy in Nipper's general direction, all he smelt was the pungent odour of commerciality.

'Cash, money,' was the Davy Truelove mantra, and Nipper wanted in.

'Layla this and Layla that,' was regularly echoed with 'Davy this and Davy that,' as Nipper and Holly got ready to go out for the evening. But as the reality of returning home to London drew ever closer, Holly's ambition finally resurfaced, and there was much plotting and planning about the how, the why, and the wherefore, that would be involved in porting the whole E vibe back to London. There was one little problem though, every enterprising individual who'd spent time in Ibiza during the summer of 1987 was on a similar wavelength.

During the next twelve months, the entire club scene became revolutionised by the drug. London DJ's like Paul Oakenfold, Danny Rampling and Nicky Holloway had been in Ibiza at exactly the same time as Nipper and Holly and had seen the potential. Initially they threw parties for people they had met out on the island or who were returning and wanted to recapture the vibe. Then came clubs nights specifically playing out remixed house singles which encapsulated that whole Balearic feel. Ecstasy was the drug of choice, and Nipper, in league with Davy Truelove, wasted no time lining his pockets with the cash of clubbers eager to experience what all the fuss was about.

'Happy Happy Happy' flyers promoted the first E club called Shoom. Danny Rampling and his girlfriend Jenni had started Shoom in a gymnasium in Southwark Street, South East London, and Nipper along with

Eggy Barnes and Fatboy Green, had been on hand 'serving up' pills to the couple of hundred people or so fortunate enough to find themselves in its cramped, mirror walled confines.

Pete designed a T-shirt with a yellow smiley face on it and wore it down to Shoom one night. Holly and Trixie loved it so much they had some more screen printed and started selling them at Heroes and Babelicious. Within a matter of weeks the 'smiley' became visible everywhere. T shirts, badges, bandanas, even E's themselves bore the logo belonging to what the media was now hyping as the acid house generation.

'Sorted!' chuckled Pete to himself, every time he saw a 'smiley'. 'Not half.'

7

December 1988

THE TROUBLE WITH PETE

'Come along, come along, come along and sing this song … we're the boys in blue, Division Two and we won't be here for long.'

'I'll be honest with ya,' said Chiller, cracking open a can of Fosters, 'I never thought that I'd be singing that song again, its fucking ridiculous.'

'Yeah, well that's Chelsea for ya mate,' replied Pete, looking out of the minibus window and frowning at the queue of red tail-lighted traffic leading away from Stoke City's Victoria Ground. 'I hope we don't have as much grief getting home as we did getting up here today, it could ruin our evening.'

'Fair point,' said Nipper looking at his watch and resisting the urge to light a cigarette. 'We should be back by 9pm at the latest, we'll be all right.'

'Definitely mate,' nodded Pete, '3-0 to the Chels, and two bags of sand in the hand … very nice.'

'Silly innit,' said Nipper, coughing loudly as he succumbed to his nicotine craving. 'A couple of years ago, we'd have been having a row up here. That Stoke mob, the Naughty Forty, they're well handy … and look at it now. They can't wait to meet us to buy two grands worth of jack and jills.'

'That's about the only benefit to having got relegated,' chuckled Eggy Barnes, fumbling through a selection of Chiller's mix tapes. 'All these football casuals from the provinces all wanna get on it, and we can serve em up and make a nice few quid.'

'Yeah, well I'd rather be watching First Division football,' grunted Fatboy Green, looking up from the match programme he was trying to read in virtual darkness. 'There was only 12,000 at that match today, it's fucking rubbish … no atmosphere.'

'A few more results like today, and your wish will come true Mr Blobby ... we must be well second in the league now eh,' said Nipper, leaning over the seat in front of him to blow smoke into Danny Green's thick mop of hair.

'Watford are still top ... look fuck off you cunt,' replied Danny, ruffling his hair vigorously with his hands when he realised what Nipper had done. 'I reckon we'll piss the league this season,' he continued, holding the programme up in such a way that the streetlamps on the road outside provided sufficient light for him to be able to scrutinise the table printed on the inside back cover.

'Yeah, and if we do Ken Bates will have to sort the team out,' interjected Solly Lewis as he inserted the cassette that Eggy Barnes had selected into the stereo.

'I agree. Peter Nicholas ... what a liability, fancy getting sent off so early in the game today,' said Eggy, turning the volume control right up as the stereo clicked and whirred, its mechanism engaging the cassette.

'He never headed butted that cunt Stainrod,' offered Nipper inarticulately, as the post-match debate teetered on the brink of argumentation.

'We were lucky,' replied Eggy, grinning as he counted his fingers, waiting for the inevitable tirade of abuse.

'Lucky! ... 3-0 ... Fucking lucky! Lucky my sweaty fucking bollocks, we're the nuts mate,' countered the hitherto quiet Riddler Rowan, as Eggy Barnes tried to contain his mirth when Fatboy instigated his latest chant.

Darren Wood is the white Eusebio ... Darren Wood is the white Eusebio.

'Yabadabadoo!' yelled Solly Lewis, finally getting the transit out of second gear as the traffic began to thin out.

Roger Freestone is our leader, la la la la la, la la la la.

'Right enough of that shit ... let's have it,' he continued, deserting the vocal homage to Chelsea's goalie in favour of cranking up the stereo which silenced each and everyone of them as the haunting Indian vocal motif that signified the start of A guy called Gerald's, 'Voodoo Ray', splintered through the bass bins of the vans heavily customised speakers.

Wah ... wah, ha ha ... wah, ha ha yeah.

'TUNE!' yelled Nipper, as the tracks eccentric acid-house-bhangra crossover electro bleeps played on his nerves as if they were piano strings, the volume producing a tingling resonance of pure aural stimulation.

Voodoo Ray ... Voodoo Ray.

Fucking brilliant, he thought to himself ... money, and all this. I'll be bang on it tonight all right. Nipper's mind wandered as he closed his eyes and listened to the music.

Just as he'd thought it would back in Ibiza last summer, Ecstasy had unified youth culture in a way never seen before. Football casuals had embodied the 'baggy' ethic of cross over pop groups like the Happy Mondays and the Farm, and the trouble on the terraces had gone underground. As expected, the media had derided this new 'rave' culture as the scourge of the twentieth century, describing in detail the all night parties and the effect that E had on the supposed thousands of clubbers involved.

It was all bollocks of course, by talking up the numbers of people 'getting on it' they simply fuelled the thirst of those kids hungry to get involved. They wanted to find out what they were missing out on, and find out they did. Holly kept reminding him that it was a bit like the old days of punk, which at its outset had originated in London and Manchester.

Fair play to her. Last month, she'd got Steve Bruno to put five grand up front to promote a party in a derelict warehouse on the Isle of Dogs. The venue, indirectly brought to Nipper's attention by Beery Barlow, had been kept a secret for as long as possible. Promoted by word of mouth and flyers designed by Pete, the night had been a great success, right up until 4am when Old Bill raided and successfully stopped the party.

Fuck 'em though, everyone involved had slipped through the net, and by the time the filth had turned up, any drugs they'd hoped to find had long since been ingested. The good thing was that no law had been written to cater for this type of occasion and its fall out.

This time around Holly had recognised the need for greater discretion and better organisation. Tonight's venue, a disused aircraft hanger adjacent to an old RAF airfield in Buckinghamshire had been selected because of its close proximity to the M25 London orbital, and the fact it was several miles from the nearest urban conurbation.

It was all about the people, the drugs and the music. If one part of the trinity wasn't right, it just didn't work. Holly and Pete were responsible for promoting the event. Nipper and Eggy Barnes, in league with Davy Truelove, took care of the chemical aspect, and Chiller was responsible for the music.

Tonight's late night convoy of party people heading for Holly's 'Orbital Rave' would only be able to ascertain the exact location of the party by calling the number printed on the flyer, or tuning into anyone of a number of pirate radio stations that had begun broadcasting underground dance music illegally from the top floors of tenement blocks across London.

Being sorted for transport tonight was a result as well. Nipper had invested some of his ill gotten gains in a BMW that Pete spent most of the time driving. It was a lovely motor which deserved better than being ploughed through farmers fields in the middle of no-where, in the middle of the night, by a fully fledged space cadet fed on a diet of disco biscuits. Since Holly didn't drive, the Beamer would be safely parked up outside the flat in Ifield Road for the duration of the evening. Even Solly Lewis had resisted the urge to try and steal it.

★ ★ ★ ★ ★

'That's fucking amazing,' said Nipper, a jaw dropping look of incredulity forming on his face as Sniffler Barlow, and a couple of hired doormen he didn't recognise, slid back the huge door to the aircraft hanger.

It was difficult to gauge the size of the event, at each end of the cavernous hanger there was a huge raised platform with a sound system underneath. The warm up DJ was playing out from a pod adjacent to a lighting rig which had been skilfully suspended from the centre of the roof. A huge red laser beam was reflecting intermittently from mirrors along the walls. Each time it pulsed, the already sizeable crowd cheered.

Search lights with coloured lenses and strobes offset the effect, and the fractal images which were being projected onto large drop down screens reminded Nipper of the time he'd seen Hawkwind play at Hammersmith Odeon.

'Very cool,' said Pete, putting two E's in his mouth and taking a swig from a can of Red Stripe, 'very cool indeed.'

'Holly's got it sussed mate,' replied Nipper, shaking his head as he watched his friend 'double drop' a couple of the pills from the batch they were serving up this evening. 'You wanna be careful with them mate,' he continued, tapping his jacket pocket to make sure the pouch containing 100 'Red Playboy' E's was still concealed there. 'They're a special order from that mate of Davy's, the old Yiddo chemist Mordi up in Islington … double strength apparently.'

'Double strength, yeah right.'

'Easy son, you're in danger of becoming your own best customer.'

'Yeah, well carry on. I'm gonna dance these up in my system. My sales pitch works best when people come up and see me having such a good time they wanna know who served me … and that's when I tell 'em … Its me! See ya later alligator.'

'In a while crocodile.'

'Later today Madame Cholet.'

'Maybe next week DJ Sneak.'

Nipper laughed as he watched Pete disappear into the pea soup thick fog of dry ice which had enveloped the dancefloor. When it came to drugs he was like the conductor of an orchestra, he always knew exactly what part of the symphony was coming next.

★ ★ ★ ★ ★

By 2am, the hanger was buzzing along nicely. A temporary community, black and white, straight and gay, rich and poor, Millwall, West Ham, even Chelsea, all dancing together in sweet harmony.

Everything had fallen into place. Holly could enjoy herself now, she'd resisted the temptation to indulge earlier in the evening, but now, with everyone paid off and the balance of the door takings safely on their way back London, it was time to party.

'You may as well have a couple. It'll bring you up quicker', Pete had said half an hour or so ago as he'd handed her a couple of the unfamiliar looking E's.

'Yeah, er right', she'd replied hesitantly.

'Just do it babe'.

'Yeah ... I'll do it, I'll do it all right!'

Here was Holly, in the middle of the party she'd organised, that brilliant feeling fizzing through her cortex, playing catch up. Catch up, she thought to herself, looking at Pete stood in front of her striking that familiar star shaped, glassy eyed pose, I'm ahead of the game.

'Break ... for love. Break ... for love.'

'Tune!' exclaimed Pete, pointing his finger at the DJ booth where Chiller, who was firmly establishing himself as a serious contender for musical man of the moment, had just seamlessly mixed Mr Fingers', 'Can You Feel It', into the Raze track, 'Break 4 Luv'.

'Break ... for love.'

'I love you sis,' mouthed Pete, reaching out to Holly.

'Love you too bro,' replied Holly, certain that she could feel each and every single nerve ending tingling in her body.

'Baby don't you worry, I want to be the man that you want me to be ...'

Even though there were enough beats per minute to keep committed ravers like Pete happy, the bump and grind sensuousness of the track combined with a serious dosage of E, was sucking him into a trancelike state and Holly's magnetic female presence was bewitching him.

This was more than just another one of those famous 1000 yard stares, this was hypnotic. Holly recognised it, but was powerless to react as the first wave of nausea engulfed her.

'There's no need to worry ...'

'Pete ... Pete, I've lost it!' she squealed, panicking as her ability to focus diminished and the room began to spin.

'I'm gonna give you love the way you want it to be ...'

'I'm here sister,' shouted Pete, reaching out and grabbing Holly as she momentarily lost consciousness and fell forward into his arms.

'I'll be there every morning to hold you tight ...'

Pete held her in the air for a split second, dropping her down and kissing her fully on the lips as he carried her off the dance-floor, making his way to an area sectioned off by gaffer tape and populated by rusty old oil drums.

'And that's why baby you don't have to wonder why ...'

'Nipper ... Nipper,' cried Holly, eyes closed, stomach cramping as she tried in vain to summon the strength to resist her brothers advances. Tripping backwards and falling to the floor, the side seam of her skirt tore as the material rode up her legs.

'I love you, I need you ...'

Holly was in a state of catatonic shock. She could feel the dampness of the ground against her buttocks, and she could feel the floor vibrating in time with the beat of the music. She sensed everything, but was unable to protect herself as the involuntary paralysis brought on by the drugs allowed Pete, who had unbuckled his jeans and dropped them to his knees, to force himself on her.

'Got to have you ... oh, right now.'

'You want it sister, you've always wanted it,' hissed Pete, his sneering face masked by a vile veneer of sweat and spittle.

Holly's body convulsed as she vomited and lost all sensory perception.

* * * * *

'There's someone here to see you doll face,' said Nipper, placing a cup of tea on the bedside table and beckoning Layla Goss to enter the room, 'I'll leave you two together eh,' he continued, swallowing hard to clear the lump in his bone dry throat. 'I'm off to the Finborough, I'll be back straight after the game.'

Holly waited until she heard the front door click shut before she spoke. Her voice trembled as she acknowledged her friends presence. 'Layla ... Layla ... I knew you would come,' she said, tears welling up in her dark ringed eyes as she motioned Layla to sit down on the edge of the bed.

'Oh my God, what has happened to you? asked Layla in a concerned manner. 'What has that brute done to you?'

'No Layla, its not Nipper,' replied Holly, drawing her knees up to her chin and frowning, 'he's been as good as gold, really he has ... it's, it's ... its someone else, something terrible happened last weekend.'

Layla picked up the packet of red Marlboro's that she'd dropped on the floor as she'd sat down, and opened the box slowly.

'I could sense it in your voice when you called me,' she said calmly, pausing to light two cigarettes and handing one to Holly before continuing. 'Your brother, right? I think from what you told me in the past it's your brother.'

Holly took the Marlboro Layla had lit for her, cupped it between thumb and forefinger so the filter was facing outwards, and smoked it in the same way a borstal kid would, inhaling deeply and moving her hand away from her mouth in an accentuated arc.

'Come on Holly, I'm not stupid,' said Layla, tousling her peroxide hair in a coquettish manner which wasn't in keeping with the gravity of the discussion. 'Under the bell jar of denial, all that can blossom is rage,' she added eloquently, the profoundness of her words taking Holly by surprise.

'You know the party I'd organised last week, the one at the airfield?'

'Yes, I remember you telling me.'

'Once everything was sorted, all in, all up and running to plan ...'

'Yes.'

'Well I fancied getting on one, and Pete had these pills that Nipper was serving up ... and, well ... I double dropped.'

'Snide pills?'

'You could say. Nipper's taking things to another level, he's having them made up by this chemist in North London.'

'Yeah, well I know what you're gonna tell me now.'

'What?'

'They weren't snide, they were uncut, pure MDMA ... we've had the same trouble on the island. It's a great idea, but peoples tolerance to the dosage aint what it should be.'

Holly smoked the Marlboro to the filter before stubbing it out and hauling her body out of the bed. 'Tolerance, TO ... LER ... ANCE!' she shrieked, gripping her forearms and biting her red raw bottom lip, 'My so called FUCKING brother r r r raped me on that shit ... HE FUCKING RAPED ME!'

As Holly collapsed back onto the bed sobbing uncontrollably, Layla raised her clenched right fist to her mouth but said nothing as she waited patiently for her friends visible anguish to subside.

Several minutes passed before the graveyard stiff silence was broken as Holly regained her composure to speak. 'I knew it all along ... all along,' she whispered, her tones hushed despite the fact that their was nobody else in the flat. 'Ever since I was a young girl, I could see the way he looked at me.'

'But what about Trixie?' asked Layla, reaching for the Marlboro's again and inwardly cursing herself at the insensitivity of her question.

'Trixie? ... Yeah what about Trixie?' sighed Holly. 'She's just a front for him, he's fucking twisted, Trixie fucking nothing.'

'Yeah sorry, I know.'

'No, Layla … you don't fucking know.'

'No I do … sorry babe, sorry,' replied Layla, steadying herself, patently aware of the fraught situation she was being availed of. 'Have you told Nipper … have you told anyone about this?' she asked, shaking her head as the reality of Holly's ordeal began to sink in.

'No-one … who could I tell?'

'And Pete?'

'The bastard!'

'Yes, the bastard.'

'No … I haven't seen him since … I never want to see him again.'

Layla pondered for a while, smoking her cigarette and wondering how the beginning and the middle of the horror story she had just been made a party to could ever have a happy ending. Any ending. Mesmerised, she watched over Holly and waited for her to speak.

'I told Nipper, I'd lost it … told him, the Red Playboy pills were too much and that I'd fallen over … E'ing my tits off, I even laughed at the situation. What a fucking Muppet.'

Layla noticed a detached coldness in the tone of Holly's voice as she spoke which made her smile. Leaning back on the bed, she rolled her shoulders in a confident, masculine manner that didn't go unnoticed. 'Would you like me to take care of it Holly?' she asked precisely, in a deep resonating voice that evoked memories of a thousand gangster films.

'You can do that for me?'

'I can do this for you … my precious friend Holly.'

'Really?'

'I can do anything. Hell hath no fury …'

'Like a woman scorned,' interjected Holly, stubbing out her cigarette purposefully.

'No!' countered Layla harshly, looking at the time on her watch and clicking her tongue against the roof of her mouth, 'Hell hath no fury … like a woman.'

★ ★ ★ ★ ★

'Hoorah, Hoorah … Pompey will go far.'

'Listen to that lot will ya,' said Fatboy Green, doing up the neck toggle of his Chevignon duffle coat and pointing at Portsmouth fans gathered on the North Stand terrace.

'It aint a bad support though is it,' replied Nipper, turning up the collar of the sheepskin jacket he was wearing and thrusting his gloved hands into its pockets. 'They must be fucking freezing though,' he continued, feeling his eyes water slightly as he yawned.

'Mind you, there's a good few of em who wont feel the cold this afternoon,' chuckled Fatboy, resisting the urge to get to his feet as Gordon Durie flighted a trademark long throw into the box.

'Not half son, I got rid of the last of those Red Playboy pills in the Finborough earlier. Their 6.57 crew will still be rolling way past midnight, did you seem em dancing away at half time?'

'Yes mate, mind you look what happened at the aircraft hanger last weekend.'

'Yeah well, I told em not to double drop.' Nipper got to his feet as David Lee flicked the ball towards the Pompey goal. 'Yes Rodders ... ooh fucking hell!' he shouted, clapping his hands as much to warm them, as to celebrate the seemingly inevitable Blues opener. Lee's strike rebounded off the post into the path of Kerry Dixon. 'Go on Kel ... YES!'

'Fucking quality!' yelled Eggy Barnes, jumping into the group hug that ensued as golden boy Dixon gave Chelsea a fourth minute lead.

'One Kerry Dixon, there's only one Kerry Dixon. One Kerry Dixon, there's only one Kerry Dixon.'

'How's Holly feeling now?' asked Eggy, teeth chattering as he tried to concentrate on the game which was becoming increasingly difficult as the cold winter air leaked through the vents in his brand new Paul & Shark windcheater.

'Yeah she's okay, that Layla bird from Ibiza has come over to see her thank Christ,' replied Nipper, taking off his gloves and lighting a cigarette. 'She's been as moody as fuck all week, refusing to eat ... it's been a nightmare to be honest with you mate.'

'Did you ever get to the bottom of what actually happened?'

'Nah, she just overdid it with the Jack and Jill's, fainted and whacked herself on the floor silly cow ... Oi Solly ... SOLOMON!' Nipper stood up and waved at Solly Lewis who he had just spotted walking down the central gangway of the middle tier of the East Stand where they were sat. 'Her brother wasn't much help, he was completely off his tits as usual, still it's all sorted now. Oooh go on Jukebox, go on you Jock cunt, hit it. Yes!'

'We are top of the league, said we are top of the league.'

The conversation broke down in the face of jubilant celebration as Gordon Durie showed pace and skill before whacking the ball past Alan Knight in the Portsmouth goal to give a cockily confident looking Chelsea side a 2-0 lead.

'Talk of the devil, where the fuck is he today?' said Fatboy, slapping

Nipper heartily across the back and picking up the dialogue where it had been left a few minutes previously.

'Who Pete?'

'Yeah, it aint like him to miss a game ... not like Chiller, now he's a famous DJ.'

'He's gone to Goa, went on Thursday.'

'Goa, where the fucks that? Malta?'

'Nah mate, that's Gozo. Goa's in India. Full of hippy's so I've heard ... Oh for fucks sake ... you fat pork pie eating cunt.'

Nipper buried his head in his hands as portly Pompey striker Mick Quinn headed in just before half-time to give the visitors some hope.

Fatboy lead an ironic chorus of *'who ate all the pies'*, which he persisted with right up until the referee blew for the breather. Contemplating a half-time cup of Bovril, he once again picked up the thread of his inquiry into Pete's hasty departure to India.

'Yeah, go on mate,' he pestered inquisitively to Nipper's increasing chagrin. 'Has he gone out there with Trixie, or on his Jack Jones?'

'On his Jack mate,' replied Nipper, blowing out a mouthful of irritated hot air as he reached into his back pocket for his money clip. 'Yeah, he had a row with Trixie last Sunday and she told him to fuck off,' he continued, pausing to count through the twenty pound notes harnessed in the showy silver frame. 'She was meant to have gone with him, had a visa and everything. They were gonna be away for the whole of Christmas and the New Year.'

'Loadsamoney,' said Fatboy, imitating the Harry Enfield character as he disregarded Nipper's words and leered enviously at the wedge of money his friend was displaying unashamedly.

'Yeah, maybe I should lend some to Ken Bates so he can buy a new defence. What the fucking hell was that you fucking Muppets?' howled Nipper derisively. Within a minute of the restart, Martin Kuhl had levelled the match with a twenty yard screamer that had flown past the Chelsea keeper, Roger Freestone.

When Portsmouth had the audacity to take the lead, the police found themselves pressed into action to quell a Duncan Disorderly led assault on the *'Play up Pompey'*, chiming fans from the south coast.

Chelsea pressed forward, searching for a face saving equaliser which eventually came their way when Kevin Wilson scored a sweet 70th minute goal.

'2-0 up, to three a piece ... fucking typical Chels!' bawled Eggy Barnes, fists clenched as the minutes ticked by increasingly slowly.

'We love you Chelsea, we do. We love you Chelsea, we do. We love you Chelsea, we do. Oh Chelsea we love you.'

'Thank fuck for that,' shouted Fatboy, getting to his feet as the referee blew for full time. 'C'mon, lets go and have a beer back at the Finborough with the others.'

'Yeah, good idea,' replied Nipper, 'it's fucking freezing, that daft twat Pete had the right idea heading out to Goa, I wonder what he's been up to.'

★ ★ ★ ★ ★

Pete was sitting cross-legged on the sand, arms outstretched, marvelling at the spellbinding iridescence of the full moon. He wasn't alone on the beach, far from it. People who'd gathered to watch the sunset were still milling around, smoking, drinking beer, and chatting amongst themselves.

In the few days he'd been there, Pete had already established that Goa was the kind of place where you could lose yourself quite easily if you wanted to. It was a place where mystique and friendship were respected and, more importantly, a place where he had no visible reminders of the past he had just left behind.

Anjuna beach, situated to the north of Goa had originally been the final destination for western hippy travellers in the '60s. Arriving with little in the way of money, these hippy pioneers, having seen the raw beauty and natural karma Anjuna offered, had been keen to find a way to fund a prolonged stay. All manner of personal belongings were bought, sold and exchanged for money and food with fellow travellers.

Over the years, photographs of the Anjuna flea market had found their way onto the pages of holiday brochures and travel guides alike, making it a 'must see' part of any itinerary for visitors to the area. Pete had drawn comparisons with Las Dalias in Ibiza, but he knew this place was different.

On Wednesdays, the market covered almost the entire stretch of the beach, with resident Westerners vying with hawkers from Gujurat and Rajasthan and the colourful Lamanis from Karnataka for the tourist rupee. This was barter town and everyone there seemed to have a sense of purpose. People would spend hours haggling over what amounted to a few pence for the pleasure of owning something they would never contemplate buying at home.

Animal, mineral, vegetable. You name it, you could buy it at the market, and a steady stream of insistent children would scurry between the pitches like industrious worker ants, cajoling and pleading with tourists to pay a visit to a nearby stall which had commissioned them to find prospective customers for anything from wild Saffron to tie-dyed sarongs, sandals, wood carvings and heavy duty silver jewellery.

★ ★ ★ ★ ★

Pete had arrived earlier in the week via a charter flight that had landed at Goa's Dabolim airport some twelve hours or so after it had left Gatwick. The scheduled stop over in Bahrain had been a blessed relief from the honeymoon couple he'd found himself sat next to, and a welcome opportunity for him to stretch his legs which were still stiff from the weekends chemically enhanced exertions on the dancefloor.

He'd initially decided that he needed to keep his mind occupied to stop himself thinking about the Holly situation and the subsequent row he'd had with Trixie, however a drink fuelled sleep had been the welcome answer to his problems on the final leg of the flight.

The searing intensity of the early morning sun had fatigued him further as he'd emerged, bleary eyed and squinting from the plane and trudged across the runway to the welcome shade and organised chaos of the arrivals hall. Hand-me-down British Colonial bureaucracy was very much in evidence. Queues lengthened and tempers frayed, as airport staff pedantically checked the visas and stamped the passports of travel weary tourists impatient to get on with their holidays.

Pete had been met at the airport by Harry Boyer, a whippet thin ponytailed veteran of the sixties hippy generation, whom he and Trixie had met in Ibiza during the summer. Harry owned a large villa in Goa and rented rooms on a word of mouth basis to people he could trust, people he'd met and vetted out when he took his annual summer holiday in the Balearics.

It was Trixie that had been taken with Boyer's insouciant geezer charm, and whilst Pete was grateful that he had a place to stay, he was in no mood for the lively banter on offer as they'd clambered into a well preserved Morris Oxford saloon, complete with gear change on the driving column, and made their way slowly out of the airport.

Pete offered nodded answers to Boyer's questions, focussing his attention instead on the strange new world outside. Besides the stray dog signs of cloying poverty, other oddities had already grabbed his attention.

Westerners, astride pristine examples of Royal Enfield motorcycles, travelled at life threatening speed along the dusty roads, swerving occasionally to avoid the sacred cows that wandered aimlessly and unimpeded across a landscape dotted with the sun bleached white facades of Christian churches.

Swastika emblazoned elephants stood on the street corners of each of the towns they passed through. Lazily they flapped their ears, oblivious to the constant blaring of horns belonging to cars whose industrious looking owners had no concept of the highway code.

Harry Boyer's villa was located behind the quaintly named Blossom Soda Factory near the anarchic looking village of Calangute. Despite the journey from the airport taking less than an hour, by the time they'd arrived Pete was already consumed by jetlag and the desire to lie down on a comfortable bed and close his eyes had been overwhelming.

The villa itself, a grandiose red brick affair, was set back from the main road and traffic noise was muffled by the gnarled trunks of trees and verdant bushes that surrounded the property. The chirrupy sounds of children playing outside the gates of the nearby Piety Chapel added to the quaint ambience making Pete feel totally at ease with the environment.

'Perfect', he'd said to Boyer, as he'd handed over 6000 rupees and slid his suitcase along the marble tiled floor of his bedroom, 'absolutely perfect'.

'You'll find me at a beach bar called Laxmans most evenings. If you need anything give us a shout', had been the reply, which barely registered with Pete as he'd laid down on the large bed and promptly fallen asleep.

★ ★ ★ ★ ★

For the first two weeks Pete did absolutely nothing apart from sunbathe, get drunk, smoke dope, and try to forget the past. Most mornings he would take a leisurely stroll to the nearby Infantaria bakery and buy some freshly baked rolls, eating them as he made his way slowly along the Baga Road until he arrived at the Turret Bar. Here he would sojourn for a cup of milky tea and his first cigarette of the day, taking time to read the local English language daily newspapers, curiously written whimsical affairs called the Navhind Times and the Herald.

The Turret was located at the T-junction formed by Three Toes Lane which extended from the beach to the Baga Road. Its location, pavement café style seating and roof terrace made it the perfect place to sit and watch the world go by. Dependent on the time of day, most of the people that passed by the Turret were headed for Three Toes Bar, one of the main meeting points for both travellers and tourists alike.

The Turret had its early morning regulars, one of whom was a huge mountain of a man who sported a moustache that would not have looked out of place under the nose of a '70s porn-star. The bar owner always made a fuss of him, calling him boss and taking great care with the preparation of the full English breakfast 'Boss' always ordered.

'I am the Walrus,' said 'Boss' on Christmas morning, as he made his way across to where Pete was sat and pulled up a chair. 'Merry Christmas boss,' he continued, a frown forming across his puppy dog features as he realised that he'd unnerved Pete.

'Yeah, and I'm the Eggman,' chuckled Pete, thinking about the old

Beatles song. 'Well er Merry Christmas to you as well mate … the names Pete,' he continued, standing up to shake the Walrus' hand.

'Nice one boss.'

'What is it with this 'boss' thing?'

'Boss means friend.'

'Friend ha ha,' laughed Pete ringing a teaspoon on the side of his mug. 'I thought that was your name … well before you said you were the Walrus.'

'No mate, my name's Randy Carver … but everyone calls me the Walrus.' It hadn't been Pete's intention to befriend anyone in Goa, but the Walrus had a warm and welcoming demeanour that he'd found instantly engaging. He didn't ask too many questions, and was refreshingly sketchy about his past, unlike the majority of the me, myself, and I people that he generally met on holiday.

With the exception of his size, everything about the Walrus was understated, and his fugitive outlaw persona, coupled with a penchant for openly smoking potent smelling hashish made him easy company for Pete who hadn't had a decent conversation with anyone, apart from himself, since his arrival.

Beyond saying that he'd lived in Goa for seven years the Walrus stuck with the here and now, explaining how he steered clear of Three Toes in the evening, preferring to hang out at Poppy, a low key bar near Vagator Beach just to the north of Anjuna.

'The police don't bother with Poppy, it's too medieval for em over there,' he elucidated, skinning up an impressive looking spliff which had Pete licking his blistered lips in anticipation.

'Are you in trade then?' enquired Pete in a hushed voice, 'cos I might be looking for some work, if you know what I mean.'

'I thought you might,' said the Walrus, lighting the joint and taking a long relaxed drag before passing it under the table to Pete.

'Fucking hell!' spluttered Pete, coughing as he drew the smoke down into his lungs, 'this is top gear.'

'Arpora weed mate, the best draw on the Indian subcontinent. You've gotta be careful though. The police are on the case. They raided the Shore Bar last week and banged a couple of tweeker birds up in Saligao nick for a couple of nights,' said the Walrus, pausing and shaking his head before continuing. 'Two sleepless nights in the piss stinking, mosquito infested darkness, sharing a cell with eight other men held on a range of charges from robbery and rape to murder, that aint my idea of fun.'

'So discretion's the key then eh,' said Pete, motioning the bar owner to bring him another cup of tea.

'Definitely,' replied the Walrus, nodding in such a way that his jowls wobbled like kids party jellies freshly turned out of their moulds. 'The police did secure one conviction as a result of their endeavours that evening. An Anglo-Indian lad called Thakkar, who was known for dealing quite openly to tourists at Anjuna market. They caught him with an ounce of weed in his backpack. You know yourself Pete, back in the UK that'd be worth a bottle on the street at best, here its worth four fifths of fuck all. He'll get fifteen years detention in Fort Aquada for that.'

'Fort Aquada?'

'Yes mate, you should look concerned. It's Goa's notorious central jail, and the worst occupational hazard there is out here, well discounting death of course. In Goa once you're incarcerated, no amount of lobbying by any foreign government will secure an early release if you've been found guilty on drugs charges. That kid's done for, if malaria, AIDS or a knife doesn't claim him, then insanity borne out of boredom will surely drive him to top himself.'

* * * * *

Pete hadn't taken too long to reconcile himself with his new occupation. Despite the fact that he hadn't been in Goa long, he still smiled as he saw the 'tweekers' idling down the dusty, dilapidated Baga Road searching for the tourist brochure idyll. The quiet solitude of sun, sea, sand and whispering palms, certainly wasn't to be found in Baga or Calangute, and Pete had little intention of sharing with his potential customers the locations in relatively close proximity which he knew would fulfil their dreams.

Pete's business blueprint was a simple one. On Boxing Day, he'd 'borrowed' a kilo of the finest Arpora weed from the Walrus and bought a large box of clear plastic ziplock bags from a hardware shop in Calangute village. Back in his room, he divided the kilo up into four 'bars', weighing each one in turn on the Statue of Liberty style scales he'd bartered his shirt for at Anjuna flea market; the 'bars' were then bagged and refrigerated.

The following morning he'd taken a 'one bar' out of the fridge, sat himself down in the garden and re bagged half of this into ounce bags, re bagging half again into eighths. The eighths he proposed to sell to 'tweekers' for 1000 rupees, this was the going rate on the Baga Road, double what the Walrus charged at Poppy.

'Sorted,' he'd said to himself, standing up and rubbing the leafy residue from his hands as he'd cautiously surveyed the grounds of the villa. The distant view from the back garden was spectacular, capturing centre frame, the stunning white washed twin towers and central dome of the beautiful church of St. Alex. The church was over four hundred years old, and the line and beauty of it's architectural style was yet another reminder of his time in Ibiza.

There was a traditional, unsullied ambience to be found at this end of Calangute, and Pete fitted in perfectly. He was polite and friendly with the villagers who lived nearby, and even though he was a newcomer they would often invite him to share a glass of Feni with them in the late afternoon when they returned home from work. Feni was a tongue loosening hooch distilled from palm trees, whose distinct taste Pete likened to nail polish remover.

The more Feni the locals drank, the more nostalgic and argumentative they would become about their old haunts, places like St. Anthony's Bar, Tropicana, Britto's and Jacques Corner. Eventually the conversation would drift from English to the local Konkani dialect, at which point Pete would bid them good day and go to work. The locals thought he worked in one of the many bars in Baga and had no reason whatsoever to suspect his newfound occupation.

At the Turret Bar, Pete would carefully observe the latest influx of female tweekers. Pale skins that had a hint of first day sunburnt redness and freshly inked henna tattoos were a dead giveaway. He'd watch and wait patiently as groups of girls passed by swathed in colourful sarongs chatting idly amongst themselves.

Some were confident in their manner as they walked on by, others less so. Indecision was the key, and he'd try and catch the eye of anyone looking furtively back at the bar. He could almost hear the whispers, 'that bloke looks quite cool, he might know what the score is'.

'Can I help you out?' he asked the flame haired, freckled faced girl who was dawdling outside the bar with two friends.

'Maybe,' she replied, blushing slightly and smiling. 'We've just got here, and we were wondering where it all happens.'

Bingo, he thought to himself, even though the ginger girl reminded him of Sissy Spacek in the horror film Carrie . 'Let me buy you girls a drink, and I'll pass you on some friendly advice. You can take it or leave it. My name's Pete by the way.'

After a very brief consultation, 'Carrie' introduced herself as Laura and her two friends as Hayley and Emma, they'd agreed unanimously that it would be okay to join him for a drink.

It was perfect, Pete bought a round of drinks and then struck up an easy conversation which he peppered with references to various bars and beach shacks. Assured of their undivided attention, he went on to describe the market at Anjuna and, even though he'd attended neither, the full moon parties that were held at Paradiso and Bombay Micks. Now it was time to put a herbal spin on the discussion to gauge their reaction.

'Of course, they probably told you at your welcome meeting about the drug thing here. Well everything they've told you is true. You really can't be too careful … people get ripped off all the time.'

Laura winked at Hayley and leant across the table. 'So do you know where we can get hold of something decent to smoke?'

Result. Pete sat back, reached for his cigarettes and offered them around the table to the girls before speaking slowly and deliberately. 'I can take care of that for you, finish your drinks and I'll walk up to Three Toes with you. It's gonna cost you a thousand roops for an eighth … that's okay isn't it?'

It was the silent, assumptive close he'd used to good effect serving up pills back home, and he had no reason to suspect that it wouldn't work here.

Laura furrowed her brow, engaging in some rapid mental arithmetic before shrugging her shoulders and nodding at her friends.

'Sounds okay Pete, good stuff is it?'

'You know that! It's the very best. They call it Arpora weed, you'll love it. Come on we can sort it out on the way up to Three Toes.'

Pete sniggered as he got up from the table. Good stuff? This flakey lot would be quaking at the knees in spliff induced paroxysms of laughter within minutes of rolling their first joint. It was barely a five-minute walk to Three Toes from the Turret and Pete made the most of it, revelling in the dramatic tension he could invoke from the circumstances. This was the fifth such deal he'd done in the last couple of days and he was supremely confident in his abilities.

'Okay Laura, lets take a walk up the road. Just before we get to that brightly lit shop on the right I'm going to give you a hug and your gonna feel me place a plastic bag into your left hand. That's the deal. The money you give me when we get to the bar. I cant say fairer than that.'

Pete knew there was no need for this level of covert behaviour but he loved the reaction he got , the way the girls were like putty in his hands, playing along with his game just for a measly eighth. Laura was no different, and he felt a tingle in his groin as he held her close and smelt her fragrant freshness.

Three Toes was awash with people, it's reputation as a meeting place for visitors to Baga was unprecedented. The Walrus had told Pete how the business had been built up at the start of the '70s by an enterprising, well-travelled Englishman called John 'three toes' Fair, who'd recognised the commercial potential of a venture which could cater for the needs of visitors to such an outstanding area of untainted beachfront beauty.

At that time, the silver sands of Baga beach stretched right up to the gardens of Three Toes house, but over the years they had been pushed back towards the sea to accommodate the increasing number of travellers and tourists that arrived with every new season.

The bars main seating area, a huge sandpit with plastic tables and chairs arranged haphazardly across its surface, resembled a cattle market. Groups of girls, not unlike those Pete had arrived with tonight, would find a table and sit down. Within seconds they would be accosted by surly looking youths from every corner of the globe keen to try their luck.

Pete found watching this scenario unfold hugely entertaining, particularly if there was a language barrier involved. As one group of lads were forced to retreat, failed by their linguistic deficiencies, another group would arrive. Occasionally a drink fuelled fight would break out which would be settled within seconds by the intervention of Baba Johnson, Three Toes head of security, a man as wide as he was tall.

Disregarding his new occupation, to Pete's discerning eye it was clear that the seeds of something unhealthy and unwanted had already been planted here. If things didn't change, it wouldn't be too long before the lager louts that frequented the Spanish Costa's arrived along with their beer guts, football shirts, and small town racist mentalities.

Fuck it though, that wasn't his problem. Business was business, and Pete wasn't going to get too sentimental about things. He pointed in the direction of a kiosk where drink coupons were exchanged for cash, and as agreed Laura gave him 1200 rupees. With that, the transaction was complete.

Pete bought three coupons for 120 rupees and pocketed the change. He exchanged the coupons for three bottles of Kings beer at the bar and walked over to the wall at the back end of the sand pit where the girls were now stood. Three likely lads had already moved in, and Pete smiled at them as he handed over the drinks to Laura, Hayley and Emma.

'Listen girls I've just seen an old mate up by the house so I'm gonna leave you to it … enjoy yourselves and be lucky.' He winked at Laura, nodded at Hayley and Emma, and made his way round the edge of the sand pit back over to the wall nearest the kiosk.

'It's all about eye contact, you use it to build rapport and trust,' he muttered to himself, as he walked back down the lane to the Turret Bar, eager to repeat the process again. 'A language without words', that's what Nipper had called it, fucking quality!

Two deals later, and Pete had sold the weed he'd come out with, now he could go home and chill out.

'Well you didn't wake up this morning, cos you didn't go to bed. You were watching the whites of your eyes turn red …'

With a spliff in one hand and a large glass of ice cold Kingfisher in the other Pete sat himself down in the garden, gazed up at the starry cloudless sky, and tried to concentrate on the old The The track that was playing at low volume on the cassette player by his side.

'This is the day your life will surely change ... this is the day when things fall into place.'

Though he tried hard, it was difficult not to think about Holly. As the Arpora weed worked its way into his system, he wondered if she might be looking up at the heavens searching out the brightest star in the firmament just like they had done when they were children.

'But the side of you they'll never see ... is when you're left alone with your memories ... that hold your life ... together, like glue.'

Mum had pointed out to them the bright North Star and told them that when they were apart, no matter where they were, if they both looked up at the sky at that bright star, then their souls would be together. That thought had stayed with Pete throughout his life, but he knew now, in his blackest heart of hearts, that Holly would never intentionally look up at the North Star again. 'Fuck it!'

★ ★ ★ ★ ★

On New Years Eve, Pete found himself sitting halfway down the well worn concrete steps that led from the Shore Bar down to Anjuna beach. Whilst watching the greying sea swallow up the golden globe of the sun as day had turned to night he'd felt a creeping sense of unease.

The terrifying self loathing which had led to night-sweats and panic attacks, he'd kept at bay with coma inducing Arpora weed, but this felt different. Day to day confidence gained from regular business deals was being knocked by a paranoid feeling that he was being stalked. Day by day, hour by hour, he double checked his surroundings, looking at people to see if they were looking at him.

All he saw was the same regular faces in the same regular places, creatures of habit just like him. The arcaic Swiss hippy with the grey beard he called Methusala was stood behind him smoking his shit from a huge hollowed out elephant's tusk. The Walrus, Randy Carver was lurking in the shadows. His landlord Harry Boyer, and a host of tweekers he'd sorted out were all proffering knowing winks and 'hello mate' gestures. It was easy to see how people could lose the plot here, but that kind of madness wasn't for Pete, he was being consumed by something far darker, far more sinister.

As the night moved on Pete felt compelled to relocate. He picked himself up and walked further around the headland at the north end of Anjuna Beach, the tide was on the turn and he knew he had to tread carefully if he wanted to make it safely to Paradiso. This was the legendary venue he'd heard so much about, a favoured location for full moon parties aligned to the Goan trance music scene.

His conscience was gnawing away at him, lowering his self esteem and making him feel powerless. The vicious cycle of drug abuse that had blighted his life, he now saw as a way to combat the emotional disorder that had come on top for him. Uncharacteristically, he felt powerless to fight. He didn't want the battle, somehow he knew that everything happening to him now was predetermined, this was his destiny.

'It aint my fucking fault,' he cursed, balancing precariously on the rocky outcrop that melded the opaque sea with the sandy beach at the foot of the cliff face into which had been hewn the three shelves that formed Paradiso. 'Really it aint my fault.'

Pete clambered across the rocks and made his way along the beach to the narrow staircase which skirted the cliffs and enabled him to gain access to the balconied area on the third and highest level of the club.

The venue was getting busier and Pete wasted no time in rolling up a spliff that comprised solely of Arpora weed. Lighting up and looking out to sea from his vantage point his dark mood eased as a combination of the herb and the vista fired his imagination.

He was the pilot of a plane, looking out on the broad horizon. The perspective was angular and things appeared smaller than they really were. Pete gazed down at the tops of the palm trees and then up at the stars, all the while drawing heavily on the industrial catering strength reefer he'd assembled.

Intoxicated by the view, the pulsating music, and the psychotropic drug he was smoking, Pete was unaware of the time ticking by. The clock of his heart had stopped several weeks previously.

He hummed deeply and resonantly to himself, following the metronome-like beat of the vocal free twisted synthesiser rhythm that was gorging itself on Paradiso's megawatt sound-system until the urge to dance became unshakable.

Pete made his way down the claustrophobic spiral staircase that led from the balcony to a narrow gallery along which he jostled with other party goers who were equally taken with the desire to move their bodies in a freeform environment. Unwittingly, he stumbled into a cavernous room that was decorated with fluorescent psychedelic paintings which were illuminated by low voltage ultra violet lighting that seemed to bring their subject matter to life.

'This is it!' he yelled, unheard and ignored by the gathered throng. Pete felt the heavy techno bass lines surge down his spine and through to his feet, he closed his eyes and let the music build him up allowing it to take him to the other place. 'This is the acid house.'

Oblivious, Pete danced in the way that only he knew how to dance. Eyes closed, arms aloft, hands together, forming a triangle with thumbs and forefingers, he swayed with the heaving crowd.

When he opened his eyes, it was the fractal paintings on the wall that he saw moving and not the people around him. They were like statues, with the exception of one person. At the far end of the room, his eyes focused on the slim figure of a girl who was grooving without restraint. The white stitching in her clothes picked out by the ultra violet light, silhouetted her frame against the wall behind her like cats eyes on an airport runway. It gave her an ethereal quality.

Pete looked at the girl and shivered. Supernatural, that's what it was, the feeling that he was being drawn inexorably towards her.

'You know me don't you? You know who I am?'

The girl mouthed the words at Pete, reaching out and grabbing his arm, leading him out of the 'acid house' and down the short flight of rickety wooden steps that brought them to the main dancing area in front of the DJ's stage.

Pete's cognitive powers, suppressed as they were by the weed, were vainly working overtime. He'd overcooked it this evening, and he knew all too well that when he was in this fabled 'other place', his drug infested mind could, would, and was, playing tricks on him. But like the advert, was this real, or was this Memorex?

The girl looked so familiar. The peroxide white shorn hair, the tanned toned arms, the wide long lashed feline eyes that were heavy with mascara. Pete was sure he'd seen her before, but somewhere else, not here in Goa.

'Dance with me ... dance with me Pete,' she said in a slow deliberate open mouthed manner that was easy to lip-read.

Pete looked at her, but his vision kept blurring. The words he was trying to string together, about how and why she knew his name, just wouldn't come out. The girl pulled Pete towards her, kissing him, forcing her tongue into his dry but willing mouth. When he started to respond, she pulled away, taking him by the hand and walking briskly around the dancefloor to a set of steps which led down to the beach.

As he stumbled down the steps, Pete turned his head and looked back up at Paradiso. Fucking mental, he thought to himself, trembling as he viewed the balcony from whence he'd come. He swore that from its parapet he could see the sylphlike raven haired figure of a girl waving at him, a girl who looked for all the world like his sister Holly.

Chilled to the bone, Pete's body shuddered as he tried to engage his brain in gear. 'It can't be … Jesus C C C Christ,' he stammered as the girl tugged his arm insistently, distracting him from his latest mental trauma.

She led Pete down to the shore, and they started to trudge slowly along the waters edge, away from where other people were gathered partying on the beach. After walking for ten minutes or so she looked round at Pete and beyond him, back along the shoreline. Pete looked round too, he could still make out Paradiso, but its dissonance was muffled by the waves breaking on the rocks nearby.

'Here we are,' she said calmly, letting go of Pete's hand and bending down to remove her sandals.

'Where?' replied Pete, watching the girl as she stood up slowly and eased herself out of the dress she was wearing.

'You'll see my friend,' she replied, taking a deep breath and sighing as she walked naked over to Pete and embraced him. 'Come with me … come let's swim together in the sea.'

Pete cocked his head to one side and looked at her, he felt so certain that he knew her, but once again, just as he began to form the words in his mouth, she began to kiss him with an ardent fervour that he was compelled to reciprocate.

As he began to lose himself in the moment, the girl pulled away from him and walked into the sea. Pete followed her with his eyes, marvelling at the perfect globes of her buttocks as they disappeared into the water. She continued until just her head and shoulders were visible above the water-line and then turned around and beckoned him to join her.

Pete felt giddy as he bent down to untie the laces on his trusty old Adidas Forest Hills, watching all the while as the girl continued to wave pleadingly at him. Steadying himself he removed his combat trousers and T-shirt, placing them next to his trainers on the sand before walking gingerly into sea.

As he waded out towards the girl, he tried fleetingly to convince himself that this was all a dream. Was it? Or was it a nightmare? Would he wake up suddenly, head bathed in sweat, lying in bed next to Trixie Fowler relieved that the only real thing he had to worry about was the chances of Chelsea being promoted back to the First Division? Nah, this was all too real.

'Kiss me Pete … kiss me.'

Pete looked at the girl awkwardly as she took him in her arms, his thoughts distracted by her actions and the surprising coldness of the water which had sobered him up slightly.

'How do you know my ...?'

Pete's question was cut short as the girl put her mouth over his and kissed him with the snake tongued passion of a lover. Naturally, he responded, running his hands down to the small of her back, pulling her close so she could feel his hardness.

He could sense the girl widening her stance. With her hands around his neck, she used the buoyancy the water afforded her to pull herself up. Kissing him, she bit down hard on his tongue, moaning softly as she felt his prick enter her.

As the girl fucked him, making the most of the undulating motion of the sea, Pete lost all sense of perception. Feeling his orgasm building up, unaware of her grip tightening around his neck, he opened his eyes and groaned as he came, his back arching spasmodically as he pushed his cock in deeper to its hilt.

Satiated, Pete closed his eyes again as the girl continued to push down, her legs looping behind his, a quick bend of the knees unbalancing him in the water. As he fell backwards, she eased herself off his still firm cock allowing her body to float up in the tranquil sea.

The swiftness of the move caught Pete completely off guard. To no avail, he began to struggle, his shaking head now submerged beneath the water stifling the panic of his screams. In vain, he tried to loosen her strangulating hands from his neck, but with the guile of a deadly assassin she pressed her thumbs inwards and upwards on his Adams apple forcing his mouth open.

As the salty water invaded his lungs, and he began to lose consciousness, Pete opened his eyes and saw the starlight shimmering on the surface of the water. The North Star? His mind whirled one last time. Thoughts of Holly, Trixie, the innocence of youth, Nipper, Fatboy, the mighty Blues ... gone forever.

8 *January 1989*
MEMORIAL

It was three full days before Pete's naked body was brought ashore, caught up in the nets of the St. Xavier, one of many small fishing boats that set sail every morning from the creek where the Baga River flowed into the sea.

Two or three people drowned every month in the area. More often than not skinny dipping tweekers, much the worse for wear, falling foul of the treacherous currents that snaked around the waters off the Anjuna headland.

Pete hadn't been missed yet, people were still recovering from celebrating the New Year. He'd paid his rent three months in advance, and the locals he drank with in the afternoon would assume that he had gone travelling for a few days, such was their experience of the transient mentality of most Westerners living in the region.

The crew of the St. Xavier had disentangled his body from their nets and carried it unceremoniously up the beach to Laxmans, the bar favoured by Harry Boyer. This was standard practice in these matters. Eldrich Corduroy, Laxmans owner, having asked the fishermen to place the decomposing body in the storeroom at the rear of his bar, had thrown a tarpaulin over it and called the police.

It was a busy time of the day for Eldrich. Despite the fact that he was sure he recognised the tattoo inked into the top of the deceased mans left arm, he had better things to do than play detective, the police could take care of proceedings from hereon in, he didn't want to get involved.

His only Christian concession had been to notify the priest at his local church that the fatality involved a Westerner. Father Francis da Silva took an interest in such matters, logging descriptions of unidentified bodies well before they were removed from the local mortuary and committed for burial in the grounds of his church.

Over the years he'd learnt that Westerners dying in such tragic circumstances would in the long run be missed by a friend, loved one or relative. Sooner or later someone would turn up, questions would be asked and answered, and the final pieces of the jigsaw would be put into place. Along with closure came the grateful donations that went some way to maintaining the upkeep of the church and the well-being of Father Francis.

When the police finally arrived late in the afternoon, the mystery of the body's identity had already been solved. Father Frances, the parish priest of the Church of St. Alex in Calangute, had cycled to Laxmans immediately after he'd received Eldrich's phone call.

'This is Peter Philips', he'd said, putting his hand over his mouth and nose as Eldrich had pulled back the tarpaulin to reveal the corpse that had begun to fester in the heat. 'Look, the tattoo ... the lion crest and the name Chelsea', he'd continued, stepping back and resting his arm on Eldrich's shoulder, 'it's him, poor boy'.

'Yes, of course', Eldrich had said, replacing the cover over the body which had drawn the unwanted attention of a swarm of flies. 'He came here once or twice to drink with Harry ... also I think to sell drugs, but tell me how do you know him?'

'He came to visit me at the church on several occasions', Father Francis had replied, his voice tinged with sadness. 'A generous boy, peace of mind was his agenda, and he'd often come to sit for an hour or two on one of the pews by the vestry before he went to work in the evening'.

Eldrich was sure that Father Francis knew more than he was letting on, but respected the priests vow of silence and didn't ask any further questions.

★ ★ ★ ★ ★

The police, accompanied by Father Francis and Harry Boyer, made a search of Pete's room and found his passport with which they were able to formally confirm his identity. The next of kin details at the rear of the passport had not been completed, and they found no other personal effects linking him to his past life in England.

Fortunately, no drugs were found on the premises, and despite Eldrich's suspicions, the police, based on statements made by Father Francis and Harry Boyer, came to the rapid conclusion that Pete's death by drowning had been an act of misadventure.

The British Consulate in India was notified of his death and owing to the lack of mortuary space at any of the local hospitals, Pete's body had soon been released for burial.

On the morning of January 3rd, at the cemetery behind the Church of St. Alex, four of the villagers that Pete had drank Feni with helped lower the coffin containing his body into the ground. Father Francis had commissioned a small head stone that read:

PETER PHILIPS
died 01 01 89
a true friend of St.Alex
may you find peace at last
RIP

★ ★ ★ ★ ★

The knocking at the door was persistent enough to rouse Holly from her near narcoleptic waking state.

'Who is it?' she grumbled, wondering what time it was and remembering that she'd unplugged the phone before retiring to bed the previous evening.

'It's me Holly, your old man,' came the gruff reply. 'C'mon love, open up … I've got the police with me.'

'Police … er yeah, gimme a minute to get decent.' Naked, Holly sprang out of bed and walked over to her dresser. 'Jesus, look at the state of me,' she muttered, glimpsing her reflection in its mirror as she picked up the ornate rosewood spliff box lying on the table and placed it in the bottom drawer under a pile of lacy underwear.

'C'mon Holly, it's Pete for fucks sake!' roared her father impatiently, hammering his fist against the front door so violently that the bedroom window rattled in its frame.

Donning her dressing gown, Holly skipped along the hall and opened the front door to her dad and a young, edgy looking, WPC.

'It's Pete,' said Tommy Philips, his face ruddy with exertion. 'He's dead!'

Holly stood stock still for a moment before her father flung his arms around her almost knocking her to the ground.

'Dead! Drowned! Died last week in India,' he sobbed, as the WPC calmly moved them further along the hall and closed the door.

'Dad, dad, please,' said Holly unsympathetically, 'your squeezing the life out of me.'

Tommy relaxed his hold on his daughter and rested his head on her shoulder.

'How did it happen? asked Holly, her face expressionless. 'Are you sure it's him?' she continued, turning to face the WPC.

'Yes I'm afraid it's true,' replied the WPC, fidgeting with the cord on her two-way radio nervously as she spoke. 'Peter was identified by an acquaintance he'd made, and subsequently via his passport photograph.'

'Acquaintance?'

'Yes, a local priest.'

'Priest! How strange. What about his stuff?' enquired Holly, stroking the back of her fathers head.

'That's all the information I have Miss,' replied the WPC courteously, her confidence returning as it became clear that Holly Philips wasn't taking the news as badly as her father had thought she would. 'He was buried in accordance with his wishes. Once the Foreign Office are able to confirm all details, your father will receive Peter's personal effects through the post. It should take about a week,' she continued, genuinely surprised by the lack of emotion Holly was displaying, 'I'm sorry to have to be the bearer of such bad news, would you prefer it if I left now, so you can be alone with your father?'

'Yeah, er thanks for everything,' said Holly politely, showing the WPC out and pausing at the door to collect her thoughts before making her way back into the living room.

'Pour me a gold watch love,' said Tommy Philips, with a forlorn look on his face that made Holly melt. 'What did she mean by "in accordance with his wishes?",' he continued, fumbling in his pocket for his handkerchief. 'D'yer think it was er suicide?' Tommy sniffed and wheezed into the hankie whilst Holly remained silent as she fixed him a glass of twelve year old malt.

'I dunno dad,' she whispered in a soothing manner, handing him the glass into which she'd poured a generous measure of the Scotch that was normally reserved for the infrequent visits that Steve Bruno paid her. 'Nipper and that Trixie bird of his said he'd been fooling around with the gear again before he'd left for Goa … who knows what frame of mind he was in … but top himself … I dunno.'

Tommy slugged back the Scotch and coughed, rubbing his eyes before reaching into his jacket pocket and producing a dog-eared postcard. Like a gumshoe detective looking for clues, he scrutinised the photo, a print of the Church of St. Alex, before turning it over and reading out loud Pete's neatly penned missive.

'Dear Dad, Merry Christmas! I hope this card finds you in the best of health. This is the view that I have from my back garden, it is so peaceful here, especially at night with just the stars for company. You'd love it mate, cheap beer, curry and friendly people. Maybe you should think about taking a holiday,

flights are cheap, sort yourself out and come and stay. I don't think I will be coming home again, well maybe once more just to say goodbye to London. You can write to me c/o Father Francis at the church if you choose to. Up the Blues. Love Peter x

Holly sat in silence, looking at her father, grateful that he didn't know the truth about his precious son. That bastard had it coming to him.

'Peter! Whats wrong with Pete?' exclaimed Tommy, having re-read the postcard several times again. 'Bloody hell that's all a bit serious, d'ya think he got into religion or something?'

Holly heard her dad, but only superficially. She was miles away thinking about something and somebody else, but her father persisted.

'Well ... c'mon, this is your brother ... my fucking son! I never knew what was going on in that addled mind of his. D'yer think he was back on that heroin shite?'

'Dunno dad,' said Holly, shaking her head and playing the game. 'I'm kinda in shock ... I always knew something like this would happen to him one day.'

Tommy began to cry, as he did so Holly bit down hard on her bottom lip trying to stem the flow of her own tears. She felt pity for him, but at the same time the burning hatred she harboured for Pete prevented her from sharing in her fathers grief.

* * * * *

Tommy came to stay with Holly for a few difficult days which she spent trying to comfort him in the best way she could given the circumstances. He went through a phase of blaming himself for everything, for her mum's death, for Pete's death, for being a poor father, and for not being a family man.

Fortunately for both of them Nipper took charge of the situation, displaying a level of maturity which surprised even himself. A church memorial service was hardly appropriate, so instead Nipper rallied their friends together and organised an afternoon gathering in the Finborough Arms.

Holly was aggrieved at the turnout. Everyone Pete knew had made the effort, and Nipper paid tribute to him with a simple eulogy that encapsulated precisely what he meant to them. The cunt didn't deserve this, she thought to herself, controlling the urge to voice her anger.

'Let's show some respect for the man,' said Nipper, banging his fist on the table in front of him as he got to his feet. 'All of you here today knew Pete, and you all knew the kind of life he led. He was always pushing himself to the edge, when we took two steps forward ... Pete took three. He brought a lot of colour into our lives ... he lived and breathed this crazy scene we love and it won't be the same without him. Earlier this year when we were out in Ibiza, he'd told me that he wanted to find more balance in his life ... to make good what he had made bad ... I ... I wasn't too sure what he meant by that ... but then that was Pete.

I don't really know if he found what he was looking for out in Goa ... I'd like to go there ... visit his final resting place ... say goodbye properly. I truly hope his tortured soul finally found the peace he was desperately looking for ... I don't really know what else to say. The thought that we will never enjoy his company again is deeply saddening for all of us, and I'm sure that we all share the deep sense of loss that his dad Tommy and sister Holly are feeling right now. Let's have a drink to his memory, raise your glasses ... friends and family, the toast is Pete!'

The pin drop silence that followed lasted for a few seconds only before everyone got to their feet and applauded.

'Nice one Nipper,' said Fatboy Green draining his pint, 'fucking quality speech.'

'Right, I think Pete's old man, who most of you know, would like a few words,' said Nipper, putting the index finger of his right hand across his lips as he helped Tommy to his feet.

Tommy Philips coughed loudly. It was unintentional, a sign of nerves perhaps, but it served to silence all the small talk.

'For those of you that don't know me,' he said, his voice faltering slightly, as he looked round and took strength from the nods of encouragement, 'I'm Pete's dad Tommy. I just want to say thanks to all of you for coming here today. Holly and I appreciate it. I can't say I fully understood my sons life, but I find it reassuring that you lot seemingly never did either.' Tommy paused briefly as the humour in his words was met by a ripple of applause and laughter. 'If he was looking down on this gathering today, I'm sure it would bring a tear to his eye. Thank you for being his friends.'

The cheering that followed, Tommy curtailed by raising his voice in an authoritative manner that took Holly by surprise.

'Finally,' he said, raising aloft the postcard Pete had sent him, 'I'm gonna be making a trip out to this place in the sun that he'd found, and that'll be the end of it. I just wanna see it for myself ... you're all welcome to come.'

Tommy handed the card to Nipper and sat down next to his daughter. Everyone looked at Holly expecting her to say something, but she simply shook her head and looked at the floor.

Fuck this, she thought to herself, pushing the play button on the tape machine that Chiller had brought to the pub. The mix he'd put together, started out with a speech by Martin Luther King ... 'I have a dream'. When the all too familiar beats heralding Ce Ce Rogers' track 'Someday' faded in, Holly pulled herself away from the crowd. Condolences! Bollocks! I've had enough of this, she thought to herself, glad of the fact she had a wrap of disco-dust in her pocket. That would see her through the rest of this afternoons tawdry affair, of that she had absolutely no doubt.

★ ★ ★ ★ ★

Nipper took responsibility for organising the trip to Goa. He could see that Holly was disinterested, but he didn't ask too many questions, in fact he didn't ask any at all. The final roll-call, including Tommy Philips, numbered twelve, all of them booked onto a one-week package holiday with the outbound flight departing on Sunday 8th January, the day after what was to be Chelsea's disastrous visit to Barnsley in the 3rd Round of the FA Cup.

Tommy Philips was okay now. He just wanted to see what it was about Goa that had so smitten his son in order to reconcile himself with the past and maybe move on. Recent ill health and a persistent cold had struck him low below the belt meaning that the insecurities he'd harboured about the trip had taken some time to dissipate. But they had, as had Nipper and the rest of the lads memories of the 4-0 thumping that Chelsea had received at the hands of the Yorkshiremen.

'Fuck the cup, we're going up', had been the chant on the way back down the M1. Nipper, was ready for a break.

★ ★ ★ ★ ★

'We are the Mods, we are the Mods ... we are, we are, we are the Mods.'

'Fuckin look at him,' shouted Eggy Barnes every time Tommy Philips sped full throttle up Three Toes Lane astride the antiquated Vespa scooter he'd hired for the price of daily pint.

'I'm ready now', he'd said, nursing a bottle of Kingfisher beer as they'd sat outside Laxmans on the second night of their sojourn watching the sun set on another perfect day. 'Let's go for it this evening yeah', he'd continued, his manner of speech deliberately lackadaisical making Nipper think twice about his motives for sorting out the trip.

'Fuck this evening, let's do it now!' shouted Holly, making light of situation and wanting to get things over and done with. 'I've had enough of this bollocks, and I'm sure my dad has too. C'mon lets go there now.'

Silence is golden, thought Nipper, gripping Holly's hand as they walked through the churches ornate arched entrance. As he looked around, even the in house jokers, Fatboy Green and Eggy Barnes were looking respectfully sombre. In a preordained manner they sat, row by row on the Spartan wooden pews drinking in the reverential ambience afforded them by the church of St. Alex.

Holly did her best to mask her apprehensiveness. Her vertebrae chilled and her neck twitched as she remembered the saying that accompanied the way she currently felt. 'Someone's just stepped on my grave,' she whispered, for the benefit of no-one other than herself as she fought back the temptation to be drawn into the vortex of parochial pity

The funereal silence embodied everyone as they sat and waited. Holly closed her eyes and did her best to erase her memory of the violation she had endured at the hands of her brother, but it was of little use. By the time the priest made his modest unaccompanied entrance into the church, she had already marked Pete down as a devil whose soul should be cast into the dark abyss.

Father Francis walked down the centre isle towards the altar, pausing to genuflect on one knee before rising slowly to his feet and making the sign of the cross.

Awkwardly, he turned to face the congregation, clasping his hands and rubbing them gently together, a broad smile breaking across the chiselled features of his lean tanned face.

'You must be the family and friends of the late Peter Philips,' he said deferentially, taking in a deep breath before continuing. 'I've been expecting you for sometime. Let me introduce myself ... I am Father Francis da Silva. Welcome to the Church of St. Alex.'

Father Francis was one of those people whose age was difficult to determine. Clearly a handsome man in his time, his looks owed much to his Portuguese ancestry. Holly looked at him intently. The crew cut greying hair and steely blue eyes likened him to Paul Newman. Not bad, she thought to herself, what a waste to see a good man like that end up living the celibate life of a Catholic priest.

Holly glanced across at Rebs and smiled. She knew Rebs was thinking the same way, on the flight out they'd flirted with one of the stewards, an outrageously camp but striking young man called Jaffa. 'Shame isn't it', Rebs had said, eyeing his pert bottom, 'the best looking men are always unavailable because they're either married, gay or priests'.

'Come, we will go and take some tea on the veranda at my house,' said the priest, scanning the faces of the people gathered in front of him. 'I will share with you what I know of Peter, and then I will show you to his final resting place where you can pay your respects in peace.'

★ ★ ★ ★ ★

The house where Father Francis lived was an imposing three-storey residence with a faded kind of grandeur and moody dusty atmosphere redolent of the past.

'Nice place you've got here Father da Silva,' said Nipper, breaking the silence as they waited for tea to be served. 'It must pay well this priest business,' he continued, nodding at Eggy Barnes and Chiller who were casting admiring eyes over the dainty form of Father da Silva's housekeeper.

'Ah the English humour, very good,' replied the priest, his broad smile revealing a perfectly straight set of pearly white teeth. 'Yes it is a rather splendid house, I share it with three other priests, the local schoolmaster and of course my housekeeper. The house was built in the seventeenth century by a wealthy landowner who left it to the church when he died.'

Nipper looked at Holly, trying to gain her attention, but she seemed miles away. Again he racked his brain trying to figure out just exactly what her problem had been with Pete, but yet again he came up with nothing. Families eh, he thought to himself, glancing around the room at all the people present. This lot are my family, thank fuck I'm an orphan, all that shit about blood being thicker than water. What a pain in the arse.

Father Francis put his teacup down on the trestle table in front of him and stood up. He had a presence that commanded everyone's attention, Nipper included.

'You know, looking at you all,' he said, weighing his words carefully, 'I am drawn to think of the twelve disciples of Jesus Christ. Now before you think I'm going to preach to you, I say this because it stirs my memory about the first time I met Peter Philips.'

The priest paused, it was as if he was selecting and filtering the anecdotes and insights he was about to share. As he did so Nipper's hand sought Holly's and gripped it tightly. Both of them were thinking the same thing. How on earth did Pete manage to make such an impression on a man of the cloth in such a short space of time?

'It was very late one Sunday evening when I thought I heard the door to the church opening,' said the priest, setting the scene in true storyteller fashion. 'The house of God is always open, well almost always. You can't be too sure these days, the nefarious dacoites that lurk the streets at night have no respect for religion, one has to be careful. I went to investigate, and entered the church through a small door which backs onto the cemetery. Now dacoites are many things, they are thieves and vagabonds who will steal the shirt off your back if they think they can get away with it. But one thing they do not do, is smoke hashish. At first I considered raising the alarm, but then I saw the moonlit silhouette of a man kneeling, head bowed, about half way up the central aisle. I walked up to him and asked him who he was.

'Jesus Christ', was the reply, 'I AM JESUS!'

'JESUS CHRIST!' exclaimed Nipper, interrupting the priest as all and sundry began to laugh. 'He must have been smoking really big hashish.'

'Yeah, you know that,' said Tommy Philips, with a chuckle. 'That was Pete for you ...,' he continued, before stopping himself mid-sentence to apologise to the priest for disrupting his sermon.

Father Francis smiled, reached for his teacup, and took a couple of sips before carefully placing it back on its saucer and continuing with the story. 'So I walked over to this fellow and remarked that smoking wasn't permitted in the house of God. To which he replied, 'what sort of place is this, where a man is not allowed to smoke in his own house?' The priest began to laugh and sat down again, as he did so his entire congregation applauded enthusiastically.

'Well I never had my son down as a comedian, but that is funny. You obviously thought so too Father,' said Tommy Philips, the laughter lines on his face fully expressed.

Holly nudged Nipper and they both smiled approvingly. Tommy's happy go lucky demeanour had returned, and the emotional inadequacy that had paralysed his feelings since hearing the news of Pete's death had been eased simply by listening to Father da Silva.

'Yes, indeed sir,' continued the priest, fidgeting with the heavy silver cross that hung from his neck. 'Over the years, I have had to accept the fact, that Westerners come here for more than just the sunshine and the beauty that Goa has to offer. I cannot say I approve of this decadent behaviour, however I have other things to concern myself with. Now would you like to hear the rest of the story?'

'Of course,' said Tommy, clapping his hands and shushing the others.

'I introduced myself to this individual and asked if he would kindly like to step outside the church if he wished to continue smoking. I was surprised when he agreed, and I followed him out into the courtyard over there where we sat down.'

Father da Silva got to his feet once again and pointed to a row of benches arranged around a heavily pitted white marble statue of Christ on the cross.

'We sat there until the sun rose, and during this time I learned that I was in the company of Peter Philips, a man whose long and fitful dependency on drugs had seen him plumb the depths of nihilism. He told me that he had come to Goa to escape from the insanity of life back home, to escape the demons that were torturing his soul. The house he'd rented had a distant view of this church. Peter told me how he would often gaze in wonder at this place, marvelling at its design, bathing in the sea of tranquillity that washed over him as he did so. He told me that it reminded him of a place he had visited many times called Ibiza.

I knew that the drugs were affecting the content and manner of his speech, but he was coherent and friendly enough to have my ear. Sometimes you need someone to listen. He came to visit me on a number of occasions in the days preceding his tragic death, and the generous financial donation he made to this church will go someway to meeting the cost of repairing the roof before the monsoons come. Well ladies and gentlemen, thank you for your kind attention. Now if you'd like to come with me I will take you to his final resting place, and then perhaps I could speak to his immediate family alone in private.'

★ ★ ★ ★ ★

'Whaddya think he was up to?' asked Nipper, as he walked with Holly through the cemetery.

'Well, we all know where the money came from that he gave to Father da Silva don't we,' she replied, holding onto Nipper's hand as tightly as a child would hold onto a parents. 'Dad won't though, he might not care about that, but he'll want to know more about the circumstances surrounding Pete's death.

The grave was immaculately tended to, the marble headstone clean and polished. As they all gathered around to pay their final respects to Pete, Nipper read, and reread the inscription on the headstone. 'A true friend of St. Alex … mmm … I just don't get it,' he whispered to himself, seeking out the priest who was stood at the edge of the cemetery talking to Tommy Philips.

'I wonder what he's saying to my dad?' said Holly.

'You'll find out now doll face,' replied Nipper expectantly, 'here he comes.'

Tommy Philips strolled casually across the closely cut sun scorched grass towards them. He seemed totally at ease with himself and announced that he was going to see where Pete had lived and then he would take a ride back up to the hotel, shower and meet with everyone for a beer at the Turret Bar later.

'I'll come with you Tommy,' volunteered Nipper, 'I think Father da Silva wants to speak with Holly. The house is only over there, so I'll come back here after and wait for her rather than go back to the hotel with you.'

'We might as well get off then,' said Eggy Barnes, voicing the wishes of the rest of the group. 'Without wanting to sound disrespectful, it's another perfect day, it'd be a shame to waste it. Who fancies the beach?'

Hands were raised in unison, and the decision was taken to depart. Everyone made a point of shaking the priest's hand as they left, thanking him for taking the trouble to talk to them and put the record straight.

'Shall we go and sit in the shade Holly?' said Father Francis solemnly, pointing at the church house veranda.

Holly nodded, walking silently behind the priest, gathering her thoughts, thinking about what questions to ask, and how best to ask them.

They sat down at opposite ends of a long ornately carved wooden bench that had been fashioned out of teak. The priest looked at Holly sympathetically. It was difficult for him to gauge her mood as her eyes where masked by the opaque lenses of her Wayfarers.

'The eyes are the window to a persons soul Holly,' he said, reaching into his cassock to produce an envelope.

'Is that so,' replied Holly, removing her sunglasses and ruffling her hair with her fingers. 'Then tell me, what's in my soul father,' she continued, arching her back in a delicate feline manner before turning to face the priest.

'I see a pain behind your eyes my child.'

'More-like a hangover.'

'Ahh, there it is again. The English way, very good.'

'Look father,' said Holly irately. 'I'm not into religion, and neither was my brother. If anything, he was the Anti-Christ. So you really must explain to me, if you can, the nature of this brief friendship you shared together. What exactly did he tell you? I really need to know.'

Father da Silva furrowed his brow and frowned disapprovingly. 'You know my child, I am bound by the laws of the holy Catholic Church. I cannot divulge any details of any confession that your brother may have made to me.'

'Confession,' sneered Holly, 'Confession! Well let me tell you something Father da Silva. If my brother did confess his sins to you, and his way of atoning for what he did to me was by donating drugs money to this church, then I have to question your morals. Do you have a conscience priest?'

'That is between the good Lord Jesus Christ and myself,' replied Father da Silva calmly, pushing the envelope across the bench towards Holly. 'Here, you must take this. It was Peter's wish for me to hand it to you personally if anything ever happened to him. He said you would come one day.'

Holly resisted the urge to argue. She reached over and picked the unmarked envelope up. Scrutinising the seal, which was unbroken and appeared not to have been tampered with, she said nothing. Father da Silva sucked in his cheeks and tutted as he watched her tuck the envelope into the back pocket of her jeans.

Holly looked directly at the priest, a scowl forming on her face as she bit her bottom lip several times endeavouring to suppress the incandescent rage that was welling up inside her.

'What did you expect Father?' she said sardonically. 'Tears? An outpouring of grief? I was raped by my own brother. Don't tell me you gave him three Hail Mary's and five Our Father's to recite as penance in exchange for absolution?'

Holly stood up and glared defiantly at the priest who was nervously clicking his tongue against his dry lips, readying himself to speak, pushing his hands down either side of his thighs in a bid to leverage himself up onto his feet.

'Hold on, I haven't finished yet,' she continued, the vitriol in her voice beginning to frighten him. 'You don't have to say anymore. Pete fucked my life up, and he fucked his own life up. If his friendship with you, and so called love of this church made him feel better in himself about what he did, then good for him. He doesn't have to live with it anymore. I do. My father has no idea about any of this, and that's the way it has to stay. Do you understand Father da Silva?'

The priest nodded, he realised that he had unwittingly stirred up a hornets nest of hatred, and whilst he was saddened by the profanities tumbling from Holly's lips, he was wise enough to realise that in certain situations religion was cold comfort for the aggrieved.

A brief 'eyes to the floor' silence ensued before Father da Silva spoke again.

'I am truly sorry Holly,' he said with genuine sincerity. 'I hope you can find a way to ease your troubles.'

'Nah. Don't worry about me Father,' replied Holly shrugging her shoulders and putting her sunglasses back on. 'I'm fine. My brother can't touch me anymore. My brother doesn't exist anymore.'

* * * * *

Back at the Turret, the decision had been taken that they would attend a full moon party being held at Paradiso that evening. Even Tommy expressed interest in going. Whilst Holly was still fighting to control her anger, she was content that Tommy seemed less tormented. The visit to Goa, meeting Father Francis, and seeing the house that Pete had lived in, had enabled him to accept what had happened. Now he could embark on the time healing process. As he slugged back one beer after another, he was even talking about returning for another holiday before the winter back home was over.

'Come on doll face. Let's try some of this,' said Nipper, lying on the floor of the hotel room with a copy of Elle in front of him. Vigorously he shook the black plastic camera film tub he was holding in his left hand, before opening it carefully and sprinkling its contents over the magazine cover.

'36 millimetres is it?' chuckled Holly, her face beaming with anticipation.

'Yeah. You know that,' he replied, arranging the white powder into six generous lines with the aid of a pair of travel scissors. 'Girls before boys then, here you go,' he continued, pulling a 100 rupee note out of his pocket and rolling it up tightly.

'I'm gonna use this,' said Holly enthusiastically, bounding off the bed with the enthusiasm of a five year old on Christmas morning.

'What is it?'

'A silver tooter, I bought it yesterday. Lovely isn't it, and far more hygienic than sticking a filthy Indian banknote up your nose.'

Holly crouched on all fours above the magazine. Holding the ball end of the tooter to her left nostril, she proceeded to snort one of the lines of coke in its entirety.

'Fucking hell Nipper!' she exclaimed, rocking her body back and opening her eyes unnaturally wide. 'That's a a a amazing!' she stammered, sniffing as the purity of the drug anaesthetised the back of her throat.

'I know hon,' replied Nipper, helping himself to a couple of lines. 'Right now, you could perform cranial-facial surgery on me with a Swiss army knife and I wouldn't feel a fucking thing.'

'Imagine having gear like this to sell at home.'

'Yeah, imagine.'

'We'd be rich.'

'Very rich.'

'Right let me have another one then. I'm handing my controls over to the automatic pilot for the rest of the evening, I'm going to the fucking moon.'

'Yeah! The full moon.'

'The full moon party, c'mon let's go.'

★ ★ ★ ★ ★

'My God, look at this!' said Nipper excitedly, looking through the rusty iron railings that skirted the perimeter of Paradiso. 'Y'see doll face. See all the partygoers, it's fucking unreal.'

They both looked down at the swaying sea of people, figures brightly illuminated by the huge spotlights suspended from palm trees, all dancing to the heavy industrial sound of European techno booming from the over-loaded, generator powered sound-system. Firecrackers fizzed and popped, serving to further engorge the volume, and for one split second Holly thought she was somewhere else. Shuddering at the memory, she put her arm around Nipper's waist for comfort, all the while wishing that she'd resisted the temptation to powder her nose.

The tap on Holly's shoulder was a gentle one, familiar almost. She turned around and there was Layla Goss. Her Layla, shimmering in a simple white cotton dress, skin so dark, hair shorn boyishly, an impish grin on her face. Layla held out her hands and gripped Holly's pulling her gently towards her but stopping before she got too close.

'Layla!'

'You what?' said Rebs, shaking her head disbelievingly.

'Shit that was fucking weird Rebs,' replied Holly, rubbing her nose. 'I thought you were Layla.'

'Layla, bloody hell. I don't think so.'

'Yeah, sorry. Must've lost it for a second then.'

'Listen, d'ya fancy a smoke? I've had enough of this racket already.' Rebs smiled as she asked the question, thrusting a bottle of Kingfisher into Holly's hand and motioning her away from the railings as she turned to face Nipper. 'Eggy and the others are over there by the stage Nip,' she said calmly, 'why don't you go and see them, they're having a right old laugh.'

'Yeah, nice one,' replied Nipper. 'You two look after yourselves, don't stray too far.'

'Of course my love,' said Holly, pecking Nipper on the lips and watching him as he made his way to the staircase that led down to Paradiso's main dance-floor.

'C'mon let's go over there,' said Rebs, pointing at a rocky outcrop that was far enough away from the party to allow them the opportunity to unwind a little.

'I am fucking wired girl,' gurgled Holly, taking another swig of beer and grinning frenziedly as Rebs produced a spliff box from the trendy little backpack she always carried with her.

They made their way over to the outcrop and sat down. Rebs busied herself with the task of skinning up whilst Holly reached into her pocket and pulled out the tightly folded letter that Father Francis had handed her earlier in the day.

With some trepidation, she carefully split the seal with her thumbnail, extricating a piece of notepaper on which was pencil scrawled a brief message.

My dear sister Holly,

If you ever get to read this missive, then it will have come into your possession because I have left this life for ever. I never meant you any harm, you are my sister and I love you with all my heart. I cannot erase what happened from my memory, nor should I be allowed to, because what I did cannot be excused. The person that debased you, was that really me, or was it me with the E? What does it matter now? All that remains for me to say is that I am truly sorry, and I know that if it makes you feel better, I will never be able to rest in peace.

Pete X

Holly read the letter twice and said nothing. Her face bore no expression as she tore the paper up into small pieces and screwed them up into a ball which she held in her left hand.

Rising slowly to her feet, Holly looked across at the Bacchanalian sight that was Paradiso. In the distance, she was sure she could just make out the figure of a woman in a white dress, waving at her from the balcony of the outhouse at the top of the cliff. She raised her left arm above her head and clicked her fingers, watching as the shreds of paper fluttered, ticker tape style, down the beach.

'What was that?' asked Rebs, standing up and handing the spliff she'd just made to Holly.

'That Rebs, was nothing.'

'Are you feeling safe now honey?'

'Safe? Yeah … Yeah I'm safe all right Rebs, I'm as safe as fucking houses.'

9

May 1997
WHEN WISE WENT UP TO LIFT THE FA CUP

'Let me tell ya sumink abaht this jam jar,' roared Stevie 'Sniffler' Barlow, embarking on a verbal portraiture of his favourite car in his own inimitable style. 'It's fully prepared for international classic rallying, gotta twin cam engine, straight-cut close ratio gearbox, limited slip diff, sump and tank guards, full cage with harness belts, foam filled alloy auxiliary fuel tank, and it's got the Minilite alloys. Yeah! That's right, Minilite's ... it's the best there is babe, you ask anyone who knows.'

Sniffler sat back in his chair and pushed his fingers through his lank, streaky blonde hair. The filthy slag would get it, he thought to himself, running his dark rodent-like piercing eyes along the length of Holly's milky white thighs. Tapping out a Benson, he gripped it between nicotine stained teeth and waited for her to reply before lighting up.

Holly was singularly unimpressed. She still hadn't learned to drive and had no passion motor vehicles whatsoever. Sniffler, who reminded her of a Dickensian street urchin, a latter day Johnny Rotten in fact, could swivel. Nipper was just as bad. Given half a chance, he would bore her to tears with the detailed specifications of the latest four wheel drives. Land Rovers, Range Rovers, dog called Rovers ... fuck em all, childish bastards.

'You don't fuck with this motor', he'd kept reminding her, extolling the virtues of what to him were the most important features of the latest 4x4 he so desired. Nipper was waiting for the new Shogun to come out. Holly didn't think she was being obtuse, but she'd cackled like a fishwife, when he'd revealed the name of the company that manufactured this particular model. Mitsubishi, a company whose distinct logo had, for some bizarre reason, found its way onto a container load of E's which were the current flavour of the month in clubland.

Eight years on since her brothers death, and things had changed. Well you'd expect that wouldn't you. Holly's faith in Nipper had been repaid. 'Ambition's got a hold of you doll face', he'd said, as she'd pressed him into exploiting the burgeoning friendship he'd developed with Barry 'Beery' Barlow. 'Yeah, and you don't like the money', she'd retorted, playing him at his own twisted little game.

'Look, listen and learn', had been Steve Bruno's mantra as 'New' Labour had swept back to power following 18 years in the political wilderness, and Holly had paid attention. Nipper also. Putting everything they'd seen and learnt back in the halcyon days of Punk and New Romanticism into practice hadn't been too hard, especially when other people were taking the brunt of the financial risk. Hysteria, was the name of the club night Holly was now successfully promoting, and Nipper was doing very nicely trafficking narcotics on the back of it.

Keeping everyone sweet was the name of the game, and that included the irritating offspring of their principle benefactor Beery Barlow. 'Just be patient with the twat', Nipper had whispered to Holly on more occasions than she cared to recall. 'Let him feel involved, make him feel important ... but nothing else'.

Yeah, yeah, yeah, thought Holly, as she endured Sniffler Barlow's extended 12" remix version of 'me and my motor'. Mind you, she knew she still had the ability to wind the tosser up whenever she wanted too, and right now was beginning to sound like a really good idea.

'Yeah but my Nipper says that it's a Ford Cortina though,' she replied, contemplating a line of coke as she looked at the time on her watch. 'A little bit on the pikey side that innit. You got them furry dice hanging off the rear-view mirror then or what?' she continued, watching Sniffler intently as he returned to the task of counting the evenings door receipts, wishing that her boyfriend would appear and sort her out with one of his celebrated 'managers specials'.

'It's a Mk1 Lotus Cortina. Your boy knows fack awl abaht motors, that's why he drives them tanks. No class, no charisma, no style,' snapped Sniffler, looking up and tapping his nose as he pointed at the floor mounted safe behind him. 'Now me I've ...'

Sniffler's self publicising speech was cut short as the back office door swung open.

'When Wise goes up to lift the FA Cup, we'll be there ... we'll be there. When Wise goes up to lift the FA Cup, we'll be there ... we'll be there.'

The three-handed chant was loud and purposeful. Nipper, Eggy Barnes and Riddler Rowan bundled themselves enthusiastically into the room, subjecting Holly and Sniffler to several more patience trying refrains of their song, before finally regaining a modicum of composure and closing the door.

'Faaack it! You Chelsea cahnts … I've lost me place wiv the numbers nah,' growled Sniffler, scowling as he banged the flat of his hand down on the table.

'Holly dearest,' said Nipper, camping it up as he tapped her on the shoulder and raised his eyebrows in mock surprise. 'What have I told you about letting S count the takings on a Friday night?' he continued, pursing his lips and blowing a kiss at Sniffler. 'It's too busy, we're making too much money. Look what happens when he runs out of fingers and toes to help him count ha ha.'

'Wanker!' replied Sniffler, having failed to come up with a suitably witty response.

'Come on Sniffler lighten up son,' said Eggy Barnes rubbing his hands together in anticipation. 'It's cup final day … COME ON YOU BLUES!'

'Facking mouthy Chelsea cahnts,' replied Sniffler predictably. 'You can stick yer blue flags up yer blue arses, you wankers,' he continued, shaking his head and admitting defeat as the verbal baiting finally got to him. 'Tell me one fing though, have you ever seen Chelsea win the league? Have you fuck.'

Sniffler's grin stretched from ear to ear as he made his final point and gave up trying to count the takings, bagging the money instead and placing it in the safe.

'Right you lot. Who fancies one of me manager's specials eh?' asked Nipper, producing an envelope from the breast pocket of the indigo blue heavy denim Armani jacket he was wearing. 'I'm gonna line up ten lovely chubby ones. Cos me, Eggy and Riddler here have gotta keep going right?' Nipper looked up from the table onto which he'd just emptied the entire contents of the envelope, seeking the acknowledgement of his friends.

'Right!' was the unanimous reply.

'We're gonna do this. Stay up all night, and then fuck off to Fulham Broadway for a fry up. Do you know why were gonna do this Sniffler?'

'No … er let me guess,' replied Sniffler, rolling up a twenty pound note in readiness.

'Because Sniffler …'

'Well come on. Let's av it.'

'*We're gonna Wembley … We're gonna Wembley, you're not, you're not.*'

Holly, playing the role of the quintessential English garden party rose, turned her button nose up and grimaced. Look at the fucking state of this lot, she thought, singing their songs, doing their sparkle. Going to Wembley? They'd be fucking lucky; if they carried on like this they'd be going to Charing Cross Hospital in a bloody ambulance.

'Right! Ladies first,' she said, snatching the note from Sniffler's hand. 'Come on. Out of my way you common louts,' she continued, in her best Mayfair housekeepers accent. 'One's been waiting for a decent toot for at least half an hour. A managers special, oh yes, one loves it, one knows that.'

Holly had developed a penchant for disco dust that Nipper considered to be a habit, but he hadn't said anything to her. Topper Townsend called it the live'ner, and he was right. The good stuff kicked like a mule. No matter how jaded you were, it would always bring you round.

She hadn't touched E since that fateful episode with Pete, and didn't want to either. For Holly the c in cocaine, represented control with a capital C. Nipper would occasionally test a new batch of E's himself. When he did, she'd always politely decline his offer to join him in reliving the old days. He couldn't understand that, and she couldn't be bothered to explain. It was over now. End of. The deep mental scars Holly bore were a sibling legacy she could never rid herself of, so she kept them covered up as best as she could, adhering to a strict policy of avoidance.

'You're fucking weird sometimes', Nipper would say.

You're fucking selfish sometimes, Holly would think, choosing not to reply. Anyway, cocaine was the clubbers drug of choice at that moment. At fifty quid a gram it wasn't cheap, but then it wasn't expensive either. Sparkle and booze went hand in hand like E and water. Which punter was going to spend the most on a night out? Easy, the coke-head.

★ ★ ★ ★ ★

Hysteria, had been up and running for eight months. It had been a struggle at first, and they had lost money. Holly's initial investment of £60,000 had been devoured during thefirst month of trading, but now they were ahead of the game.

The overheads for the first year were projected at £682,500 against a turnover of £685,000, so there wasn't going to be much in the way of an initial profit to be realised by the principal investors. They had plenty of reason to be pleased though because Hysteria was already operating from a breakeven position.

It couldn't have been made easier. The rent and rates for the property had been 'fixed' by Barry Barlow at a very manageable £45,000 for five years. An initial loan to cover the £200,000 refit had been agreed at a favourable apr through Steve Bruno, and the rest of the up front costs for stock, advertising and wages had been met, in the main, by Holly who'd ploughed the profits from Babelicious into this new venture. Nipper was responsible for illegally financing their lifestyle through the sale of drugs. The books balanced, and the bills were paid on time. Everyone was happy.

Holly and Nipper were in this for the long-haul. Both could see the benefit to be gained in investing money into the club, even if it was 'their' money. It was all about pulling in the crowds. Having Jack 'Chiller' Chillman, who had by now established himself as one of the leading House DJ's in the world, as a friend had been fortuitous. His name had helped them launch Hysteria, and the tills never rang louder than on Friday nights when he had his residency.

Variety was the key. More money meant they could hire name DJ's from different genres of the scene. Each scene had its own devoted crowd, show them a good time and they'd be back for more. More money paid for a better sound and lighting system, essential when these DJ's would often play out at several venues in the same town or city over the course of an evening. Inside three months, Hysteria was hosting two capacity nights on Fridays and Saturdays with an occasional specialist night on a Thursday.

★ ★ ★ ★ ★

'Oi lover boy,' said Holly, artificially reinvigorated. 'Are you coming back upstairs for a dance, or shall I take this fella here with me?' she continued impatiently, wrapping herself lithely around a blushing Riddler Rowan.

'Yeah, yeah,' grinned Nipper, pointing at the last two lines of coke on the table. 'Finish your supper first my girl.'

Holly nodded and laughed, extricating herself from Riddler's clutches and wiggling her backside as she sashayed across to the table.

'I getcha,' said Eggy Barnes, winking at her as she brushed past him. 'You aint interested in my mate Nipper. It's Riddler innit.'

'Oi, oi. Leave it out,' interjected Riddler, tugging at the oversize collar of the black viscose Gucci shirt he was wearing. 'You can't blame the girl for reminding herself.'

'Reminding herself of what?' enquired Eggy, puzzled by Riddler's turn of phrase.

'Y'know, reminding herself what a top geezer I am innit.'

'You're a fucking plum Riddler and a priceless one at that,' said Eggy, sniffing in an exaggerated manner and laughing.

'C'mon, listen it's my tune!' exclaimed Holly, bouncing up white nosed from the table like an animated marionette.

'You're not alone. I'll wait 'til the end of time. Open your mind, surely its plain to see.'

'C'mon Nipper. C'mon.' Holly grabbed Nipper by the hand and led him out of the office.

'You're not alone. I'll wait 'til the end of time for you. Open your mind surely there's time to be with me'.

The atmosphere in Hysteria's main room was electric. Hot sweaty hands punched the air in unison as the bodies they belonged to jacked in time to the music. This was it, the tune. Diva style vocals over a perfectly amplified four to the floor beat that assaulted human senses whose perception had already been deregulated by a life-threatening combination of intoxicants.

'This is what its all about Nipper … look at em,' shouted Holly, pausing momentarily to survey the scene in front of her.

'Chiller's taking the roof off tonight,' replied Nipper, pointing at the DJ booth as they bustled their way through the crowd onto the middle of the floor.

Chiller always finished his set by playing out the current chart topper. Not any specialist dance music chart. The Top 40. So far since the club had opened, this had yielded a mixed bag of music ranging from U2 and the Chemical Brothers, to the Spice Girls. It was a fun way to end the evening, and very well received by the crowd. Last week however, ex Take That heartthrob, Gary Barlow, had succeeded in saving Hysteria's security team the arduous task of clearing the floor. Thankfully his tenure at the top had lasted for just seven days.

'You're not alone' by Olive, was top of the pops this week, and Holly couldn't get enough of the track. It had received its first commercial release last year and she'd danced her pert little tits off to it then, now it was number one, fantastic! She was mesmerised by the uplifting quality of the tune, and the singer Ruth, with her huge mass of frizzy hair and fantastic facial bone structure, was a true star of the scene.

'Fucking brilliant!' proclaimed Holly, as Chiller faded out the tune to thunderous applause from his devotees.

'Definitely,' agreed Nipper, embracing her, his mind already turning to thoughts of what might lie ahead in the next few hours.

★ ★ ★ ★ ★

'All right ya boys. You wanna threea fulla Eengleesh break-a-fasts innit ha ha,' croaked Beefy Trykush hoarsely, mopping the sweat from his brow with a sheet of kitchen roll.

'Yes please Beefy,' replied Nipper, rubbing his hands together in eager anticipation.

'Fantastico Meester eh Neeper. Why you not seet downa over there with your friend Meester eh Green, he already haves two breakfasts to eat himself innit.'

'Two, fucking hell! Oi oi Fatboy.' Nipper turned away from the counter as he spoke, waving at Danny 'Fatboy' Green who was shaking hands with Eggy Barnes and Riddler Rowan.

At 10am on the morning of the FA Cup Final, the café adjacent to Fulham Broadway tube station was alive with the sound of excited banter. Generations of Chelsea fans sat across tables sharing opinions as they wrestled with the morning papers whilst trying to cut the rind off Beefy Trykush's brown sauce smothered bacon rashers.

The steam rising from mugs of hot tea competed for airspace with the plumes of blue cigarette smoke hanging like storm clouds in the centre of the room. A small boy, perched precariously on the edge of his chair, was writing a message into the heavy condensation that had formed on the café window. It read, Chelsea Cup Winners 1997.

'Nice one son,' said Fatboy, belching loudly as he got to his feet to applaud the youngster. '*We are the famous, the famous Chelsea … ,*' he chanted, raising his hands to ensure that everyone in the café joined in.

'Go on Fatty sing us another one,' said Riddler Rowan through a mouthful of fried egg sandwich.

'*Oh his name is Tommy Baldwin, he's the leader of the team. What team? The finest football team that the world has ever seen. We're … … … … … ,*'

The young lad who'd written the message on the window had a puzzled look on his face, as did several other sprogs who were prodding elder brothers, fathers and grandfathers for an explanation. None was given, as everyone in the café beyond a certain age stood on their feet, backs arched, mouths open as they held the '*we're*' for as long as their breaths permitted.

Fatboy, resplendent in an oversize replica of the shirt worn by Chelsea in the 1970 FA Cup Final, breathed in deeply before continuing with the chant. '*… the Fulham Road supporters and we're louder than the Kop? What Kop? And if you want to argue, we'll kill the fucking lot … tra la la la la.*'

Like a terrace Pavarotti, Fatboy Green, beads of perspiration trickling down temples that visibly rippled as his blood coursed through them at an unhealthily high pressure, bowed to the acclamation of his audience.

'Hard night then lads?' he said, sitting back down and picking his plate up. 'Got a bit of PMT then eh?' he continued, putting the plate to his face and licking it clean.

'Oi lip up fatty,' replied Eggy Barnes, flicking at the edge of the plate. 'There's no pre match tension here.'

'*Fatboy Fatboy give us a song, Fatboy give us a song …*'

'Hey a Fat-a-boy, all right ya. Eet sounds a like your fans, they want a you to seeng some more,' said Beefy Trykush, snatching the plate from Fatboy, and patting him across the back as the patrons of the café, which was now packed to the gunnels with passing supporters keen to join in a singsong before embarking on the tube journey to Wembley, got to their feet and chanted their request in deafening unison.

Fatboy didn't need any encouragement, he loved being the centre of attention. Leveraging himself up with the help of Nipper's shoulders, he climbed onto his chair which creaked loudly in protest.

'Shhh ... shhh.'

Fatboy authoritatively shushed the cafés denizens and waited for his cue from Riddler Rowan.

'Out from the Shed, came a rising young star. Scoring goals past Pat Jennings from near and from far. And Chelsea won, as we knew that they would, and the star of that great team was Peter Osgood ...'

Again there were some bemused looks on younger faces, as Fatboy led the chant which was sung to the un-seasonal tune of the Christmas carol, the 'First Noel'.

'*... Osgood, Osgood, Osgood, Osgood. Born is the King of Stamford Bridge.*'

★ ★ ★ ★ ★

The stretch limousine, provided by the Black twins, arrived on cue at midday. Jamie and Leighton Black weren't into football as such, but this was a guaranteed craic. Their father Doogie, currently detained at Her Majesty's pleasure in Parkhurst, would be with them in spirit only.

A true blue, he'd been at Old Trafford when Chelsea had defeated Leeds United in the 1970 FA Cup Final replay to win the famous old trophy for the first and, to this date, only time in their less than illustrious history. A year later he'd been in Athens to witness the replay victory over Real Madrid in the Cup Winners Cup Final.

The last time the limousine had been commandeered for football purposes, Nipper and the boys had travelled to Wembley in style only to witness the Blues capitulate 4-0 to Manchester United. This time though, there was a genuine belief that the result was going to be different.

Having regained their First Division status under Bobby Campbell, Chelsea had established themselves back in the top flight. Ian Porterfield and '70s hero David Webb, the latter albeit briefly, had built secure footings on the foundations laid by Campbell, but it had been the appointment of Glenn Hoddle that had sparked a mini revolution at Stamford Bridge.

His signing of Ruud Gullit had been pivotal in enabling Chelsea to attract the cream of continental talent, and when Hoddle resigned in May 1996 to take stewardship of the national side, the Dutchman had been the natural choice to succeed him.

Vialli, Lebouef and Di Matteo had joined in the close season augmenting the youthful exuberance of Eddie Newton and Frank Sinclair, and the experience of players like Hughes, Petrescu and Clarke, with their own brand of Mediterranean style, wiliness and élan. Born leader, Dennis Wise, was the captain of this tabloid perceived band of mercenaries.

It wasn't all plain sailing. Chelsea had stuttered through the opening months of the season, losing heavily at Liverpool and embarrassingly against Blackpool, before back to back victories at home to Spurs, and away at Manchester United finally got things back on the right track.

Gullit's masterstroke, was the signing of the mercurial Sardinian, Gianfranco Zola, who had joined in November. Chelsea were now a force to be reckoned with. The team went on to finish 6th in the League, their highest placing since 1990, and with their Cup Final opponents Boro having endured an arduous season that had recently ended in relegation to the First Division, many assumed that Dennis Wise had one hand on the cup already.

* * * * *

'Cheers lads,' said Nipper, shaking the Black twins hands. 'This is fucking quality, thanks for sorting it out. By the way, I've got a nice surprise lined up for the journey back. Win or lose, it'll be quality, you'll see.'

'You've always got something lined up,' replied Jamie Black, nudging his brother and tapping his nose.

'Yeah, and some of that,' laughed Nipper, clambering into the limousine and sliding across the black leather seats.

The journey to North West London was tortuously slow, but that didn't matter, it just added to the enjoyment. Nipper loved riding in the limousine, he felt like an A-List celebrity, sipping a chilled glass of champagne, looking through the darkened privacy glass at the common people on the pavement. He imagined their minds would be turning cartwheels as they wondered what depravity might be going on right there in the middle of their high street.

There was no debauched licentious behaviour to contemplate right now, just the repugnant behaviour of Fatboy Green whose head and torso was protruding from the limos sunroof likening him to a surreal tank commander.

'They're fucking Geordie's aint they ... the Boro?' he said, dropping down into the cabin for a brief moment.

'Yeah, sort of,' replied Eggy Barnes, looking up from the TV screen he was watching absorbedly.

'Look at her there in the Boro shirt,' he said, pointing at a middle-aged woman who had just emerged from the exit at Hanger Lane tube station with a bewildered look on her face. 'OI LOVE, ANY ANAL?' bellowed Fatboy as she was joined by several younger men all wearing the red of Middlesboro.

'*Who ate all the pies? Who ate all the pies? You fat bastard, you fat bastard, you ate all the pies,*' they chanted back, giving Fatboy the middle finger, much to the amusement of Nipper, Eggy and the rest of the lads sat in the limo.

'Come on Fatboy, that's enough,' said Leighton Black, putting his arms around Fatboy's waist and hauling him down carefully. 'Why don't you tell us a decent joke eh ... come on. How about the one about Simon eh?'

'What jokes this?' enquired Jamie Black.

'The one about Simon Lewis,' replied Nipper.

'What, Simon 'mad-axeman' Lewis?'

'The very same.'

'I thought his name was Solomon.'

'Nah ... I've seen it on his passport ... It's Simon, Solomon's his middle name.'

'But he aint here.'

'Exactly, Mad Axeman Lewis aint here, and that's why this gags gonna be even funnier.'

'Yeah right. Well carry on Fatboy, carry on.'

Fatboy squeezed himself onto a seat in-between Riddler Rowan and the Chiller jerking his chin forward several times as he cleared his throat.

'Right then,' he said, pausing to gulp down the glass of champagne that Nipper had just handed him. 'You all know Solly Lewis, or should I say Simon Lewis, and how well he can sing. He's a right diamond on the Karaoke, and me and the lads have been telling him for ages that he should send a tape down to Mathew Kelly and get on Stars In Their Eyes. So anyway he did right. Next thing, he gets a phone call inviting him and a friend or relative up to Birmingham for an audition ... all expenses paid. So Simon phones his Uncle Geoff up to tell him the good news and ask him if he would like to drive up to Brum with him the night before and have the full on craic. His uncle agrees, but then as they're driving up the M40 in this flash Merc that Simon's thieved, the steering goes and the motor veers into the central reservation, spins round, and is struck broadside by an oncoming juggernaut. Tragically Uncle Geoff is killed outright, and poor Simon has both his legs amputated at the scene of the accident before being airlifted to hospital.

'No wonder I aint seen the poor cunt then,' interrupted Jamie Black. 'Is he all right now?'

'In a minute J, in a minute,' replied Fatboy, using the unscheduled break to down another glass of bubbly. 'Right, now where was I?' he said, handing the glass to Nipper and burping loudly. 'Oh yeah, so anyway, out of this terrible event comes some good fortune. The consultant surgeon at the hospital informs Simon that with his consent they will be able to perform an operation that will see his deceased uncles legs, which were undamaged in the accident, attached to the stumps of his own. Simon agrees, the operation is a success, and several weeks later he is well on the way to recovery. Whilst convalescing he receives a call from Mathew Kelly who has heard the news and wants to invite him back to star on the show, no audition required. Simon concurs, and a couple of weeks later, with the aid of crutches he emerges on stage through a dry-ice mist to a fanfare of trumpets.

'Tell us Simon who are you going to be for us tonight?', asks Mathew Kelly, grinning cheesily for the camera. 'Tonight Mathew ... I'm going to be Simon and Half Uncle'.

'Simon and Half Uncle, Simon and Garfunkel ha ha ... you cunt,' wheezed Jamie Black, tears rolling down his face as he and the rest of the crew split their sides laughing. 'I thought you were seriously going on about Solly Lewis. Where is he really?'

'Goa mate,' replied Nipper, once he'd regained his composure. 'He fucked off after that stunt he pulled up in Sheffield the other week. Reckons he's at the top of Old Bills most wanted list.'

'He aint called Simon either is he?'

'Simon? Is he fuck ... Solly Lewis ... jack the fucking lad ... the mad axeman ... from now on he's Chopper Lewis.'

'*One Chopper Lewis, there's only one Chopper Lewis, one Chopper Lewis, there's only one Chopper Lewis.*'

The chanting continued unabated right up until 2pm, the time the limo pulled up outside the Green Man public house on Dagmar Avenue, a short walk away from Wembley Stadium. The driver, Ballroom Bertie, would spend the afternoon in the pub with a couple of old mates so there would be no real rush to get back, except that was for Nipper's special surprise.

★ ★ ★ ★ ★

'*Abide with me; fast falls the eventide; The darkness deepens; Lord with me abide ...*' Nipper felt the hairs on the back of his neck stand up as he joined in the hymn traditionally sung by players and supporters before the Cup Final.

'*When other helpers fail and comforts flee, Help of the helpless, O abide with me.*' Nipper shivered, the passion and fervour that surrounded him, and the true sense of occasion were almost overwhelming. He stopped singing and listened, looking around at Chelsea's blue and white army ... Mathew Harding's blue and white army, he swallowed hard as he felt a lump come to his throat. Mathew Harding, a true Chelsea supporter. How the man would have loved to have been here today, to see the club he'd recently bankrolled with his own money, finally achieve something worthwhile. But it wasn't to be, his life had been cut tragically short back in October when the helicopter he was a passenger in had crashed in bad weather. Mathew had been flying back to London after watching Chelsea lose a mid-week fixture away at Bolton Wanderers.

'*Heaven's morning breaks, and the earth's vain shadows flee; In life, in death O Lord, abide with me.*'

As the hymn drew to a close, Nipper's vision blurred as his eyes moistened. 'What a fucking waste of life,' he mumbled to himself, drawing his right hand across his face to wipe away the tears. And if the death of Mathew Harding had been tragic, what about Peter Philips? How much would he have loved this, the poor cunt? he thought, steeling himself to join in the National Anthem, melancholy giving way to patriotic pride.

The roar at the end of the anthem was deafening. Unanimous cheering and rapturous applause from both sets of supporters left no-one in any doubt, least of all Nipper, that this was what football was all about.

'Come on you mighty blue boys!' yelled Fatboy Green, his face turning crimson with his exertions on what was turning out to be a very hot humid sunny afternoon.

'*Mathew Harding's blue and white army, Mathew Harding's blue and white army ...*' The Chelsea fans chant reached an almighty crescendo as the referee whistled to signal the start of the game.

'Go on Wisey, get in there son ... nice one,' said Eggy Barnes, rocking back on his heels and clapping as the Chelsea skipper dispossessed Robbie Mustoe and passed the ball to Roberto Di Matteo.

'Go on Bobby,' encouraged Nipper, an unlit cigarette dangling patiently from the corner of his mouth as the Italy midfielder began an unchallenged run from the Chelsea half. 'Go on son, go on Bobby ... shoot you cunt.' Nipper leapt in the air as Di Matteo rifled his shot from almost thirty yards out. The ball sailed over Boro's hapless keeper Ben

Roberts and crashed off the underside of the bar into the back of the net.
'GOAL … YES!!'

The blue half of the stadium was ecstatic. The goal was timed at 42 seconds, making it the fastest scored in an FA Cup Final this century.

'One Di Matteo, there's only one Di Matteo, one Di Matteo, there's only one Di Matteo.'

Nipper finally lit the cigarette and clenched his fist, 'Come on the Chelsea.'

'I tell you what that Juninho aint got it has he,' observed Chiller, as the match settled down.

'Nah, it was meant to be all about Juninho against Zola,' said Eggy Barnes knowledgably, 'but if you look at it, Di Matteo, Eddie and Wisey have got him and the rest of the Boro midfield in their pockets. We'll piss this.'

'Robson aint got a clue what to do has he,' said Fatboy, contemplating a half time hot-dog. 'He shouldn't have picked Ravanelli, he was fucked before he started and he's already taken Mustoe off because he's having a mare.'

'You can see why this lot got relegated … oooh fuck me,' added Nipper, his contribution to the running commentary curtailed by a Dan Petrescu lob that was cleared off the goal line.

'Gianfranco Zola … la la la la la la, Gianfranco Zola … la la la la la la …'

'He deserves a goal, go on Franco,' said Riddler Rowan, bracing himself, along with all the other Chelsea fans, as the little wizard lined up a free kick. 'Fucking hell! Fair play to the keeper,' he continued, gasping in amazement as somehow Roberts managed to acrobatically keep the ball out.

'You thought you had scored, you were wrong, you were wrong.'

'That's it mate innit,' said Fatboy, several minutes later, as Boro had a Festa header disallowed for offside on the stroke of half-time. 'We is gonna win da cup.'

★ ★ ★ ★ ★

'D'ya think he'll let Vialli have a run?' enquired Jamie Black, almost tempted to join in a chorus of 'One Man Went To Mow'.

'Not if Zola carries on playing like that,' replied his twin, as Boro's tormentor in chief skipped passed three defenders and was denied a goal by a fortunate piece of keeping by Roberts.

'Come on you Blues, Come on you Blues …'

'Sweet Eddie. Yeah, nice touch super Dan. Go on Franco!' shouted Nipper, breaking off from the chant as Zola picked up on Petrescu's pass and ran in at Boro's far post. 'Fucking brilliant son,' he continued, as the Italian flicked the ball with the outside of his boot into the middle of the box and into the path of Eddie Newton who was following up on the move he'd started. 'GOAL!'

Newton scooped the ball into the net with his left foot, and Chelsea celebrated in style. Chelsea's second, and final goal came with only a couple of minutes left on the clock. If Di Matteo had rightly earned the title of man of the match, it was Zola whose wizardry had been the icing on Chelsea's victory cake and he received a standing ovation when Gullit substituted him as time ebbed away.

'Vialli, Vialli, Vialli, Vialli.'

The popular Italian, Gianluca Vialli, whose appearances this season had been restricted by the form of Mark Hughes, and his oft publicised differences of opinion with the manager, entered the fray to the sound of his name being chanted repeatedly by Blues supporters readying themselves to celebrate victory.

'Fucking brilliant!' exclaimed Nipper, throwing himself into a group hug as the referee blew the final whistle.

'Blue is the colour football is the game, we're all together … and winning is our aim. So cheer us on through the sun and rain, cos Chelsea, Chelsea is our name.'

When Denis Wise eventually made his way up the hallowed Wembley stairs to be presented with the trophy, Nipper found himself overcome with emotion once again. Quality, he thought to himself. Fucking quality. All those years of disappointment, all those years of anger and frustration, now it was over.

'We've waited so long, but we'd wait forever. Our blood is blue and we would leave you never. And when we make it, it'll be together, oh oh oh … Chelsea, Chelsea, Chelsea, Chelsea … we're gonna make this a Blue day.'

As the celebrations continued unabated, Nipper made for the ladies toilets. On reaching the top of the steps he turned and saw the team running hand in hand towards the Chelsea fans and he joined in the euphoric cheers as they dove forward onto the turf.

'Fanfuckingtastic!' he shouted, his voice echoing off the empty toilet walls as he entered a cubicle and slammed the door shut behind him. Nipper sat in silence as he fumbled with his wallet, finally extricating the neatly folded lottery ticket that he'd tucked behind his Amex card which he also removed.

'Time for a live'ner,' he muttered, opening the wrap and spooning a healthy measure of coke up with the credit card. 'Something for the nose ha ha,' he continued, snorting the powder up his right nostril.

'*D-I-MAT-TEO* ... *D-I-MAT-TEO*', the chant, sung to the tune of 'D I S CO' the old Ottawan hit from the '70s was reverberating around the toilet walls as Nipper sat back on the seat and enjoyed the buzz. The first line of the day was always a live'ner all right, no matter how tired you were.

★ ★ ★ ★ ★

'COME ON!' was the unified shout, from the group of men as they leered at the two naked women cavorting in a realistic display of lesbian lust on the floor of the limousine.

'Sorry mate,' said Nipper unapologetically as he tapped Ballroom Bertie on the shoulder and instructed him to lift the opaque glass panel that divided the drivers compartment from the passenger area. 'You need to concentrate on your driving.'

'Girls ... girls,' said Eggy Barnes, tugging at the ribbed collar of his Paul & Shark jersey. 'Kneel on all fours, I wanna do something.'

'Yeah I bet you do,' sniggered Nipper, chopping out the contents of a Henry's worth of bugle onto a hard backed copy of the London A to Z.

'Line em up on their arses,' replied Eggy lasciviously.

'Fucking good job this things got blacked out windows innit Nipper,' guffawed Chiller, the sight of cocaine on naked female flesh finally stirring him into action. 'Look we're just driving past Edgware Road nick,' he continued, bursting into laughter as Riddler Rowan, rolled up twenty in his hand, hoovered up a couple of the lines that were so invitingly presented.

'Our girls wouldn't approve, would they,' mused Eggy.

'Nah mate. I'm also starting to get a bit of stick off Holly about not coming home after I've been watching the Chels,' replied Nipper.

'You do go home though, don't you?'

'Yes mate, via the club.'

'If she said, "it's me or Chelsea", would you miss her?'

'Dunno mate, maybe. Fuck that shit. We've won the cup, let's party.'

Nipper refocused his attention on the matters at hand, ensuring that everyone had the opportunity to go nose down on the girls. It was pretty cramped in the back of the limousine, but it was worth it. Chelsea didn't win the FA Cup every year.

Considering the degrading circumstances they found themselves, the two girls remained in high spirits. Mind you, a monkey between them, a few drops of Cristal and a sprinkling of disco dust was a good enough sweetner and besides, everyone had abided by Nipper's rules. The main one being that no 'intimate touching' was allowed.

Privately, Nipper thought he'd love to 'intimately touch' the darker haired girl. Looking at her upturned, slightly bucking rump, his mind was pervaded by perverted thoughts of degradation and depravation. A little bit of Percy went a long way if you wanted to corrupt a female body. If drugs had taught Nipper one thing, it was that women, and he supposed men as well, were frighteningly willing to do just about anything sexually if they were chasing a cocaine high.

'Oh West London … is wonderful. Oh West London is wonderful, it's full of tits, fanny and Chelsea … Oh West London is wonderful … OH WEST LONDON!'

'Tits, fanny and Charlie more like,' chuckled Riddler Rowan, as the limo glided down Park Lane towards Hyde Park Corner

★ ★ ★ ★ ★

'Nipper, if I said it's me or Chelsea, what would your reply be?' Holly held the passport sized photograph of her boyfriend between her thumb and forefinger and scrutinised it. Of course he wasn't there to answer the question she'd posed, he was out celebrating Chelsea's cup final victory.

She'd seen the news, she'd seen that goal. Apparently the fastest goal ever scored at Wembley eh, and that Roberto Di Matteo, he was such a handsome boy, gorgeous in fact. Holly placed the photo back inside her purse and tossed it onto her dressing table.

Another night at Hysteria beckoned, and as she opened her wardrobe and contemplated what to wear, Holly found herself questioning not only Nipper's commitment to their relationship, but her own. Trying to crystallize her haphazard hopes for love was a random task addressed in moments of solitude. She bemoaned the lack of romance in her life, fantasizing about unrequited sexual encounters with the people around her, both men and women.

Layla. Claire the pale and interesting doe-eyed girl she'd just hired as a manager, suave Eggy Barnes, ice cool Chiller, even Sniffler Barlow. Twenty years with one person was a long time, half a life time. Love, honour and obey one person? Fat chance, thought Holly, as she ran her hand across the knee length, black pleated Prada skirt she'd bought on a whim several weeks ago but had yet to wear. Love, honour and betray more-like. Men were all the same, and she had little doubt that Nipper was any different. Hysteria, Chelsea, drugs, the craic, he had it all, living a mans life in a mans world. The very same mans world that she had so successfully encroached.

Fidelity or infidelity? Holly lifted the skirt out of the wardrobe and held it against her skinny frame. I'd look like a fucking librarian wearing this, she thought to herself, shaking her head and wondering how the look could be enhanced. With a pair of Jimmy Choo's killer heels perhaps? If she ever found out that Nipper had been unfaithful how would she react? Would she be angry, or maybe relieved? What about him? Yeah, what about him?

Holly placed the skirt back on the hanger rail and tousled her hair. Her teenage love for Nipper had bordered on the stomach churning obsessive. A love borne out of solitude, a love to replace her mothers affection she'd lost at such an early age. Drugs had heightened the physical aspect of their relationship, cocaine in particular helping her numb the emotional pain she'd endured when Pete had violated her. Together in bed, things were guttural and dark, sex without boundaries, sex without love. The love they shared was a selfish love.

Holly sat down cross legged on the floor and closed her eyes. Saturday night was no time for self appraisal, but five minutes worth wouldn't do her any harm. It was a simple conundrum. Did she want to maintain her high octane lifestyle, enjoying all its fringe benefits, both chemical and financial? Or sacrifice it in favour of a serene life? The sort of life in which she would go to work at a normal time, wearing the Prada dress she'd just put back in her wardrobe with sensible shoes and a knitted cardigan. A life in which she could find a calm enduring love. A conventional life.

The phone rang, distracting her thoughts.

'Yeah, I'm on my way Claire.' Holly concluded the brief conversation and placed the receiver back in its cradle. No time to waste now, the other side of love and life would have to wait.

10

Autumn 1997

THE DRUGS DON'T WORK

'Dan, Dan, super Dan, Dan, Dan super Dan, Dan, Dan super Dan, super Dan Petrescu.'

Holly stood up along with Nipper and the rest of the boys as they celebrated Chelsea's opening goal of the match, a twenty yard Petrescu chip that had beaten Southampton's keeper Paul Jones and gone in off the far post.

It was a beautiful late summer afternoon and the verdant Stamford Bridge pitch was bathed in bright, eye squinting sunlight. Holly wasn't entirely sure why Nipper had invited her along to the game, none of the other lads girlfriends were in attendance, but she wasn't complaining. Things seemed different. Out of sight, out of mind, she thought, remembering her teenaged experiences of watching Chelsea and wondering what had happened to the vicious thugs and racists that had once been associated with the club.

She looked around, things had definitely changed. The ground for a start, what a transformation. It wasn't complete yet, but impressive nonetheless. Holly laughed as she recalled the time she'd first stood on the Shed, too petite so see much of what was going on. 'Don't worry love', Nipper had said, 'you're not missing anything'.

'Ed de Goey oi! Ed de Goey, Ed de Goey oi! … Ed de Goey,' chanted the Chelsea supporters in the pristine new Mathew Harding Stand to the tune the old Gary Glitter track 'Rock & Roll'.

'Dodgy keeper, dodgy keeper,' countered the visiting Saints fans, as the giant Dutchman, making his home debut, fluffed an attempted clearance allowing Kevin Davies the opportunity to equalise.

It wasn't long before every Chelsea fan in the ground was on their feet again as the Blues raced into a 4-1 lead. In the space of six breathtaking minutes, Frank Leboeuf, Mark Hughes, and Dennis Wise all found the net.

'He's horny,' crowed Holly, pointing at the shaven headed French defender.

'He's here, he's there, he's every fucking where … Frank Leboeuf, Frank Leboeuf.'

'Easy tiger,' laughed Nipper, checking the time on his watch as he accepted a cigarette from Eggy Barnes. 'You'll be wanting to come every week,' he continued, joining in the rapturous applause that ricocheted around the ground as referee Wilkie blew for the lemon break.

'Nice kettle,' said Riddler Rowan pointing at Nipper's wrist. 'Looks familiar,' he continued, taking closer order as a bemused Holly looked on.

'Kettle?' she enquired, pursing her lips and blowing a kiss at Riddler.

'Uh huh … sorry treacle,' he replied, face flushed with embarrassment. 'Kettle and hob, fob … er as in watch fob.'

'Ridiculous,' replied Holly pushing her tortoiseshell framed Gucci sunglasses back up the bridge of her nose. 'Why don't you just call it a watch?'

'Yeah, cheers mate,' interjected Nipper, choosing to ignore Holly's comments. 'It's a Monaco re-issue. Made by Tag. Steve McQueen wore an original Edouard Heuer piece in the film Le Mans.'

'That's where I seen it,' nodded Riddler. 'Very nice.'

'An expensive watch is an essential part of every gentleman's wardrobe,' added Nipper, drawing his finger lightly across the Monaco's glass.

'Why have you got one then?' enquired Holly jokingly.

'Because I'm a gent doll face,' he replied, playfully spanking Holly's pert denim clad backside, which she'd noticed had received plenty of admiring glances during the course of the afternoon.

* * * * *

'It all went a bit pear-shaped in the second half I thought,' said Holly, tugging at the zip of the figure hugging Christian Lacroix dress she'd worn to Hysteria that evening. 'Undo me darling, there's a love,' she continued, picking up a half smoked spliff from the ashtray and relighting it.

'Listen to you now,' replied Nipper, pouring himself a generous glass of neat Southern Comfort and walking into the bedroom. 'That's Chelsea love, and 4-2 aint a bad result at the end of the day.'

'Do you love me Nipper?' asked Holly, turning around and blowing several large smoke rings into the air.

'You know that doll face. How many times have I told you, I love you more than I love myself.'

'No I mean it.'

'So do I.'

'Do you still fancy me?' she breathed huskily, as Nipper undid her dress and ran his hands slowly down the front of her body.

'Course I do,' he replied, thankful for the fact that he'd had the presence of mind to pop one of Chopper's diamond shaped performance enhancers as soon as they'd arrived home.

Nipper pushed Holly onto the bed; She was encouraging him to be rough, slapping at his face and trying to pull at his number one cropped hair. He just laughed, loosely gripping her neck whilst holding her at arms length safe in the knowledge that his face was out of the reach of her rakish fingernails.

'You know you can't win you little slut … don't you eh?' he hissed, taking closer order and placing his left forearm across her neck and the full weight of his body on top hers.

For a split second Holly's mind flashed back to the trauma she had endured at the hands of Pete. But this was different. Of course she knew she could have moved. She could fight back like a kicking, gouging, feral wildcat if she wanted to, but she didn't.

Nipper knew that Holly would yield; she wanted to submit, she wanted to be abused. She fucking loves it, he thought to himself, sensing his hardness and groping roughly at her sex through the flimsy cotton g-string she was wearing, feeling the goose-bumps rising on her thighs as he bit her earlobes and the nape of her neck.

'Come on then you dirty bastard,' she snarled gutturally, rearing up and drawing her razor sharp nails down the length of Nipper's back causing him to yelp with pain.

'You little bitch,' he growled, sitting back up on the bed and grabbing a fistful of her hair. 'I'm going to have to teach you some manners,' he continued, pulling her head down to his groin and forcing his manhood into her willing mouth. 'Respect my cock!'

Time stood still as Nipper heightened his pleasure by sniffing amyl nitrate from the bottle that was never too far away from his grasp. Breathing heavily, he summoned every ounce of will power he possessed to delay his orgasm, but Holly was intent on finishing what she'd started.

'Fucking hell Holly!' he groaned, clenching his buttocks and arching his back as Holly deep throated him to the point of no return. 'Stop … stop,' he whimpered as she continued to suck him dry, his sensitivity heightened, pleasure quickly turning to discomfort.

Nipper laid back on the bed, his pounding heart feeling like it was about to erupt from his chest Alien fashion. Holly drew her hand slowly across her mouth and licked her lips, reaching for the bottle of Southern Comfort that was on the bedside table next to the remote control for the TV.

'What about me, you lazy bastard,' she purred, looking at Nipper's prostrate form before taking a slug from the bottle. 'I'll have to pleasure myself then eh,' she continued, picking up the remote control and switching on the TV, stabbing at the buttons in a failed bid to engage the video.

'What the fucks happened now?' she muttered to herself, looking at the imagesbeing displayed by ITV. A series of stills showed what looked like a serious car wreck under some sort of a bridge. Holly focussed her mind quickly, turning up the volume so she could listen to the newsreaders dialogue.

The mangled car she could see on the screen had crashed in a tunnel running alongside the River Seine in Paris. Inside the car had been Diana, Princess of Wales, her boyfriend Dodi al-Fahed, the driver Henri Paul, and Dodi's bodyguard Trevor Rees-Jones. Dodi and the driver were reported as having been killed, whilst Princess Diana and the bodyguard were thought to have been very seriously injured.

'Nipper wake up,' said Holly, prodding his face in vain with her index finger as she got off the bed. Donning a towelling robe, she turned off the TV, picked up the bottle of Southern Comfort and her spliff box and walked through to the living room, turning the lights on and dimming them low before sitting down on the sofa next to Jezebel the cat who was sound asleep and purring contentedly.

Holly built and lit a joint before switching on the lounge TV and concentrating on the bulletin being broadcast. The newsreader couldn't hide her emotion as she explained that it had now been confirmed that the Princess of Wales was dead.

'What's the date today Jezebel?' said Holly, stroking the still dormant cats heavy fur coat. 'August 31st ... August 31st,' she sighed, beginning to sob as the 'breaking news' banner flashed along the bottom of the screen displaying the date, the time, and details of the evolving story.

The date was indelibly etched like a tribal tattoo on Holly's heart. August 31st, the anniversary of her mother Lexie's death. 'Twenty five years ago today mum,' she whispered to herself, her voice trembling as the tears rolled down her face. Sorrow renewed. Two lives lost at a preciously early age. Two lives wasted.

Holly fumbled with the spliff, her moist eyes stinging as its acrid smoke pervaded them. 'Enough of this, enough now,' she said, flicking the still lit roach into the fireplace and clasping her hands together around her drawn up knees.

Suddenly Holly felt that her life was in some supernatural way inextricably bound with Diana's, a woman whom previously she'd mocked for displaying a myriad of weaknesses in public. She'd viewed the Princess with suspicion. Another immensely wealthy celebrity with a broken marriage; a posh girl with a hatred of the media who garnered public support with her compassionate view of humanity and its lost causes. Never once during the well documented breakdown of her marriage to Charles, in which the minutiae of her foibles were exposed for all to see, had Holly ever felt sorry for her, let alone identified with her, and yet here she was enduring that same gut wrenching emptiness that she'd done all those years ago when her mother had died young.

★ ★ ★ ★ ★

'Where to love?' asked the taxi driver, as Holly stood shivering on the edge of the pavement directly outside the smart Victorian terrace in Lavender Gardens that she and Nipper had bought two years previously. At 9am, it was still too early for gentrified Battersea to be rising from its Saturday night slumbers, and Holly had stood like a zombie waiting for the taxi she'd summoned to arrive.

She'd felt compelled to do something. Overtired and wired, sleep was never going to be an option. Instead she'd showered and dressed, glaring at her icy androgyny in the mirror, alarmed by her ghostly make up free pallor. 'Death warmed up,' she'd muttered to herself scrawling Nipper a brief note explaining where she was going.

'Love, can I help you?' enquired the cabbie patiently, his 'seen it all before' demeanour unfazed by the extra-planetary apparition in denim that was stood before him.

'Don't worry I won't throw up in yer cab,' grinned Holly, shrugging her shoulders and pulling herself together as she climbed into the car.

'Where can I drop you sweetheart?'

'Kensington mate ... High Street Kensington.'

The cabbie smiled at her and nodded. 'You going there too love?' he asked, the cockney robustness of his voice giving way to a more sympathetic lilt. 'Terrible thing innit,' he continued, looking over his shoulder to double check on the well-being of his troubled fare. 'I've been working all night. Heard the news on the wireless when it happened. Rang the missus straight away, the poor souls inconsolable she's 'ad to go over to me sister's.'

Holly sat in silence as the cabbie went onto explain that he'd already ferried several people up to Kensington this morning. Kensington Palace was Diana's home. Shrouded in a mysterious cloak of woe, Holly had felt spiritually guided when she'd taken the decision earlier to embark on the brief journey she was now undertaking.

Scores of people, male and female, young and old, were gathered on the pavement outside the Palace. With every minute that passed, more arrived, some laying floral tributes and wreaths along the railings that skirted the palaces gardens, others, like Holly, just standing stock still in stunned disbelieving reverential silence, captivated by the contagiously mournful serenity.

Holly was reminded of Goa and the quaintly beautiful church of St. Alex, her brothers final resting place, but the similarity ended there. This felt spiritual for her. The people that came to the Palace seemed to meditate, there were tears in their eyes as there were in hers. For the first time ever in her life, Holly did not feel alone in her grief, she felt that she was in the presence of something omnipotent, something tangible, something with a deep and hitherto hidden meaning.

★ ★ ★ ★ ★

Over the course of the following week Holly returned to the gardens on four separate occasions. The inner feeling was always the same for her, but the funereal spectacle had changed shape. The spectre of commerciality loomed large, as unscrupulous people sought to profit from the shared grief of those who congregated to pay their respects. At night, generators powered lights which, along with all the candles, bathed the never ending sea of flowers in an eerie almost daylight glow. This was all too much for Holly, finally she'd seen enough.

Nipper was driven to distraction by Holly's behaviour. The inevitable arguments had been intense and short lived. He'd viewed the events surrounding Diana's death with cold detachment, speaking of hypocrisy and mass hysteria, whilst she was still trying to navigate her way without a map and compass through every available human emotion.

The fragility of Diana's life, did it mirror her own? Was she grieving for herself or for Diana? Maybe she was grieving for the loss of her mother. What about the gear, what part did that shit have in muddling her feelings? There were so many questions that neither of them could answer. Nipper gave up, and Holly felt increasingly isolated and alienated.

'All this talk of getting old, it's getting me down my love. Like a cat in a bag, waiting to drown, this time I'm coming down.'

On the Monday following the burial ceremony, Holly sat in doors and worked her way through a couple of wraps of coke listening over and over again to the melancholic lyric of The Verve's chart topping song, 'The Drugs Don't Work'.

'And I hope you're thinking of me, as you lay down on your side. Now the drugs don't work, they just make you worse, but I know I'll see your face again.'

There was something in singer Richard Ashcroft's tortured vocal delivery that resonated with her subconscious, tugging at her heartstrings and yet somehow filling her with a steely resolve.

'Cause baby, ooh, if heaven calls, I'm coming too. Just like you said, you leave my life, I'm better off dead.'

★ ★ ★ ★ ★

All cried out, and just when things looked like they couldn't get any worse, Holly received a telephone call from Chopper Lewis informing her that her father Tommy was gravely ill, suffering from acute hepatitis.

Tommy had spent the summer out in Goa keeping self styled fugitive Chopper company during the monsoon season. In the intervening years since his sons death, the bottle had got the better of him, and his liver, consumed by cirrhosis had been slowly and painfully ceasing to function properly. When his GP had told him that he had less than three months to live, Tommy had kept the news to himself, deciding to head out to Goa where he could drink himself to the grave in relative privacy. A grave that he'd planned would be next to that of his sons. In death, if not in life, he wanted to be close to Pete, reasoning that somehow the real truth would be revealed to him.

Displaying a degree of care and concern that impressed Holly, Chopper made all the necessary arrangements for her arrival in Goa. Out of season, she'd had to take a scheduled flight to Bombay. Chopper had sent a driver to collect her and bring her to Calangute where she was to stay with Father Francis in the old house adjacent to the Church of St. Alex. Nipper wasn't on the guest-list, nor was anyone else from London.

★ ★ ★ ★ ★

The rain was incessant, beating down on the tiled roof of Panjim Hospital with a machine gun-like intensity that made it hard to concentrate, let alone sleep, as Holly sat with her head bowed at her dying fathers bedside.

'Death is the ultimate force in the world,' said Father Francis sombrely to Holly, after performing the last rites on her father. 'When it comes into your life, no matter how well prepared you are for it, you cannot counter the dread drenched feeling of apocalyptic desolation that embraces you. I will leave you now my child. Be strong for your father in his final hours, and be strong for yourself.'

Holly looked on her fathers frail body, at the yellowed skin drawn tautly across his bony face, a face that she'd remembered as a child being so full and handsome, a face that had once sparkled with the joy and laughter of a happy family man. The mask of death he wore now painted a different picture. A portrait of someone tortured, not only by the physical pain that had ransacked his body, but also by the unanswered questions that had ravaged his soul.

What if this? What if that? What if? What? Holly's mind ticked over to the tappety tap beat of the still falling rain. As her fathers life finally ebbed away, she closed her eyes and wept. Tears for herself, and tears for her family.

PART TWO

11

HYSTERIA

The basement toilets at Hysteria are fantastic. Marble floors, gleaming black and white tiles, miles of chrome piping, pristine porcelain sinks with heavy duty faucets set into a slab of reclaimed granite that bevelled nicely into the show-stopping art-deco mirror running along the entire length of the back wall.

Hands on hips, Holly stood in front of the mirror, admiring its sculpted frame and marvelling at the intricacy of the craftsmanship. The lifetime work of a poor post-modernist who never got to saw his masterpiece hung somewhere meaningful. The mirror had originally been commissioned by Beery Barlow and intended for the drawing room of a clients property in the London millionaire enclave of Eaton Square.

Fashion being a fickle thing, by the time the frame was complete, art-deco home décor was out, and so was the mirror. Hysteria, undergoing a dramatic phase of refurbishment, was the perfect location. It was just a question of where? Beery wasn't sure about it, but Holly knew the club game and she'd convinced him that it would get the attention it justly deserved in the ladies toilets.

A lady loves a mirror, and none more so than Holly.

'I did love you once,' she said for her own benefit, frowning at her reflection whilst applying and re-applying her lipstick with the vim and vigour of a teenage girl who'd just discovered the keys to her mothers vanity case and boys on the same day. 'But it didn't last,' she continued, her voice hushed as she realised that a couple of the cubicles were occupied. 'Y'see I'm far too flighty to form a meaningful relationship, and far too selfish for all that give and take innit Holly my love eh.'

Too late for all this self-criticism now, she thought to herself. The figure was still there for all to admire, but the telltale creases around the eyes and mouth were just that little bit too pronounced for Holly's liking. Botox? Yeah, that might be something worth considering. She was a self-celebrating part of the nip and tuck, shop and fuck generation, but needles and the surgeons scalpel scared the living shit out her.

Checking her watch and wondering where the toilet attendant was, Holly snatched at the small but functional Fendi clutch bag that Nipper had given her last Christmas and made her way to the cubicle furthest from the entrance door. UFT, Holly thought to herself, sniggering as she bolted the cubicle door shut. The best 'user friendly toilets' in London town. Well, anything else would have been inexcusable, hypocritical even.

'That'll do nicely,' she muttered, using her black American Express card to fashion two chubby lines of coke on the stainless steel ledge conveniently located above the low level cistern. There was no need for it, not here. Holly could have fed her habit in the privacy of her office, but this was more fun. Having said that, Davy Truelove, who these days was known to one and all in clubland as Mr Sheen, apparently because he brought sparkle into peoples lives, was one of the worst offenders for cutting his coke with baby laxative. The last thing anyone needed at 5am was to be caught short by an epic bowel loosening experience of Train Spotting proportions, so it was better to err on the side of caution.

'Sweet, you know that,' said Holly, flushing the toilet to mask the sound of her snorting the lines through a rolled up £50 note. Sweaty, dirty, sexy, that's how coke made her feel. The good stuff, you can't beat the good stuff. Right now she felt so high, she thought that she could kiss the sky. On unlocking the cubicle door, Holly was greeted by her own reflection in the mirror.

'Look at me all shiny eyes and full red lips ... ha ha,' she trilled, flicking her hair and sniffing her nose as she made for the exit door. 'I'm a fucking drink on a stick.'

★ ★ ★ ★ ★

With the night due to finish at 6am most of the revellers had left, only those fuelled by Class A's remained. The living dead, thought Holly, walking though the club and taking care to avoid the edgy vacant stares of pill popping last gasp chancers, whose dilated pupils were struggling with the menacing strobe lights, their bodies trying with varying degrees of success to keep up with the hard step drum and bass rhythms pumping from the speakers in the main room.

For the first time this evening, Holly was right up there with them. She had that weightless feeling in her stomach once again, the cocaine roller coaster ride was about to begin. She clenched her fists pushing her finger-nails hard into the palms of her hands, sniffing hard and swallowing, grimacing at the bitter taste of the cocaine tracing its way through the back of her nasal passages and into her throat.

'Hello treacle,' said Riddler Rowan, tapping her on the shoulder and distracting her from the dark thoughts that had suddenly filled her mind.

'Hey, Riddler,' replied Holly, greeting him with a long lost lovers clinch. 'This fucking coke is wicked. Did you move much tonight?'

'Believe, Miss Philips, believe.'

'Well come on then,' said Holly, tracing her finger across bashful looking Riddler's cheek.

'Sniffler's doing the paperwork now, I can tell you it's a good one though.'

Holly laughed, she adored the effect she still had on some men. Forty something, so what. Riddler Rowan was like putty in her hands.

'Love it fella,' she said, rubbing her hand down Riddler's right arm and squeezing at his bicep whilst blowing a kiss at him.

'Yeah Holly. Cor blimey, pack it in love,' he replied, unnerved by her attention. 'I'll have to go and wax my dolphin if you carry on like this.'

Holly backed off, grinning as the cocaine buzz tightened its familiar grip.

'Wax your dolphin?

'Put one down the sink.'

'Ha ha. Oh yeah, I get ya. You dirty old man.'

Riddler couldn't tell if the scowl on Holly's face was intentional, or all part of her elaborate little game. Whatever it was, he wasn't about to push his luck.

'Sorry love, just a joke.'

'Tune!' exclaimed Holly, disregarding the fact that Riddler had just called her 'love', something she'd never been down with.

'Alex Reece, nice one. Listen I'm gonna crack on, I'll catch you later at closedown.'

'Yeah later.'

Holly suddenly felt the urge to dance, clicking her fingers as the infec-tious pioneering tempo of 'Candles' broke down from the intro to the vocal.

'It's the way the candles light up your face, that I know that no-one could take your place.'

Holly two stepped, tilting her head back, tracking the criss-cross red, blue and green lasers across the room. The moves still came easily, Dad

Tommy had always said, her brains were in her feet, like a regular dancing queen. Holly span round slowly, perfectly segued with the music. Perks of the job ha ha, she thought to herself, widening her eyes as she caught sight of Camp Kenny and his entourage of ragtag and bobtail glamour 'girls' tottering across the dancefloor, high on heels, coke, poppers, the ubiquitous E, and anything else they could ingest.

Talk about pills, thrills and bellyaches, how Camp Kenny had managed to avoid a terminal encounter with the ace of spades was beyond comprehension. Nipper always used to make Holly laugh when he said that Kenny was such a slut he must have an arse like a clown's pocket.

Camp Kenny and his 'girls' were the club pickers, employed by Holly to ensure that Hysteria's reputation as a cutting edge venue remained. As a paying punter back in her New Romantic days, Holly had graced the bars, dancefloors and darker recesses of various establishments safe in the knowledge that she was part of the elite. It wasn't for everyone, you had to make an effort. No effort, no admission. No admission, no fun.

If you got past Kenny's rigid door policy you knew you were in with the in-crowd. He'd mince up and down the queue forming outside the entrance doors with a clipboard in his hand, critical eyes weighing up the punters, and the lads in particular.

'What's yer name? Where yer from? What yer on?' was reserved for the lucky ones. Those turned away could expect anything from, 'yer names not on the list, yer not coming in', through 'sorry lads it's couples and ladies only tonight', to 'sorry lads no style'.

Holly always laughed at that one. Nipper had told her a story years ago about watching Chelsea away up north, Newcastle, that was it. After the game they had gone into the city centre planning to have a few drinks before getting the train back to London. No chance, the burly doormen protecting the interests of the patrons of every drinking establishment they tried to gain admittance to had taken one look at the sharp dressed, self-styled 'Tea Bar Casuals' and repeatedly turned them away with the line 'sorry lads no style'. Every girls crazy for a sharp dressed man, it just wasn't worth the aggravation.

'*Chelsea boys we are here, shag your women and drink your beer.*' Everywhere but Newcastle!

As far as Camp Kenny was concerned, 'no style' meant just that. You hadn't tried hard enough. Holly sometimes overruled his decisions, but by and large she revelled in the entertainment to be had watching straight, suitably attired working class boys flirting outrageously with her door queen in a valiant bid to secure entry. They all knew it was worth it though, because once inside they knew that they would be able to indulge themselves in the simple pleasures of life. Alcohol, chemicals, tunes and if they got lucky, a tour of duty with the Hysteria beaver patrol.

'Hi Holly honey. Ooh what a wonderful night darling.' Kenny stood in front of Holly looking like a Warhol styled pantomime villain. Larger than life and in her face, his pupils were dilated to the extent that he looked like he was wearing black contact lenses. Sometimes Kenny went all the way down transvestite lane, but tonight he was resplendent in a sheer Gaultier vest that he'd pulled tightly across his finely honed black torso and tucked loosely into a pair of red lycra cycling shorts.

Although in his early thirties, Camp Kenny, the crown prince of kink, still held the attention of the fawning group of sycophants that traipsed around after him hanging on his every word. They were his boys, and they were young. They looked up to him as their lifestyle guru. He had everything they aspired to, and gave them everything they needed. Everything!

The trouble was though that sometimes what Kenny gave, wasn't exactly his to give. Sniffler had long suspected that he was lining his own pockets at the expense of the club, and despite the fact that he'd mentioned it on more than one occasion to Nipper, nothing had been done about it. Now he'd mentioned it to Holly, she thought maybe it was time to exercise a little authority, especially since she'd dumped Nipper.

Sniffler was aware that Nipper knew Camp Kenny was serving up pills meant for Hysteria's punters elsewhere. Nipper allowed it because he recognised that it wound his adversary up like an old clock. Tick, tock, tick, tock.

The black iron, getting away with it again. Fucking liberty! thought Sniffler, it made his Aryan blood boil. Holly still found it funny even though her man was no longer on the scene. Nipper courted respect, people didn't cross him. A problem aired, was a problem dealt with when he was around. But that was then and this was now. All Holly had to rely on these days was trust, goodwill and Stevie 'Sniffler' Barlow.

'Mug', was Nipper's definition of Sniffler. 'The blokes a fucking bully, all verbals'. Holly kept out of it, she knew just as well as anyone that a little nepotism went a long way, and being the son of Barry Barlow helped son Stevie fulfil what Nipper referred to as his 'plastic gangster dream'.

Sniffler loved to play up to the GQ new male stereotype, but the reality was somewhat diametrically opposed to the image. The only thing GQ conformant was his dress sense. The man's psyche was borne out of a disturbed childhood that had seen him bullied by his overprotective father, ignored by his mother and derided by his classmates at school for being dim-witted.

As an alienated teenager, he'd been perfect raw material for the right wing propagandists who'd peddled their ideologies about white supremacy and freedom. He'd joined the Cockney Red army just to be a part of a gang. Manchester United were incidental, and the football a fucking chore. But he was in a gang, and that made him a gangster, just like his dad. One day things would change though, when his dad became old and slow. One day he'd have the stage and the audience, and then people would see what Stevie Barlow was really made of.

Of course Holly didn't know any of this, but with Nipper vacating the leading mans role in the film of her life, it was time to hold the first audition for his replacement, and Sniffler wasn't going to pass up on the opportunity.

'Fancy a drink Kenny? You look like you could use one, come to the office in ten minutes.'

'Of course darling.'

Holly prodded Kenny in the ribs and pinched her nose. She felt edgy now, the coke had sharpened her up, and she was ready for the curtain to rise on the evenings final performance

★ ★ ★ ★ ★

Nipper has been sitting on the edge of the bed for less than half-an-hour, but it seemed like an eternity. That was the gear and the booze. A whole day of it, mind you 4-1 away at West Brom had been a terrific tonic. Chelsea always took his mind off things, and right now they were on level points at the top of the Premiership with Arsenal and going well in the Champions League, happy days.

'It's me or Chelsea, Nipper', yeah right, 'Slag.'

There had to be more to it than that, but Nipper just couldn't figure it out. A tableau of naked emotions, his mind was working overtime with at least five different trains of thought criss-crossing his already paranoid state of self consciousness. Runaway trains, out of control, seemingly headed for the same chicane destination with inevitable results.

Jose Mourinho, Jose Mourinho, Jose Morinho.

Nipper rocked back and forth on the edge of the bed, his feet on tip toes, moving up and down rapidly in time with the football chant playing in his head.

'It's me or Chelsea, fuck off!' he cursed, as he contemplated finishing off the last bit of sparkle he knew he still had in the lottery ticket wrap in his wallet. How could she begrudge him following the Blues? All those years of bitter dismay. This was payback time.

Di Matteo's FA Cup Final lightning strike had heralded the dawn of a new era of success. Ruud Gullit had fallen out with Captain Birdseye and been replaced by the talismanic Luca Vialli, under whose guidance Chelsea had won the League Cup, the Cup Winners Cup, and the FA Cup again.

Vialli fell foul of Bates in September 2000 and was replaced by the genial Claudio Ranieri who in just under four years managed to win nothing apart from the warmth and admiration of players, supporters, and media alike.

'Have you ever seen Chelsea win the league? Have you fuck. Have you ever seen Chelsea win the league? Have you fuck. Have you ever seen Chelsea, ever seen Chelsea, ever seen Chelsea win the league? Have you fuck!' so went the popular Manchester United chant that Sniffler was so fond of at the time.

'Glorious unpredictability? Fuck you Sniffler!' snarled Nipper, reaching for his wallet. In July 2003 with Chelsea zillions of pounds in debt, Ken Bates had sold Chelsea football club to a mysterious Russian oil billionaire. At 36, Roman Abramovich was already the 43rd richest man in the world. Rock and fucking roll, *'cos we are the Chelsea and we are the best, we are the Chelsea so fuck all the rest.'*

Out came the chequebook, and in came a dazzling array of domestic and continental talent. The boardroom door revolved controversially also. Peter Kenyon was a less than popular choice to run the club, and his appointment hastened the departure of Ken Bates. Batesy was like Marmite. You either loved him, or you detested him. Nipper and the boys loved old greybeard despite his foibles.

His one cardinal sin, the replacement of the traditional club crest had been had been unforgivable, but his titanic struggle to secure the future of the club from the hands of developers who'd sought to turn Stamford Bridge into a block of very expensive flats would never be forgotten.

17 million quid, was his return. Fair play to him, thought Nipper, lining himself up one last live'ner and clapping his hands together.

'Jose Mourinho, Jose Mourinho.'

There it was again, that fucking chant, lodged in the left side of his brain. At the end of last season, Ranieri had paid the ultimate price for failure and been fired by Kenyon. In Nipper's eyes he'd only blotted his copybook once. That Champions League semi-final away leg in Monaco, when the so-called Tinkerman had tinkered just that little bit too much and cost Chelsea a place in the final.

Having said that, if you believed the popular press, he would have been fired if he'd won the trophy anyway. Football could be a cruel business. Ranieri's replacement, Jose Mourinho, had been the all conquering manager of FC Porto, the team that Chelsea would have faced in the Champions League final had they prevailed against Monaco. Mourinho was the man destined to lead the Blues to the promised land.

'Jose Mourinho, Jose Mourinho.'

Nipper hoovered up the coke with a rolled up £20, got to his feet, and began to pace his bedroom like a caged tiger. The temperamental right side of his brain soon suppressing thoughts about his beloved team, replacing them instead with those of an angst ridden, spurned lover.

'Fucking bitch! Dirty, lying, cheating fucking bitch. Look what you've done to me,' swore Nipper, totally strung out as he rubbed the back of his hand against his nose which continued to run no matter how much he sniffed.

He looked over at the picture of Holly in the heavy wrought iron frame on the bedside table and shook his head. I gave you everything, you gave me nothing in return. Selfish bitch, he thought, grimacing as he swallowed hard, the back of his throat not cocaine numbed enough to dull the pain. Shot to pieces, that's how Nipper felt. Run down, his body had been racked by the influenza virus currently gripping the nation. Cigarettes, alcohol and cocaine were not a remedy any doctor would prescribe, the only cure for his particular ailment was the sweet tasting potion of revenge.

It had been a couple of months since Holly had dropped the bombshell that he was surplus to her exacting requirements. 'I'm sorry Nipper, but sometimes love changes shape'. Changes shape? What fucking Sex and the City shit was that all about? The timing? Yeah, that had been expected. The anniversary of her mothers death, he should've seen that one looming on the horizon, especially after the way she'd behaved when Princess Diana died.

'Fuck it!' growled Nipper, hurriedly getting undressed and walking briskly to the bathroom. 'It's time to go to work,' he continued, muttering as he stepped into the shower. The icy water rapidly extinguished his luminescent rage. A handful of Nurofen washed down with a Vitamin C supplement would balance his system and a black coffee coupled with his steely resolve would do the rest.

Holly could continue to confidently lead her life in a dazzling whirl of decadence, effervescence and self indulgence, but would she be ready when he came back at her? Nipper shrugged his shoulders at the thought, clapping his hands and healing himself. The man with a plan.

★ ★ ★ ★ ★

Holly closed the heavy wooden office door behind her. Sniffler was sat behind the desk drawing heavily on a Marlboro, slovenly fingering through the raft of paperwork piled up in front of him like some B-Movie private detective searching for clues without really knowing what he was looking for.

'Hello S. Busy then are we?' asked Holly sarcastically. 'Kenny should be here in five or ten minute's I want him sorted,' she continued authoritatively, walking over to the desk and resting both her hands on its richly waxed surface.

Sniffler eyed Holly casually, raising his left eyebrow as he reached into the inside pocket of his black Hugo Boss leather jacket that was hanging on the back of his chair.

'SORTED!' bellowed Nipper. 'I'm gonna fillet that disease riddled silvery shirt lifter,' he continued, spitting the words out malevolently as he placed the cut throat razor he'd produced from his jacket into the palm of his left hand. 'A close shave, that's what Kenny needs. He'll be shaking like a shitting dog by the time I've finished with him.'

Holly narrowed her eyes impatiently at Sniffler, but she couldn't help smiling at his reply. He did make her laugh though, it was as if he'd rehearsed everything. Sniffler lived his life as if he were the leading man in some Guy Ritchie film, the fucking idiot. He really fancied himself as a regular gangster; mind you she supposed, if the truth be told, that's exactly what she'd allowed him to become.

Not withstanding this, he did afford her a certain degree of protection and she felt safe in his company, securely and sexually. One of the biggest drawbacks about being a respectable sort in this game was the fact that just about every bloke she met viewed her as fair game for a chat up line or a bit of smutty innuendo.

Holly looked at Sniffler, remaining silent, briefly wondering why he'd never tried it on with her. Come to think of it he never really tried it on with anyone. All the lads on the payroll had an eye for her, so why not Sniffler? Maybe he'd been too scared of Nipper, maybe it was a respect thing, or maybe it was something else.

★ ★ ★ ★ ★

Nipper, sobriety regained, was sat behind the wheel of his 'limited edition' Autobiography Range Rover heading over Blackfriars Bridge towards the City. Incessant rain, lashing down from the leaden sky and driven hard by a relentless biting cold wind meant that London's streets, which would have been quiet anyway given the time and the day, were virtually deserted.

This suited Nipper, traffic and people were the last thing he needed to contend with. His biggest concern at the moment was the filth. City of London Old Bill were bigger, harder and less tolerant than their Met counterparts, he knew he needed to stay focussed and concentrate on his driving. Although the so called 'ring of steel' was no longer in operation, there was still plenty of CCTV surveillance kit out there which was diligently monitored 24 hours around the clock.

The Range Rover was discreet enough. He'd had to get rid of the BMW X5 that had replaced his treasured Shogun because the old Chelsea tractor had become a favoured target for carjackers. Not that he couldn't deal with the threat, it just meant that the police patrols paid closer attention to the occupants of said 4x4 and that was something Nipper could do without given the nature of his work.

Who says crime doesn't pay? Nipper loved the Range Rover. Blue is the colour, Cairns Blue. The paint finish, privacy glass and 20" alloys gave the car an understated presence, and the cherry wood dashboard, lush parchment hide and 14 speaker Logic 7 sound system made every ride an event. Well worth 65 bags, thought Nipper, making full use of the 710 watts of amplification available to him.

Chain smoking Marlboro Lights, and chewing on some Wrigleys Extra, he clicked his fingers in time with the beat of the music, thinking about how he was going to change things. The searing soulful vocal kicked in and Nipper involuntarily shrugged his head and shoulders as a shiver ran down his spine. Forget Eric Clapton, Kenny Bobien was God, and 'Rise AboveThe Storm' was the man at his deeply soothing best.

'Like an eagle spread your wings, take to the sky it's time to fly … rise above the storm … rise above the storm.'

* * * * *

'Ad a good one 'ave we Ken? Looks like it eh, been down the sweet shop 'ave we?' Sniffler machine gunned the words staccato style at a nervous looking Kenny from the corner of his mouth.

'Well then young man,' added Holly primly, a scowl replacing the smile that had initially put Camp Kenny at ease when he'd entered the office.

'Everything's cool innit eh … er innit?' replied Kenny, effeminately wrinkling his nose and pursing his lips in a manner that visibly angered Sniffler.

'No you silvery ponce. Everything is far from cool … innit you slag.'

'What's this all about? Tell him Holly, I aint done nuthin innit,' pleaded

Kenny, clasping his hands and pulling one of those 'I don't know what your talking about ... but really I do' faces.

'Enough of this bollocks,' snarled Sniffler, leaping out of his chair and lunging across the table, grabbing hold of Kenny by his vest with one hand, whilst flicking open the cut throat razor with his other. 'Right then Kenneth, lets see if this fine piece of Sheffield steel can loosen your tongue eh?' he continued, pulling Kenny close to him and placing the blade of the razor against his right cheekbone. 'How would you like it if I gave you a Deptford smile?'

Kenny quivered with fright, opening his eyes wide and wincing as he tried to come to terms with his predicament and the menacing threat to his features posed by the sharp cold steel wielded by Sniffler Barlow.

'Listen. I ... I'm s s s s s sorry,' he stammered, his voice trembling as he fought to hold back the tears. 'Look I ... I'll pay you back innit. Anything you want, but please d d d don't cut me.'

'It's not the money Kenny, it's the principle innit,' replied Holly sternly. 'Now a pretty boy like you should know better than to bite the hand that feeds, because sooner or later that hand's gonna slap you hard boy,' she continued, moderating the severity of her voice, feeling sexually charged by the exhilarating adrenalin rush that came with this unfamiliar territory.

'No please!' squealed Kenny, letting out a high-pitched blood-curdling scream as Sniffler drew the razor across his face, slicing through the soft flesh either side of his mouth with the fiendish precision of a deviant cosmetic surgeon.

Sniffler held Kenny at arms length whilst Holly stood transfixed, watching as his newly disfigured mouth foamed with blood which bubbled down his neck enveloping his assailants hand like a murderous crimson glove.

'That'll learn ya,' mocked Sniffler, releasing his grip and laughing as Kenny fell to the floor gurgling like a fishmongers drain. 'Let's see if we get our prop's now eh Holly.'

'Fuck me S,' she replied, raising her eyebrows. 'That was a bit over the top wannit, he's gonna need hospital treatment, and quick, otherwise he'll bleed to death.'

Both of them looked on as Kenny crawled into the far corner of the office whimpering like a newly born baby as he tugged at the loose flaps of skin that used to be his cheeks.

'Fack 'im, I'll get Riddler Rowan to drop 'im outside St.Thomas's, they get this sort of thing all the time dahn there, another faggot pill-head wiv 'is froat cut ... s'ardly gonna make News at Ten is it?'

Holly pondered the situation, picking up Sniffler's Marlboro's and nodding her head in agreement with the plan she was about to propose.

'Too dodgy. Kenny's got a big mouth … in fact he's got an even bigger mouth now thanks to you,' she said, smiling at Sniffler and pausing to light a cigarette. 'I reckon Claire's place might be a safer option than the hospital. I'll call her now and give her the SP. We're gonna need to talk this one through later otherwise before we know it we'll have his brothers on top as well as Old Bill to deal with.'

Holly wasn't overtly worried. Kenny knew he'd been out of order, and everyone that knew him knew that he'd been out of order. He was hardly likely to take out a full page advert in the Evening Standard explaining how and why he suddenly required plastic surgery on a Michael Jackson scale.

Of greater concern to her right now was the effect that his untimely disappearance would have on the way the club was run. The more she thought about it, the more Holly realised what a large part Kenny played in making her club the success it was. Okay so he'd over stepped the mark, maybe he thought he was untouchable, but a severe talking to would have been enough. Nipper would have handled it differently, fuck it! It wouldn't have happened if he'd been around. Holly's eyes narrowed at the thought, what a fucking mess.

'Sniffler,' said Holly sedately, the adrenalin rush which had replaced the coke high waning. 'Come round to the flat when you've finished up here. We need to sort a few things out, this bloody mess included, and decide how we run things from now on.'

'Yer cab's here Holly,' nodded Sniffler, pointing at the CCTVimages being beamed onto the bank of security monitors mounted on the far wall of the office. 'Go on home, I'll get hold of Claire and get things cleaned up, if you know what I mean.'

'Course you will mate. See you later,' replied Holly, ignoring Kenny's pitiful pleas for medical attention as she left the office.

What a nightmare, she thought. Everything she did was driven by the need to be in control. Everything that was happening now was beginning to make her realise just how little control she had.

★ ★ ★ ★ ★

'Deh deh deh deh, deh deh deh deh.' Ever since he could remember, Nipper would always hum the theme tune to the old 'Twilight Zone' TV programme whenever he crossed the Thames heading north.

'You are now entering the twilight zone,' he said in a fairly convincing pseudo American accent. Nipper wasn't too fond of the north side of the capital. Dodgy drinkers, dodgy clubs, dodgy boilers. Each to his own, it wasn't for him. With the exception of routine football related matters, Nipper stayed south, only venturing north to pay an occasional visit to Mordi.

Mordechai the 'chemist', a recreational pharmacist of proven ability, was in Nipper's eyes a legend, a real gem. A beautiful bright unflawed diamond that captured the light and sent it sparkling in all directions. The man was fucking invaluable.

Mordechai was a boy when, along with his parents, he'd escaped the clutches of the Nazis purge on the Yiddish communities of the Netherlands, finally winding up in Brick Lane where his Uncle Ruudi lived. His uncle, an unlicensed medical man, was an East End Legend who undertook back street abortions and provided pills, potions and various ancient Romany remedies for everything from clinical depression to gout.

Without a formal education young Mordi had busied himself with his uncle's trade, developing in particular a keen interest in synthesising stimulants which were otherwise available by two routes only. Prescription or theft. By the early '60s the dynamic duo were manufacturing and discreetly supplying half the London Mod brigade, Tommy Philips included, with their own brand of 'blues', 'purple hearts', 'bennies' and 'dexies'.

It hadn't taken long before their operation had been hijacked by one of London's leading crime families, the Hewitt's. For the next twelve years or so they'd plied their trade in the loft space above an old disused curtain factory in Liverpool Road, Islington.

With half the local plod rumoured to be on the Hewitt payroll, the 'factory' never came to anyone's attention. It was only when the Jamaican Yardies started to enforce a stranglehold on narcotic distribution in the capital that Mordechai and his ageing Uncle Ruudi's world had gone a little pear shaped.

In December 1974, Ceasar Hewitt and his two eldest sons Sam and Ian had travelled to Ladbroke Grove for a prearranged meeting with leading London gangsters Doogie Black, Balham Alan, Freddie 'fingers' Laidlaw and the McGonigle brothers. There had been talk for some time of unification, a white villains co-operative that would stand firm against the threat posed by the Yardies.

The principle was fine, but since when did villains have principles? This was the '70s, and the days of honour amongst thieves had ended with the clanging sound of prison cell doors when the Kray twins had been convicted.

Even now, nearly a quarter of a century later, Nipper remembered watching the story unfold on the TV news bulletins. In a nutshell, although the relevant connections were not made for several years after the incident, the McGonigles from Kilburn had done a back street deal with the Yardies.

It was Balham Alan who'd rumbled the connection and Doogie Black who'd fired the opening salvo of bullets in the shootout that followed. The excitement proved too much for Ruudi who called time on his career and retired, leaving Mordi to run the business. The shop was a common sense move, a front that had everyone fooled.

It was madness really, but all credit to Mordi for pulling it off, thought Nipper, grinning as he pulled up outside the Day & Night Pharmacy and reached for his mobile phone. That sort of shit just didn't happen these days, only in films.

Mordechai had been surprised by the somewhat early call, but he'd been in the game long enough to know that the illegal trafficking in drugs was not governed by the boundaries of day and night, hence the surreptitious name of the shop.

'Poxy fucking weather! For fucks sake Mordy, c'mon open the bleedin' door before I get pneu-fucking-monia,' chattered Nipper, who'd made his way around to the rear of the shop which occupied an end of terrace plot and was shuffling from one foot to the other as he sheltered from the still falling rain in the narrow porch.

'Thank fuck for that you old goat!' exclaimed Nipper, as the door was finally opened. 'I thought I was going to get swept away in the great flood. I know it's early but you 'avent got a couple of aspirin 'ave you? I've got this mingin' headache.'

'Seriously?'

'Seriously.'

'Okay. It's no problem,' replied Mordi, scurrying to the front of the shop and returning with a packet of Aspirin. 'So my boy,' he enquired, clasping his hands together and cocking his head to one side, 'what is it that you really need that brings you here at this hour, and on the Sabbath?'

With his dishevelled white hair sprouting freely from the back of a long since bald crown and his hands thrust into the pockets of the white lab coat he always wore, Nipper thought that Mordi looked just like the Doc Brown character in his favourite

film, Back to the Future

'Atropine Mordi.'

'Atropine?'

'Yes mate ... do you have it?'

'Of course ... er anything else?'

'Yeah. Can you cook up some crystal meth?'

Mordi licked his lips and handed Nipper a glass of tap water to wash the Aspirin down with, a look of concern etching itself into his wizened features as he contemplated what his visitor might be up to. He knew as well as anyone how the chemical landscape was changing. Ecstasy could be bought on the street for as little as 50p per pill, coke was down to £40 a gram, crack, smack and Ketamine were readily available at a keen price, all of which meant that dealers margins were being squeezed. A little invention could go a long way if you wanted to make the numbers work. That's if making the numbers work was your intention.

'Special er request?' inquired Mordi hesitantly, he knew Nipper was nobodies fool and would give little or nothing away, but he couldn't mask his curiosity.

'Listen old friend,' replied Nipper smiling. 'Let's say nothing for now, but maybe you and I could be looking at an unbeatable pension plan that's gonna mature very soon indeed.'

'Retire eh,' cackled Mordi, cracking the knuckles of each hand. 'A few extra shekels for your old friend Mordi … Mordi is a tired old man now, this game's not for Mordi anymore.'

★ ★ ★ ★ ★

'Well Jezebel, what sort of night have you had?' said Holly, pausing to stroke the cat that was sat contentedly on the sofa next to her. Jezebel looked up at Holly, stretching and rolling her tongue, sniffing at the air noxiously polluted by the fumes of the 'white widow' spliff which her owner was smoking.

Jezebel was a blue-eyed, seal lynx point Bengali cat, whose distinctively marked short haired coat owed much to its Asian Leopard Cat ancestry. A 40th birthday present from Nipper, Jezebel was the daughter Holly would never have. A flowing graceful creature with a soothing temperament, she was a comforting companion in times of need. Times which were all too frequent these days.

What an easy life eh? thought Holly. She didn't believe in reincarnation, but in an ideal world, if she ever did have to live her life over, she'd be returning as a pedigree cat.

'You see my beautiful Princess Jezebel, You see how I'm all alone now … see what I've gone and done.'

Jezebel purred, staring up at Holly, watching her numb her senses and deaden reality. 'You see babe, you see if six was nine it could have been oh so different.' Holly took one final drag from the spliff and extinguished it between her thumb and forefinger, wincing slightly as she crumbled the roach into the ashtray on the sofa next to her. 'C'mon girl, time for bed.'

Mazy stoned lethargy replaced hyperactivity as Holly picked the cat up and placed her on the floor, pushing herself to her feet and swaying giddily as inebriation threatened to ground her. Tottering through to the bedroom, she turned around to make sure that Jezebel was following, which of course she was.

Holly climbed into bed still fully clothed. Pulling the duvet close around her, she waited for the cat to join her, lying perfectly still, her mind drifting. Eyes welling up with tears, she could see Nipper's face morphing into her brother Pete's. She could feel the presence of her father and her mother, what would they think of her situation if they were alive today?

Holly felt her heartbeat pounding in her ears, it sounded like waves breaking on a distant shore. She thought about Claire tending to Kenny's horrific injuries, and about her soul mate Layla, a strong woman who always knew what to do.

Serenity regained. Holly's deep breathing calmed, regulating itself with Jezebel's soporific purring. Mercifully the peaceful shroud of sleep had enveloped her.

12

FROM RUSSIA WITH LOVE

'Lovely,' said Holly, almost gagging as she entered Hysteria through a rear security door. The tainted aroma of cigarette smoke and alcohol blended with disinfectant and suffused with stale sweat, wafted through Holly's coke ravaged nostrils. Lighting a Malboro to stop herself retching, she walked purposefully through the club checking that the cleaners had done their job properly the previous day, a day which Holly had slept straight through.

'Fackin ell, Hols wot kepcha?' said Sniffler irately, fidgeting with the rings on his fingers as he got up to greet Holly. 'I've bin waitin free arhs ... tryin yer mobile all morning. No one could get old of ya yesterday, we was all worried.'

'I needed to sleep,' replied Holly in an unruffled manner that startled Sniffler. 'You've dealt with everything for me haven't you,' she continued, nodding and pointing at the dried blood stains on floor.

'Course I have. The Muppet's over at Claire's, Riddler took him there just after you left.'

'Good. She's a real asset that girl.'

A nurse by profession, Claire Zhirkov had a part time job at a private hospital in Surrey which gave her access to the medical supplies required to keep her flat in the City operational as a field hospital. Over the last few years she had built up a very lucrative business stitching cuts, setting broken bones, and tending to the odd gunshot wound.

When the E craze had been at its peak, Holly had employed her specifically so she could be on hand to deal with the fallout as and when a clubber caned it just that little bit too hard. Discretion was important, and Claire never asked any questions. Word got around; certain inhabitants of

London's violent underworld now had their very own Florence Nightingale to call upon when needed.

'D'ya think I should've finished him off?' asked Sniffler, dropping the mockney gangster persona and frowning as he sat back in his chair.

'Do what?' replied Holly, trying to gauge if he was being serious or just downright stupid.

'Boss, you know what Kenny is like. He'll talk.'

'I doubt it, not after what you did to him.'

'Yeah well he had it coming to him. I'm just worried he'll grass me up to Old Bill.'

'He won't, you'll see. GBH is one thing, murder is another. Kenny's been a silly bastard who's tried to fuck us over and got more than he bargained for. In fact if you hadn't been pretending you were both of the Kray twins and stuck to giving him a few well earned slaps, you wouldn't be worrying about it coming on top for you.'

'Whadyya mean YOU?' barked Sniffler, taken aback by the alacrity of Holly's insinuation. 'You asked me to sort him out.'

'Listen MATE!' retorted Holly, scowling as she spat out her words. 'I said SORT him out, not turn his head into a fucking shish kebab! What's your fucking problem, you're not scared are you? Well are you? Where's your fucking bottle for Christs sake?'

'Yeah, yeah okay. In all fairness, I've been a cunt, but I aint lost me bottle.' Sniffler's reply was conciliatory and amusing. Well amusing to Holly anyway, who began to laugh as she hot-keyed 7 on her mobile phone.

'What's so funny?'

'Shhh let me speak to Claire.'

Sniffler sat in silence and smoked a cigarette whilst trying to second guess Claire's half of the conversation.

'Well?' he said expectantly, as Holly ended the call and pushed the phone into her jeans pocket.

'Well what?'

'What were you laughing at?'

'Oh nothing. Right come on lets go and pay Kenny a visit, we'll buy him a big bunch of flowers.'

'He's okay then?'

'Yeah. He won't be winning any beauty contests for a while though. It took over eighty stitches to repair the damage. By the way, are you holding?'

'You're joking aren't you?'

'No.'

'Nah, it's Monday morning innit.'

'Shame, a little live'ner would've been nice. Right then, let's go.'

★ ★ ★ ★ ★

Claire Zhirkov had done well for herself; a two-bedroom apartment in a renovated block just behind the Barbican represented a solid investment in anyone's book. Bought and paid for, the flat was immaculate and tastefully decorated, an oasis of understated chic and pared down sophistication that mirrored the minimalist style of its owner.

'Meadowsweet, lady's smock, lupins and hollyhocks. Very nice,' said Claire, smiling wistfully as she ushered Holly and a blushing Sniffler into her living room.

'They're for Kenny,' replied Sniffler, grimacing as he realised the inference of what he'd just said.

'Really. I didn't know you two were an item.'

'Yeah,' interjected Holly, 'they had a bit of a lovers tiff last night.'

'Very funny,' snapped Sniffler, clicking his heels together impatiently, clearly uncomfortable with the situation he found himself in.

'Come, come. It's just a joke,' chuckled Claire, tugging at the tortoise-shell and leather lariat hung around her slender neck. 'No funny stuff with Kenny please,' she continued, checking the time on her watch as she beckoned Holly and Sniffler back out into the hallway. 'I had to sedate him quite heavily yesterday. As you can imagine, it's the shock of what's happened rather than the injury which is causing him the biggest problem.'

'Two visitors for you my sweet,' said Claire, pushing open the door to the bedroom. Kenny, face swathed in padded bandages, was sat up in bed watching Neighbours on TV. His dark bloodshot eyes widened and he recoiled in fear as he saw Sniffler and Holly enter the room. 'I'll just take your temperature Kenny, and then I'll leave you three together.'

'Two,' said Holly firmly. 'Sniffler isn't staying,' she continued, turning to face Sniffler and rocking her head back authoritatively. 'You can put the flowers down over there, I'll call you later.'

Sniffler looked blankly at Holly and then at the floor. There was no point in arguing, because there was nothing to argue about. As he left the room, he resisted the urge to put his index finger over his lips and then draw it across his throat, cut-throat style. Holly was right, Kenny would never say anything, and even if he did, who would believe him? She'd been the only witness, and she was hardly likely to grass him up.

'My my,' said Holly, waiting until Claire and Sniffler had left the room before speaking to Kenny. 'You were lucky the other night.'

Kenny furrowed his eyebrows and pointed at his mouth before picking up the notepad and pen that were on the bedside table. He hesitated momentarily before scrawling down some words and handing the notepad to Holly who was now sat on the edge of the bed fidgeting with her diamond ear studs.

IS HE GOING TO KILL ME? PLEASE HOLLY I'M SORRY

'Of course he isn't,' said Holly calmly, smiling as she read what Kenny had written. 'If I'd wanted him to do that, he would've done it the other night, you know that. As for your apology, I accept it. This matter is finished with now as far as I'm concerned.'

Holly handed the notepad back to Kenny. She felt no pity for him. Pity was a sign of weakness, and she knew she had enough private flaws already. The untreated emotional disorders and low self esteem that went with them could render her powerless if they were ever exposed. And as for the coke, well everyone had a coke habit. Personal problems were best swept under the carpet, and pity was for wimps. Wimps like liberty taking Kenny, with his new Joker smile, a perfect reminder for him each time he looked in a mirror that no one double crossed Holly Philips and got away with it.

THANKS I WONT SAY NOTHING TO ANYONE

'I know you won't,' said Holly, watching what Kenny was writing and speaking before he'd finished. 'You got mugged, that's what I heard.'

MUGGED

'Yeah, mugged. The word on the street is that it was some lads that you'd refused entry to the club to the other week. Anyway,' she continued, reaching into her leather Betty Jackson bag, 'this should sweeten things up for you.'

Kenny opened the brown envelope that Holly handed to him and peered inside.

THANKS

'All done then. I'll let you get back to the goings on in Ramsay Street,' she said, leaning over to give Kenny a matronly kiss on the forehead. 'I'd go and stay with your mum if I were you. You'll get plenty of tea and sympathy there. Get yourself sorted out and ring me when, and if, you feel like coming back to work. I'll review the situation then.'

★ ★ ★ ★ ★

'Call on me, call on me. Call on me, call on me. I'm the same boy I used to be.'

'Blinding tune eh Eggy,' said Nipper, cranking up the Range Rover's stereo. 'Have you seen the video? Proper crumpet. Makes you wanna join a gym.'

'Yes mate,' replied Eggy Barnes, tapping his fingers and shaking his head in time with the beat. 'It's that old Stevie Winwood track 'Valerie' innit. He heard the bootleg floating around the clubs in Ibiza in the summer and rerecorded the vocal for that Eric Prydz geezer.'

'Call on me, call on me. Call on me, call on me. I'm the same boy I used to be.'

'It's a bit repetitive innit,' said Nipper, mirroring Eggy's moves, both of them resembling the Flat Eric puppet in the old Levi TV commercial.

'You're getting old mate.'

'Yeah ha ha. Maybe.'

'Look at those cheeky cunts in that minibus,' observed Eggy, pointing at a group of mischievous looking school kids who had been trying to attract their attention, and having done so, were now giving them the middle finger. 'Imagine being that age again ... quality.'

Nipper turned down the volume as he turned off a busy Fulham Palace Road into Queensmill Road, and the labyrinth of streets and traditional terraced houses surrounding Craven Cottage, the home of Fulham FC.

'Only one F in Fulham eh Eggy,' said Nipper, reverse parking the Range Rover into a residents only bay.

'Effing more like,' replied Eggy Barnes, looking up and down Stevenage Road to see if there were any traffic wardens patrolling the area.

'I tell you what mate,' said Nipper, cutting the ignition and reaching for his cigarettes. 'I remember coming down here in the late '70s and early '80s, it was well different then ... friendly like. Real people. No one had a bad word to say about Fulham, but It's all those trashy media types now ... moving in and pushing up the prices ... look at the motors.'

Both men laughed as Eggy pointed out two more Range Rover's parked further down the street. As they climbed out of the car Nipper remembered that he needed to make a couple of calls before they got to the airport later that afternoon. Watching the Blues in Moscow was going to be a craic, but business was business, he couldn't afford to keep people like Geezer Goodwin and Del Goss hanging around, not with all the ingredients he had in the mix right now.

★ ★ ★ ★ ★

'Nipper, Eggy ... hello boys come in. Can I get you a drink? Tea, coffee, something a little stronger perhaps? Come in, come in.' Davy

Truelove's inimitable nervous tick greeting and scattergun speech was a fabled advertisement warning against the perils of drugs. 'Ere you aint been followed have ya?' he said, peering slowly up and down the road before closing the door and following them into the kitchen.

Davy Truelove, along with Mordi, was Nipper's main source for Class A drugs. Since their first meeting at Es Parral, the two had struck up a firm business based friendship which had developed over the years. Unfortunately Davy's hedonistic Ibiza lifestyle had finally caught up with him on the eve of the Millennium when he'd suffered a minor stroke which had prevented him from working for a while, but Nipper had remained loyal. That was why he got the cream of the coca leaf crop. Despite his disability, Davy still had a portfolio of celebrity clients who liked his personal, if slightly eccentric touch. Mr Sheen, Davy Truelove's nom-de-plume on the party circuit, was still very much in demand.

'Nipper dear boy,' said Davy, twitching his nose like a rabbit. 'I hear there was some bother at Hysteria the other night. They say Holly's struggling to keep that tosser Sniffler on a lead.'

'Really,' replied Nipper wryly. 'What've you heard then you old gossip? You know you're getting as bad as Camp Kenny.'

'Funny you should mention him,' said Davy, picking up a cloth and wiping down the granite surface he had just been leaning against.

'Well come on then,' interjected Eggy impatiently. 'Let's have it.'

'Camp Kenny won't be gossiping to anyone for a while. Apparently he'd been doing a bit of private work using the firms tools if you know what I mean. Sniffler cut him across the face from ear to ear poor fucker.' Davy grimaced as he spoke, avoiding eye contact with both Nipper and Eggy, who were looking at each other and shaking their heads. 'Right lads, have a pew, I'll be back with you in a minute.'

A smile replaced the frown on Nipper's face as he watched Davy scuttle out of the kitchen and into the hall. 'Same routine every time innit I dunno what he does up there. Powdering his nose probably ... cos the work's always ready and waiting in the microwave over there.'

'I know,' replied Eggy, looking at the opaque glass front of the immaculately clean microwave oven that was fitted into the limed oak cupboard by the pristine white enamel butler sink. 'Did you know about Camp Kenny?'

'Yes mate.'

'You never said anything.'

'I know mate, what was there to say?'

'Yeah but Kenny doesn't deserve that.'

'It aint my business anymore.'

'Sniffler needs teaching a lesson.'

'Holly too.'

'I never said that.'

'You didn't have to, but she does. It'll all even itself out though, you'll see.'

The discourse, which left Eggy wondering how much his supposed best mate shared with him about his business dealings, was curtailed by the sound of Davy Truelove clip clopping back down the stairs.

'Oi Davy,' said Nipper changing the subject completely. 'How comes they call you Mr Sheen these days?'

'Well,' replied Davy, opening the microwave oven door and extricating a large Tupperware container. 'The funny thing is that everyone thinks it's because I've been diagnosed as having OCD, y'know obsessive compulsive disorder. That's bollocks, I just can't stand a mess. Clean as you go, that's my motto.'

'So what is it then?' enquired Nipper, reaching into the flap pocket of the heavy duty Stone Island duffle coat he was wearing.

'It was that Dennis Pennis cunt off the telly,' replied Davy, narrowing his eyes and grinning as he watched Nipper place four wads of £50 notes on the table.

'Who?' asked Eggy, splitting the seal on the Tupperware container and dabbing the index finger of his right hand gently onto the surface of the snow white powder.

'He was that knob jockey who used to make out he was an interviewer for the BBC, always haranguing celebrities at the Oscars and the like,' replied Nipper, waiting expectantly for Eggy to deliver his verdict on the purity of the coke as he watched him rub his flake covered finger across his gums.

'That's right Nipper,' said Davy nodding at Eggy and winking. 'Denis Pennis, the character created by Paul Kaye ... fucking funny he was. Gifted ... did you see that one where he collars Charlie Sheen's dad Martin at the Oscars?'

'Yes mate,' replied Nipper, rubbing his hands together as Eggy gave a big thumbs up to the Percy.

'Mr Sheen, Mr Sheen. Do you think you're gonna clean up at this year's Oscars?' continued Davy, 'best ever.'

'Mr fucking Sheen ... sparkle right, ha ha,' said Eggy, resealing the container and handing it Nipper.

'Yeah, very good Davy,' added Nipper. 'Right come on son, we've got to get a move on. We've got a plane to catch later.'

'Moscow?' enquired Davy, walking down the hall and slowly opening the front door.

'You know that,' replied Nipper, tucking the Tupperware container inside his coat and leaving the top three toggles unbuttoned.

'Enjoy,' said Davy, shaking both men's hands before they left the house.

'We intend to,' replied Nipper, patting Davy on the shoulder before turning to follow Eggy out onto the street. 'Don't you worry about that.'

Nipper smiled as he walked across the road. Its all coming along nicely, he thought to himself. The famous master plan. Difficult to keep to himself, but he'd managed it so far. That was the only trouble with the nose Nike, it loosened your tongue, made you over confident. You could never be too careful in this racket.

His plan had originally involved Holly, fuck her now though, she had her own agenda. She'd soon find out her limitations, and the limitations of the others around her. Sniffler, he was as useful as a dog without teeth. His dad? Yeah, Beery Barlow was still a player, but he wasn't on the money anymore. There were new people entering the game, people like Geezer Goodwin and Del Goss. Professionals who had aspirations that matched his own. It was all a matter of timing. Timing and patience.

★ ★ ★ ★ ★

'Would you like a cup of tea?' asked Claire, as Holly emerged from Kenny's temporary bedroom looking slightly drained. 'You look like you could use one.'

'Why not,' replied Holly, pushing her fringe back off her forehead and smiling. 'I need to get a cab over to Fulham a bit later, but yeah that'd be nice. Things are a bit stressful at the moment.'

'I can imagine,' said Claire, walking through to the kitchen.

Holly followed. Claire had such an elegant manner. Dressed in the girly youth uniform of low cut Miss Selfridge jeans and a pastel blue camisole top, she looked as succulent as a peach with her vanilla white skin and tawny blonde hair.

In her own mind, Holly could only aspire to Claire's health and beauty. If only she could swap self obsession for self fulfilment and quit the bleaching lifestyle that she led. But how? She was in it right up to her neck. Agitated thoughts that only led to one thing. The desire to have a live'ner. A cup of tea? Just supposing if everything was that simple. A nice cup of tea, just like her mother used to make. Fuck it.

'I've been really worried about you since the split with Nipper,' said Claire, snapping Holly out of her moody daydream. 'I know it's not my business but I thought you two were set up for life.'

'That's okay,' sighed Holly. 'Things changed, I've known Nipper most of my life. Believe it or not, he's the only bloke I've ever been involved with. I'm not the same person I used to be, shit happened that made me look at life in a different way, a way that he could never understand.'

Claire nodded, but said nothing. Holly didn't mind, what could she say? Layla was the only person who knew the real Holly, and the reasons she was the way she was.

'Have you got family Claire?' asked Holly, hoisting herself up to sit on the marble work surface.

'Yeah, sort of,' replied Claire, pausing for a moment before continuing. 'I never knew my mother, she died when I was young. My father's Russian, he was a lecturer at UCL but he's retired now and lives in Moscow, which is where I worked as a nurse for a couple of years.

Holly sat in silence, idly knocking her knees together, turning her elbows in and out in unison just like she used to do at her mothers house when she was a child. Curling her toes inside her shoes whilst chewing at the inside of her left cheek, she pondered the coincidence. So Claire had lost her mother too, interesting.

'Sit down in the lounge and make yourself comfortable,' said Claire, distracting Holly from her thoughts.

'Good idea,' replied Holly, springing off the counter onto the floor. 'Do you mind if I put my feet up?'

'You can do just as you please my dear Holly.'

'Really?'

'Really.'

★ ★ ★ ★ ★

Nipper shrugged his shoulders, winking at Eggy Barnes as he placed the coke filled Tupperware container onto the laminate riser shelf of stainless steel workstation in the centre of Mordi's immaculately clean make shift laboratory.

'Nice piece of work,' he said, rubbing his hands and resisting the urge to sample the merchandise. 'How much do you reckon old Mr Sheen steps on the gear?'

'It's gotta be 20% I reckon,' replied Eggy, flickering his eyes as he did the mental arithmetic. 'We gave 15 bags for the kilo which aint bad. Sheeny must be making himself 3 large on the deal just for skimming in some Lactose powder.'

'Mad when you think that some poor Bolivian peasant is cultivating, harvesting, and selling the coca leaves for a coupla quid a kilo.'

'How pure d'ya reckon this stuff is then?'

'60% ish, Mordi can tell us. It's a simple test with some sort of reagent, like the litmus paper test only with a liquid. The darker the liquid goes, the purer the gear. You know yourself though, you cant beat the taste test.

'Drop it down by another 50% then?'

'Yep. Sniffler will be getting 30% pure Percy for Holly's punters, and we make 15 lovely bags of sand on the deal.'

'What's it gonna be cut with, Mannite?'

'Nah, much as I'd like to hear that Holly's shit herself after yet another nose full, I've asked Mordi to spice it up a bit.'

'And like the Murphy's.'

'You what?'

'You aint bitter.'

'Fuck off Eggy, you're meant to be on my side you cunt. Now do us a favour, go and get the old goat I'll swear he's Mutt and Jeff. I bet he's havin' a beau peep.'

'I'm here my friends, I'm here,' croaked Mordi, breaking the tetchy atmosphere as he limped into the room carrying a bucket sized bright blue thermoplastic container.

'You've got the Atropine then old man?' asked Nipper, watching as Mordi placed the container on the riser shelf next to the cocaine.

'Atropine?' enquired Eggy, 'What the fuck is that?'

'Heady stuff,' replied Mordi, reaching into his pocket for his handkerchief and blowing his runny nose. 'They say it was used in witches brews in the dark ages, they used to rub it on their pulse points and genitalia … claimed it made them fly. My Uncle Ruudi cut it into the first Ecstasy pills he made, not much … just enough to augment the MDMA. Remember those Red Playboy pills? They were cut with Atropine. This is synthetic Atropine,' he continued, opening the container and tipping an even measure of the off white powder into the homogeniser on the workbench. 'It's used in eye surgery to dilate the pupils, as an Opium antidote and an anti inflammatory. You can treat asthma and whooping cough with it, and they use it to revive people who have had a heart attack. More recently it has been used to counteract the effects of Iraqi nerve gas attacks during the Gulf War.'

'Thanks for the lecture Prof,' said Eggy, standing up to applaud Mordi. 'But what's the point of cutting it with the sparkle? Why can't we use Lactose? It's gotta be cheaper.'

Nipper frowned as he reached for his Marlboro's. 'Listen mate … the point is that with the right mix of Atropine in it, this gear will have the punters right at it. They'll not be able to get enough, Sniffler will be back for more … and we, my sunny son, will make another tidy profit.'

'Those Red Playboy E's were well moody,' replied Eggy, handing Nipper his lighter.

Nipper sparked up, taking a deep drag and exhaling smoke as he spoke, 'Life's moody mate,' he said philosophically. 'Right then Mordy, you crack on. We'll be back for this in a couple of days when we return from Moscow. Oh and don't forget the other stuff.'

'Yes, yes,' replied Mordi, arching his bushy eyebrows in a manner that suggested he was suspicious of Nipper's intentions with the concoction he'd been asked to prepare. 'It will all be ready for you when you get back. You boys lets yourselves out now ... oh and enjoy the game heh heh.'

'What other stuff?' asked Eggy Barnes, as they descended the stairs.

'I'll tell you later mate,' replied Nipper, shaking his head and grinning.

★ ★ ★ ★ ★

'How does that feel?' asked Claire, hamming up a Russian accent as she stood behind the sofa Holly was sitting in and gently massaged her scalp.

'Great,' replied Holly, rocking her head back slightly. 'Where did you learn to do that?'

'Club Maximus,' answered Claire, gently kneading the knots of muscle in Holly's lower neck.

'Club Maximus, what's that? A health club?' Holly raised her right arm and put Claire's hand on hers.

'No. It's an erotic club in Moscow,' replied Claire, drawing her fingers gently across the palm of Holly's hand.

'Erotic!'

'I had to make a living while I was studying to be a nurse,' explained Claire, dropping the accent as she walked around the sofa and sat herself down snugly next to Holly. 'Some dancing, some massage, a little fucking ... you know that sort of thing.'

'I'm shocked,' said Holly, body tensing slightly as Claire leant forward and kissed her fully on the lips.

'Don't be,' replied Claire, pulling away and smiling at Holly who was blushing like an embarrassed schoolgirl. 'It probably explains why I prefer the company of women though ha ha,' she continued, the Russian accent returning as she pulled Holly on top of her and they began to kiss with ardent fervour.

'Shit! What about Kenny?' giggled Holly, thoughts of cocaine banished as a new high permeated her senses.

'My bedroom, come on,' whispered Claire, her porcelain face flushed with anticipation as she stood up, pulled Holly to her feet, and led her to her bedroom.

'I didn't ...'

'Shhh,' shushed Claire, 'try and keep quiet, it's more exciting,' she giggled, closing the bedroom door and pushing Holly onto the sumptuous duck-down quilt that was draped regally across her queen sized bed.

'I've never ...'

'Shhh ... get undressed.'

★ ★ ★ ★ ★

'Last call for passengers Barnes and Nipper travelling to Moscow,' boomed the tannoy, as Fatboy Green, Riddler Rowan and Chiller shook their heads and made their way through the departure gate.

'C'mon that's us!' shouted Eggy breathlessly, as he sprinted along the corridor trying to keep up with Nipper who was already several metres ahead of him.

'We'll be all right,' replied Nipper, puffing with the exertion and wishing that he didn't still abuse his body in the way he did.

'Gate 17 ... just up here Nipper.'

'Thank fuck for that, my lungs are gonna pack up.'

'Mr Barnes and Mr Nipper, I presume,' said the check-in steward in a camply officious manner, as the two men came bowling through the door just as the 'gate now closed' sign was about to be displayed.

'Yes darling,' replied Nipper, pausing to draw breath as he reached into his pocket for his passport and boarding pass. 'That's us.'

13

FEAR ROBBEN

'Are you awake yet?'

The sound of Claire's dulcet tones above the shrill whistle of a kettle boiling woke Holly from a hazy post alarm clock snooze.

'Mmm. Just about honey. I was drifting a little,' came the muffled reply as she poked her head out from under the comforting confines of the duvet.

'You want some breakfast?'

'Just coffee,' replied Holly sitting upright in the bed and drawing her knees up to her chest.

'Aren't I the lucky one,' she sighed huskily, as Claire glided into the bedroom carrying a large tray on which was arranged a variety of fresh fruit, a glass of orange juice, and a steaming hot mug of coffee.

'Maybe,' replied Claire, placing the tray down on the bedside table and sitting up on the bed next to Holly.

'Do all your girlfriends get this treatment?' enquired Holly, reaching for the coffee cup and thinking about her first cigarette of the day.

'You don't need one.'

'What?'

'A fag.'

'Witch.'

'Ha ha,' laughed Claire, sitting up on her haunches before turning and crawling felinely across the bed. 'D'ya wanna have a shower with me Miss Philips?'

'No. Really I'd love to, but I need to get going,' replied Holly, conscious of the time and suddenly remembering her missed appointment with her nose doctor Mr Sheen.

'I see. Love me and leave me. Just like a bloke then eh Miss Philips.'

'Yeah maybe. Oh and less of the Miss Philips. No one's called me that since the old punk days.'

'Punk?'

'Yeah … I'm old.'

'Didn't wanna say anything ha ha.'

'Bitch!'

'You know that. Ha ha.'

'Don't say that. It's my line,' trilled Holly, thinking about what Claire had just said as she got up and got dressed. Age, that was nothing but a number. The ism's, mmm, well that was her and Nipper. 'Bastard love of mine!'

'What?'

'No not you.'

'Nipper?'

'Yeah, whatever,' groaned Holly, glimpsing her reflection in the cheval mirror at the far end of the bedroom. 'How's Kenny this morning?' she continued, not caring too much about the reply.

'He's fine. Having his breakfast through a straw. I told him you stayed over and that I had my wicked way with you.'

Holly wasn't listening, her mind was elsewhere. Fulham to be precise. Mr Sheen. Sometimes she felt that she carried her emotions precariously close to the surface, people like Claire could probably see right through her. But the other side of life, now that was different. The expression 'own worst enemy' could have been conceived at her christening she thought as she pulled on her Christian Dior leather and shearling boots, the last present Nipper had bought her before they'd split up.

One last time, she could sort it all out now. The girl thing was just an experiment, Nipper was the man. He'd come back, she could get him back with a click of her fingers. Of course he'd understand, she'd tell him everything. Everything! She'd explain how she'd had to go to the dark place to understand why her behavioural addictions existed, and now that she fully understood, she could begin the process of recovery. One last time though, eh Holly. Ride the train, one last time.

★ ★ ★ ★ ★

'Fuck the tourist bit,' said Eggy, beckoning the waitress over to the table and ordering five more beers before slouching back into the leather sofa he was sat on and turning his attention to the mezzanine floor of the hotel. 'It's too cold out there, and besides I like the view from here.'

'Philistine,' replied Fatboy Green, grabbing a fistful of Japanese rice crackers from the bowl on the low slung mahogany table in front of him and cramming them into his mouth.

'Phili what?' asked Riddler Rowan, partially distracted by the sight of another poised, sculpted, incredibly thin, baby faced young woman walking across the lobby to the centrally located, glass encased elevators. 'Listen to Fatboy here, with his posh ham sandwich,' he continued, rubbing his rheumy eyes as he followed the girls passage.

'It means hostile to culture, you thick pleb.'

'Hostile?'

'Pillock!'

'Girls, girls, calm down,' interjected Nipper, diffusing the situation before it got out of hand. 'Listen we've all had a few sherbets, lets not get ourselves thrown out of the hotel just because Fatboy Green here has decided to develop his use of the English language.

'Nice one,' said Chiller languidly. 'There's too much up-skirt action to be had sitting here.'

'I'm with Chiller,' agreed Eggy, shaking his head as another stone faced beauty made her way through the large revolving hotel doors. 'I know we're only a few minutes walk from the Kremlin, Red Square and the Bolshoi Theatre but this is far more interesting. Whaddya reckon is going on?'

'They're brasses,' replied Eggy.

'How do you know?'

'I asked one of em when we got here last night.'

'What's the going rate.'

'300 US dollars for fifteen minutes.'

'A carpet for a quarter, yer avin a bubble,' said Riddler, reaching into his back pocket for his wallet.

'Put yer dough away Riddler, he aint havin a laugh.' whispered Nipper. 'It's room service only.'

'How do you know?'

'I had one this morning ha ha.'

★ ★ ★ ★ ★

'There!' exclaimed Holly exultantly, completing her coiffure and scrutinising her appearance in the mirror on her dressing table. 'Look at me ... ha ha! Living proof that any woman can return from over the hill and bask once more in the sunlit valley of her youth without resorting to cosmetic surgery.'

Self doubt followed by self-congratulation, sanity defined mainly by its absence. Honestly, thought Holly to herself, what a joke. Looking good and feeling good, she slid her favourite Louis Vuitton jewelled hair comb into place. A necklace, yeah. Big beads are out, long strings of pearls are in. Diamond earrings as big as fairy cakes, come on girl make a statement.

'Holly's back!'

As she placed the pearl necklace around her neck, Holly paused to admire the craftsmanship of the Chanel logo that was fashioned out of silver and attached to the string of pearls in the same way a cross is attached to rosary beads.

The text message alert on her Nokia distracted Holly from her rediscovered narcissism.

MR SHEEN AWAITS YOUR CALL

'Good skill Mr Sheen,' she purred, clicking her tongue against the roof of her mouth and clenching her newly clammy right hand into a fist as she pushed hotkey 5 with the thumb of her left hand which was clutching the mobile.

'Well hello Holly Philips, I've been expecting you,' said Davy Truelove, his voice sounding syrupy and seductive.

'Mr Sheen, have you got something for me?'

'Something for the nose my dear?'

'Yes of course, something for the nose.'

'Bit of a cold then.'

'You could say.'

'There's a lot of it about.'

'Definitely.'

'I have your prescription here. It's for a Henry, that should help.'

'Love you Davy, I'll call a taxi right away.'

'Love you too Holly, see you soon.'

★ ★ ★ ★ ★

'He's got a few roubles tied up in this lot aint he,' said Eggy, clapping his gloved hands together as the players took to the pitch. 'Come on the Chels!'

'Yeah,' replied Nipper, scanning the stand they were sat in, looking for familiar faces. 'Sibneft, the oil company he owns sponsor the club, but Roman aint allowed to have any ownership interest, it's against UEFA rules. Come on JT lead by example my son, lead by example.'

'D'ya reckon a deals been done?'

'Nah. We've got the beating of this lot.'

'Ha … I meant the other way.

'Nah … look,' said Nipper, pointing at the central section of the stand directly behind them. 'There's Boris Yeltsin.'

'Yeah and look who's sat just behind him,' replied Eggy, getting to his feet and waving.

'Who?'

'Duncan Disorderly, Fuck Off Colin, Big Chris, Lemon and Young Dave!'

'Fuck me, you're right!' exclaimed Nipper, standing up, whistling and giving the okay sign with his raised right hand, 'and look, there's Riddler, Chiller and Fatboy.'

'Siddahn,' brayed the Chelsea fans sat immediately behind Nipper and Eggy.

'Amazing innit,' said Nipper, nodding at the irate supporters before taking his seat, 'Chelsea in Europe, all the old faces, fucking brilliant … Go on Robben my son!'

Everyone in the Chelsea section got to their feet, collective breaths held as Eidur Gudjohnsen nodded the ball into his path.

'Give and go!' shouted Eggy, as the Holland international laid the ball off to Damien Duff on the edge of the CSKA penalty area and ran inside him.

'One two … go on Duffer!' Nipper could barely contain his excitement as Duff back heeled the ball into the path of Robben.

'GOAL!' screamed the ecstatic travelling support, as Robben rode a desperate tackle and side footed the ball with deft arrogance past the home sides bemused goalkeeper.

'*Arjen Robben, Damien Duff, Arjen Robben, Damien Duff,*' chanted the Chelsea fans to the tune of the Piranha's ska classic Tom Harks.

The supporters of Moscow's central sports club found their voices, and the home side raised its tempo forcing corner after corner. Just before half time, impressively named Brazilian striker Vagner Love had a searing shot saved by the agile brilliance of Chelsea keeper Cech. It took the Blues fans breaths away … but not for long.

'*We are the famous, the famous Chelsea.*'

'Fuck me, it's cold!' chattered Eggy, as the referee blew for half time and the players jogged off the pitch.

★ ★ ★ ★ ★

Holly sat in the taxi, pushing herself into the seat and hunching her shoulders. Her mind steeped in contradictions and insecurities, she pondered the past and contemplated the future, turning her thumbs into her hands and clenching them tight with her fingers before releasing them. Nervy anticipation on the road to Mr Sheen's.

Outside the rain was falling, a misty rain blowing into the faces of those people hardy enough to walk the streets. Ordinary people with ordinary lives. Mothers, fathers, children, everyone of them with a future, everyone of them with a past.

Despite the inclemency of the weather and the hustle in their step, the expressions of the people on the pavement seem strangely serene. No trace of anxiety, just acceptance of their own personal situations, whatever they may be. Holly's mind was strangely drawn to the memory of seeing her mother on her deathbed. Peaceful, composed, mortal agonies cast off. Gone now. Mother, why couldn't I have been more like you? she thought to herself, biting her bottom lip hard to stem the flow of tears forming in her eyes.

'Are you all right Miss?' enquired the cab driver, catching sight of Holly in his rear view mirror.

'Yes mate. I was miles away,' she replied, rubbing the bridge of her nose, welcoming the thought arresting idle banter. 'Blimey the roads are busy today,' she continued, looking at her watch as the taxi progressed slowly through the heavy traffic.

'Half term innit treacle, that and the rain.'

'Tell you what, just drop me up here by the Shell garage, I can walk the rest of the way.'

'You sure? You aint got a brolly, you'll get soaked.'

'I'll be fine, I need to get some fags anyway.'

As Holly got out of the cab she cursed herself for never having bothered to learn to drive. Wondering what car she would own if she could, she buttoned and belted the Burberry Prorsum wool trench coat she was wearing, pulled up the collar and walked the short distance to the petrol station.

Lit Marlboro Light in mouth, Holly felt reinvigorated as she sauntered down Fulham Palace Road in her knee high Bottega Veneta velvet boots which matched the purple hue of her coat. Miraculously the rain abated. Respect for her one woman fashion parade maybe she thought, acknowledging with a wink the admiring glances of a passing motorist who tooted his horn in appreciation.

'One last time,' she said to herself, as she had done the last few times she'd made this journey. Mentally, Holly never saw Mr Sheen again. Physically, here she was on his door step about to ring his bell. The relationship between dealer and addict exemplified.

'Holly darling!' gushed Davy Truelove, proffering his puckered lips like a camp 'end of pier' comic. 'How are you? Do come in.'

'Fine Davy,' replied Holly, as she embraced him. 'Oh and before you ask ... I wasn't followed.'

'Oh Miss Philips ... You do steal all my best lines,' he said, standing on tiptoes and peering over Holly's shoulder. 'Okay, ha ha. Now go on through and sit yourself down in the lounge.'

There it was again. 'Miss Philips', thought Holly, as she made herself comfortable on one of the expensive looking leather sofas in Davy Truelove's Conran inspired living room.

'You look divine my dear.'

'Why thank you Mr Truelove, or should I call you Mr Sheen?'

'Call me Mr Sheen if you must. Your ex finds it highly entertaining.'

'Have you seen him recently then?'

'He was here yesterday ... er with that Eggy Barnes character.'

'No doubt to sort Sniffler out.'

'No doubt. I'm sorry but I won't have that lout in here. You don't have a problem with that do you?'

Holly paused before answering. Davy Truelove may have thought she was mulling over his question, but she was in fact thinking about Nipper, and how she was beginning to really miss him.

'No problem. How is he?'

'Cold I expect,' replied Davy, reaching into his jacket pocket and producing a white envelope which had been folded in half and sealed with tape.

'Cold?'

'He's in Moscow for the Chelsea game.'

'Ah Chelsea, I should've known,' said Holly, clicking her tongue and smiling as she shook her head.

'Did you really finish with him over the football?' asked Davy, handing the envelope to Holly.

'There was a little bit more too it than that mate,' she replied, squeezing the envelope gently. 'What else is in here?'

Davy Truelove raised his hand miming the act of smoking a joint. 'A nice bit of jazz funk to chill you out, a friend of mine grows it in his loft.'

'Your friend should be careful about growing skunk in his loft. Old Bill use thermal imaging equipment these days.'

'My friend is Old Bill.'

'I should've known ha ha.'

Holly loved Davy Truelove. He was a real character whose quaint idiosyncrasies only added to his charm. She often wondered how he could live his life the way he did, but then he probably thought the same about a lot of his customers including her. He was the link to the people she was out of step with, people like Nipper, and that was why he was so hard to let go, it had nothing to do with the drugs really.

'Penny for em.'

'Ha! I was just thinking that I don't really come around here to buy drugs, just to catch up on the gossip.'

'That's what they all say honey.'

'Well I'd love to stay and chat longer,' she said, getting to her feet and putting the envelope in her pocket. 'Can we sort out the paperwork?'

'£120 to you doll face ... with your staff discount.'

Holly handed Davy Truelove six crisp new £20 notes. 'You've been talking to Nipper haven't you,' she said, smiling at the familial term of endearment.

'You what darling?'

'Nothing,' said Holly, frowning as she was distracted by the sound of rain hammering against the windows.

'Shall I call you a mini-cab?' offered Davy, looking slightly puzzled.

'If you have a brolly you can lend me, that'll do. I'll walk to the main road and get a black cab, I don't do run-of-the-mill gutter ponces.'

Silly cow, thought Davy, nodding as he walked into the hall and returned with a a plain black golf umbrella.

'This do?'

'Quality Mr Sheen ... I'll bring it back later this week.'

'Course you will my dear, now mind how you go.'

Davy waited at the doorstep until Holly had reached the corner of Inglethorpe Street before waving at her as she simultaneously turned to do the same.

'Fucking hell!' cursed Holly, as she fought to keep control of the umbrella which was being wrestled from her grip by a gusty wind which at times felt strong enough to lift her off her feet. 'There's never a black cab when you need one,' she muttered, shaking her head as she walked back up Fulham Palace Road, past the Shell garage, and past the hostelry that had once been called the Greyhound.

The Fulham Greyhound, now that was some drinker, she thought to herself, suddenly overcome by a potent shot of nostalgia. Watching the Count Bishops at the Greyhound with Nipper, Pete and Fatboy Green, those were the days. What was that song of theirs? 'Train Train', that was it. Holly smiled, wondering if she would still think the tune was garbage if she heard it again now, reminiscences instantly ended as she finally managed to hail a black cab.

'Elm Quay Court on Nine Elms Lane please,' said Holly, grateful that the cabbie had stepped out of his taxi to open the door for her. She was getting keen now, the excitement of her impending coke binge was gnawing at her senses, the devil inside awaking from his slumbers.

The cabbie made light work of the traffic, expertly weaving between cars and buses, cursing and gesticulating his way down Dawes Road, along the Fulham Road, into Edith Grove, and along Cheyne Walk and the Chelsea Embankment.

I still don't get it, thought Holly, gazing at Battersea Power Station's imposing chimneys as they crossed the Thames at Chelsea Bridge and filtered left along Queenstown Road, past the old gasworks and the dogs home on Battersea Park Road. It was a famous London landmark right enough, but Holly could never understood Nipper's fascination with the building, which in her eyes was a time warp monstrosity that should have been demolished years ago.

Nipper had the notion of turning it into a superclub to rival Amnesia, but it was just a fanciful idea. The cost of the project would be punitive, and besides the really big clubs in London were struggling to pull in the punters, the dance scene wasn't what it was. Having said that, new investors had rustled money in their direction on more than one occasion over the last couple of years.

Omnipotent London powerbroker, Geezer Goodwin, had courted them about running the newly refurbished Adrenalin Village club which was in the shadow of Battersea Power Station on the other side of the railway arches. He'd insisted on renaming it Mr Terry's, which had been too cheesy for her to contemplate, although at the time of splitting with Nipper, she'd been certain that there'd been more discussions that she hadn't been a party to. Despite its name, the club had opened to rave reviews. It was a place that Holly felt she should've checked out. With Nipper, they'd always done that sort of thing together, with Nipper she'd always done a lot of things. Ahh Nipper.

★ ★ ★ ★ ★

'What time is it back home?' asked Eggy, looking at his watch and winking at the burly looking security guard whose impassive glare could have frozen the River Volga.

'They're three hours behind mate,' replied Nipper, pausing to applaud as the Chelsea players emerged from the tunnel in readiness for the start of the second half. 'Half-nine here, so it'll be half-six there … Come on Chelsea!'

'Oh for fucks sake!

The majority of spectators in a crowd of over 27,000 got to their feet shouting and whistling as Glen Johnson's clumsy tackle from behind upended a Moscow player who had darted into the Chelsea penalty area with the ball.

'Fuck me! Ha ha,' laughed Eggy, wrapping his right arm around Nipper's shoulder and hugging him. 'Johnny Wilkinson would've been proud of that,' he observed, as Love spectacularly fired the ball high over the Chelsea crossbar.

'That's it mate, you know that,' replied Nipper, clenching his fists. 'Come on Chelsea!'

Try as they might, the Russian side couldn't break down a resolute Chelsea defence that had only conceded four goals in 16 matches in the current season, and by the time the referee called time on proceedings, the ground had all but emptied.

★ ★ ★ ★ ★

Holly's penthouse flat at Elm Quay Court afforded her a sweeping view east across the River Thames, taking in Westminster and the Houses of Parliament. A shrewd investment on her part, the property had trebled in value during the seven years she'd owned it. It had been let to a Japanese businessman right up until Easter, coincidentally the point in time when Holly had felt the need to start to distance herself from Nipper.

Tonight she had no time for the vista, no concern for the welfare of Jezebel, and no interest in anything else apart from the 3.5 grams of coke that constituted the 'Henry' that she'd purchased from Mr Sheen. The fact that savoury food hadn't passed her lips all day had not crossed her mind.

Holly sat at her dressing table and slid the jewelled comb out of her hair using its teeth to fashion a side-parting. She liked the look. It was evocative of the type of head turning, high maintenance women that frequented the gym in the Elm Quay complex that she infrequently used.

'Right then, lets get organised,' she said, winking at herself in the mirror as she slit the envelope open with her thumbnail and picked out the clear plastic coin bag which contained three potent looking, orangey-grey cannabis buds. 'Nice one Mr Sheen, that'll bring me down later, but first it's time to get high.'

Holly could feel her heartbeat gaining momentum as she placed the bag in her spliff box and turned her attention to the perfectly folded white cartridge paper pack which she removed from the envelope. Opening it with the precision of an Origami grandmaster, she held the pack up to her nose, closing her eyes and sniffing its contents in much the same way that a chef would check the freshness of some pre-prepared fancy piece of nouvelle quisine.

Holly remembered the documentary about drug culture she'd watched on TV recently. A group of users had been wired up to ECG and EEG machines, and had had their reactions monitored as they'd been shown the full gamut of paraphernalia associated with drug taking. The most startling responses had been obtained when the odours relating to various drugs were wafted into the room. Palpitations brought on by giddy expectation, perspiration the result of quivering anticipation.

Holly emptied the contents of the pack onto the smoked glass surface of the dressing table, sighing as she used the leading edge of a laminated playing card to tease the finely graded powder into ten fat lines which she then halved and halved again. Orderly and spaced, like miniature lime lined graves, there was a finite sense of symmetry about her work, and Holly sat back in her chair momentarily to proudly admire it.

'Okay lets have it!'

A brand new £50 note, straight from the vaults of the bank was Holly's preferred option when it came to snorting coke. Unrolled, untainted, unblemished, just the way she liked it. Nipper had once told her that 90% of all the used banknotes in circulation in London had traces of sparkle on them, now that was downright unhygienic. The funny thing was though, after the first line, you didn't give a fuck. Any old thing you found down the back of your sofa would do, all that mattered was getting your next nosefull.

One, two, three. Sniff, sniff, sniff, Holly shook her head after snorting the third line, widening her shiny eyes and exhaling through puckered lips as she blew a kiss at her reflection in the dressing table mirror.

'Shit, that is good coke!' she proclaimed for the benefit of Jezebel, who had awoken from her slumber and was stood in the doorway, observing her mistress with one of those know-it-all expressions that cats are fabled for. 'A drink and a fag now eh, oh and I need a tune.'

★ ★ ★ ★ ★

'Cheers lads,' said Nipper, holding his glass of neat vodka up in front of him. 'Chelsea ... kings of Europe.'

'Chelsea kings of Europe!'

'Just imagine, we could've been playing away at some dodgy Second Division ground tonight ha ha,' replied Fatboy, draining his vodka after the toast and clenching his fist in a victory salute.

'Roman Abramovich, Roman Abramovich, Roman Abramovich ...'

'How did you hear about this place Nipper?' enquired Eggy, following an exultant rendition of the popular Chelsea hymn praising the clubs wealthy benefactor.

'You know Claire at Hysteria,' replied Nipper, struggling to make himself heard above the cacophonous din of forgotten rock music, 'she used to work here.'

'Doin what?'

'Pole dancing.'

'Seriously?'

'Yes mate, her old man's Russian. She lived out here, did her medical training and all that bollocks.'

'I reckon she's a carpet muncher.'

'Reckon you're right.'

'I wouldn't mind munching her carpet.'

'Join the queue.'

'Ere,' interrupted Riddler Rowan, his craggy face taking on an ethereal quality as the stark white ultraviolet lights silhouetted him against the thick fog of dry ice that was billowing across the downstairs bar in Club Maximus. 'I reckon your old doll face Holly's got a thing for her, I'm telling ya.'

'Toffee apple.'

'Seriously mate, I've heard it from Camp Kenny, I took him over to Claire's place after Sniffler carved him up.'

'He cant speak.'

'Didn't have to ... he just pointed and winked.'

'Faggot!'

'Yeah, whatever Nip, but he never deserved what that cunt Sniffler done to him.' Riddler Rowan pulled back from the conversation, distracted momentarily by the sight of Fatboy Green being engaged by a sylphlike, snub nosed lap dancer, whose shock of fiery red hair resembled her to one of those oh-so-fuckable maidens in those moody pre-Raphaelite paintings that Beery Barlow collected.

'I'll have Sniffler soon,' replied Nipper, pulling Riddler towards him by the collar of his prized Helmut Lang pea coat and repeating himself just to make sure his friend got the message.

'All right Nip, I heard you the first time.'

'Nice one,' said Nipper casually. 'Enough of this shit talk now. Come on let's see what Fatboy's problem is,' he continued, walking across the bar area to the rest of the group who were remonstrating with the red haired girl and a couple of agitated looking bouncers.

'What's up Fatty?' asked Eggy, responsibly taking charge of the situation.

'She was pressurising me into having a lap dance.'

'Didn't you fancy it then?'

'She stinks man,' explained Danny Green, pinching his nose and smiling. 'She kept going, 'lap dance, lap dance', but the smell was so bad, I told her me lap was broken. I don't think she understood, so she called these goons over.'

'What sort of smell?' enquired a puzzled looking Chiller, looking for any opportunity to leave the premises, his sophisticated dance music ears complaining at the level of noise pollution.

'Jellied eels mate, and her breath smells like Satan's bottom.'

'That's bad.'

'John the Baptist?' said Riddler Rowan, pointing at the exit door as Eggy Barnes handed the distressed redhead $100.

'Good idea Riddler,' agreed a slightly embarrassed Fatboy Green. 'Let's head off. The hotels a far safer bet, and the crumpet's a bit more fragrant.'

★ ★ ★ ★ ★

Taking coke socially hadn't been on Holly's agenda for years. A toot at work kept her on the money, but that was all. She'd been around the drug long enough to see how it could turn even the most placid, reserved of people into ranting bores who craved to be the centre of attention.

Louder than the rest, the Cokemon! That had been Nipper's joke. He loved those stupid Pokemon creatures, Picachu and Meowth in particular. Cokemon had been his fictitious creation, the evil drug demon, a sort of Dr Jekyl as Mr Hyde. Silly twat, thought Holly, lighting a Marlboro and skipping into the kitchen to fix herself a large Southern Comfort and lemonade.

'Ten Years of Hysteria'. Holly smiled at the cover of the CD. That had been a shrewd idea of Nipper's. Mixed by Jack 'Chiller' Chillman, the double CD was a definitive representation of his ability on the decks, and blended upfront commercial classics, with some of the choice underground cuts with which he'd wowed Hysteria's punters over the past decade.

'You touch my mind in special places.'

Another Marlboro.

'Touch me in the morning and last thing at night.'

Another line.

'Rui da Silva … yeah love it.'

Another drink.

'It's true, I never meant to make you cry, I never meant say goodbye …'

Another Marlboro.

'I wanna come back to you and put things together.'

'Ron Carroll … love it more.'

Another line.

'To be in love with you, to me is everything.'

Another line.

'Loving you is my desire, loving you has set my soul on fire.'

Another line.

'Masters at Work … come on!'

Another line.

Hours flew over as Holly bathed in the still water of her addiction, until finally her body could take no more.

Crouching over the toilet bowl, bloody nosed and sweating profusely, she retched, gagging on the foul smelling tar-like bile she coughed and spluttered from her slack jawed mouth. 'Help me mother,' she cried, staggering to her feet, pulse racing, 'help me please!'

14

WHAT'S THE STORY ...
MORNING GLORY

'I'll be ready in 30 minutes son,' said Nipper, draining the can of Red Bull he'd just opened as he finished chatting to Eggy Barnes about the days agenda. 'There's plenty to do mate. You pick up the tea and sandwiches from Mordi's, and I'll see you in Victoria ... later yeah.'

More like an hour, he thought to himself, ending the call and tucking his mobile phone into the top of his boxer shorts as he walked back along the landing from bathroom to bedroom. On reaching his bedroom, he paused to peep through the crack between the door and the doorframe. Sometimes life was like that, he thought to himself, stifling a chuckle. Occasionally you had a stroke of luck that defied belief.

For a woman apparently cruising towards her sell by date, Trixie Fowler still had the face and figure he'd had an eye for when she'd been going out with Pete. There were some subtle differences though that betrayed her age, but Nipper definitely wasn't complaining as he felt a voyeur-like stirring in his loins.

The untameable blonde mane had been cut back, straightened, and dyed a sophisticated shade of auburn and there were a few lines around her long lashed icy blue eyes, but everything else was just as he'd remembered it. Lithe limbs, honeyed skin that really was as soft as it he'd thought it might be, pert boobs that still had a life of their own and an arse to die for.

'Do you like what you can see?' drawled Trixie huskily, rolling over on the bed and pushing her backside in the air.

'Not half,' replied Nipper, fixing the money shot in his minds eye and sighing as he glanced at the time on his watch.

Trixie sat up, licking her lips lasciviously as Nipper entered the bedroom and walked over to the bed. 'Come and get it then,' she said, cupping her breasts sensually and opening her legs.

'Be rude not to,' replied Nipper, eyes drawn to her shaven sex, his manhood engorged and ready. 'I cant walk around like this all day.'

The coupling was frantic. For Trixie, being with Nipper added a frisson of danger to the proceedings, but she was in no mood to repeat her submissive role from the previous evening. She'd remembered from her girly chats with Holly that Nipper liked to be in charge and she'd been more than happy to yield to his demands, but that was last night. This morning she was going to fuck him, that way he'd be certain to remember her. Not that he wouldn't.

Nipper's attempt at dominant penetration was met with razor sharp fingernails clawing talon-like into the soft flesh of his buttocks, his tongue probing her mouth suddenly gripped by sharp incisors, the ferric taste of his own blood causing him to rapidly rethink his sexual strategy.

With the agility and strength of a gymnast, and the self awareness and guile of a martial arts exponent, Trixie turned the tables on Nipper, flipping him onto his back in the way a tiger would its prey, guiding herself onto him, pushing down hard, fucking him fast, both hands around his throat throttling him to the point of unconsciousness.

'Yes!' cried Trixie, as the first of three consecutive orgasms ripped through her body, the second of which triggered Nipper's own ejaculation, his issue powerful and plentiful enough to have doused a fire.

'You've come for England,' she observed, grinning and wiping the beads of perspiration away from her forehead as she eased herself off Nipper's wilting member, feeling his semen ooze out of her and trickle down the insides of her thighs.

'You've killed me,' he replied, breathless from her attention. 'That was sensational.'

'I try my best.'

Nipper watched as Trixie ruffled her hair, donned his bathrobe and got up to go to the bathroom. Fucking quality, he thought to himself, I've had a right touch.

★ ★ ★ ★ ★

'Are you okay honey?'

'Yeah, I'm feeling brand new Claire,' replied Holly hoarsely, her gravelly voice a legacy of the abuse she'd subjected her body to earlier in the week.

She'd had plenty of time to think about things as she'd recuperated at

Claire's flat, not least how her relationship with drink and drugs had changed. Hedonism had been substituted by visceral nihilism, and the reasons were plain enough for her to see.

The coke binge had been an escape for a woman tired of wading knee deep through her own personal traumas. Nothing in Holly's life had ever been simple, but at least now everything was mapped out and documented in the back of her mind. Her feelings of inadequacy and pain had been soothed by Claire's antiseptic attention, slowly but surely her opaque view of life was becoming translucent.

'You haven't got that old Johnny Nash hit on CD anywhere have you?' asked Holly, getting out of bed and stretching her body.

'Which one?' replied Claire, walking through to the bedroom carrying a clean dressing gown which she handed to her willing patient.

'He only had one didn't he,' said Holly, easing herself into the robe and flicking her head. *'I can see clearly now the rain has gone, I can see all obstacles in my way,'* she sang whilst doing a reggae moonstomp on her way to the toilet.

'You sound like Bonnie Tyler.'

'Maybe I should go on the 'X Factor' then … *la la la it's gonna be a bright, bright, sunshinin day.'*

'You'd have to learn the words properly first though ha ha,' said Claire, laughing as she imagined Holly trying to impress the judges.

'Maybe I'd be better suited to 'Stars in their Eyes' then.'

'Maybe.'

Holly didn't reply, her mentioning the programme reminded her about the joke Fatboy Green always used to tell, the piss take on Simon and Garfunkel. Now that was funny. Fatboy Green, what a funny guy. They were all funny back then, even Nipper.

'Have you spoken to Sniffler today?' she asked, emerging from the bathroom and gratefully accepting the cup of tea that Claire handed her.

'Yeah he's got everything in hand for tonight, in fact he's expecting a delivery from lover boy this afternoon.'

'Please Claire,' said Holly, screwing her face up in consternation at the inference.

'Joke.'

'D'ya reckon he'd be interested in buying me out?'

'What … Nipper?'

'No, Sniffler.'

'Dunno. Why do you ask?'

'Maybe I need to do something different, chill out a bit first though,' said Holly, walking over to the window and looking down on the hustle and bustle of the street below. 'Get a regular job, whaddya reckon?'

Claire smiled wistfully, teasing her downy hair with her fingers as she shook her head. 'I cant see it honey. You are Hysteria, it's what you do.'

'Yeah, that's the trouble innit babe,' replied Holly, sipping at her drink and clicking her tongue the way she always did when she was trying to find the solution to a problem. 'I just don't know any other way of life.'

'You could get married, settle down and have kids,' suggested Claire, the sincerity in her voice surprising Holly. 'It's what most people do.'

'I'm not most people though.'

'I dunno, I reckon you might be now. It's all about timing. Our girl love's just a distraction for you.'

Holly turned around to face Claire and smiled, but kept her own counsel. A wise head on youngish shoulders, she thought as they embraced. Lucid, direct, and almost always right, that's what Claire was. Not to mention shrewd. At her worst Holly saw herself as naïve, disingenuous and downright incongruous. In other words, her exact opposite, hence the attraction. Claire was right, she wasn't the answer to her problems, just an aide in finding the solutions, the real work would be down to her and her alone.

★ ★ ★ ★ ★

'So anyway, honey when can I see you again?' enquired Nipper, getting an eyeful of Trixie's cleavage as he deftly reversed the Range Rover into a vacant parking bay outside the Apollo Theatre in Wilton Road, Victoria.

'That depends on you,' she replied huskily. 'I'm going down to Brighton to visit my son for the weekend, but I'll be back on Monday.'

Parking manoeuvre completed, Nipper leant into Trixie and brushed her hair off her face with his right hand. 'Yeah sexy, I've got a busy weekend too. Monday would be great,' he said, pulling her close and kissing her fully on the mouth.

Nipper's mobile rang, distracting both of them.

'Saved by the bell,' laughed Trixie, prizing herself out of Nipper's amorous clutches. 'Go on answer it, I'm off,' she continued as she opened the door and swung her legs out in a manner that suggested she'd been to a top Swiss finishing school.

'Very ladylike,' observed Nipper as he accepted the call. 'No, not you Eggy you tosser.'

'And on that note Johnny Nipper, I'll take my leave.'

Nipper frowned as Trixie slammed the door shut and crossed the road in front of him, but his mind was soon re-occupied with the matters at hand. Finishing the conversation with Eggy Barnes which had revolved around whether or not he wanted a sandwich or not, and if so sausage or bacon? He'd then called Mordi and Sniffer Barlow in quick succession, firming up the arrangements that he'd made with them the previous day.

'Oi Oi saveloy!' grunted Eggy by way of a greeting, as he clambered into the Range Rover. 'How's it going?'

'Not three bad mate, not three bad,' replied Nipper, spinning the steering wheel and indicating to pull out of the parking bay. 'Which is better than not two innit,' he continued, accelerating quickly through amber lights at Wilton Road's junction with Victoria Street.

'Cup of tea and a sausage sandwich mate, here you go,' said Eggy, settling himself into his seat and placing the package containing the drugs into the glove compartment.

'Didn't Mordi have no bacon then?'

'Nah mate just sausages. Ere by the way, you'll never guess who I just saw as I was walking to yer motor.'

'Let me guess … er Trixie Fowler.'

'How did you guess that, did you see her too?'

'No mate, I dropped her off.' Nipper kept his eyes on the road ahead, smiling as he waited for his friend to react.

'You did what?' replied Eggy incredulously.

'She was with me last night.'

'Fuck me son, you should change your name to Black Beauty.'

'Why?' asked Nipper, easing the Range Rover confidently across the lanes of the Parliament Square gyratory.

'Cos you're a fucking dark horse,' replied Eggy, giving the middle finger to an irate motorist who'd just been cut up by Nipper's reckless driving.

'She's a still a proper sort mate, you cant blame me,' said Nipper, cruising over Westminster Bridge at a slow enough speed to allow him to look back down the River Thames. 'If you wanna get over it, you've gotta get under it.'

'And did ya.'

'Is a frogs arse watertight?' chuckled Nipper, one eye on the Range Rover's satellite navigation screen and the other on the road in front of him. Lambeth North, Elephant and Castle, Old Kent Road, his mind was like an A to Z of London, but he liked the way sat nav system tried to keep up with his short cuts and double backs by making helpful suggestions in an automated posh voice that sounded like it belonged to a middle-aged bird who needed a serious seeing to.

'D'ya reckon Sniffler will have the correct paperwork for this lot?' asked

Eggy, opening the glove compartment in front of him and retrieving the small nylon holdall he had wedged in there 20 minutes earlier.

Nipper hesitated before he replied, checked his rear view mirror and indicated left, turning off the A2 into Deptford High Street. 'Course he will mate,' he said, driving with due care and attention along the busy road, slowing to a halt as they reached the junction with Mary Ann Gardens. 'He wouldn't wanna miss out on a deal like this now would he?'

Eggy nodded, lighting up a couple of Marlboro's and handing one to Nipper. 'I expect not,' he replied, pausing to take a decent drag before continuing, 'although I did hear his old man was in serious trouble with the bookies.'

'His old mans in trouble with the bank as well. He lost a shed load of cash on a planning deal that went pear shaped and I know for a fact that Geezer Goodwin is putting the squeeze on a couple of his other operations.'

'I bet Sniffler doesn't know that though.'

'I bet he doesn't.'

'Are you gonna front this deal then?'

'Yes mate,' said Nipper buzzing down his window exhaling smoke as spoke. 'It means you might have to sample the merchandise with him though.'

'I don't have a problem with that.'

Nipper guided the Range Rover into a narrow parking space between two identical dark blue BMW's nodding as he did so. 'I know you don't, but don't forget we've still gotta get back up to Mordi's and I wanna pop in and see Kenny as well before we've done today, so go easy on the taster.'

'Blimey Nipper, this is like a proper job.'

'Yes mate, you know that!'

★ ★ ★ ★ ★

Sniffler happened to be looking out of an upstairs window as Nipper and Eggy arrived and was at the front door waiting to greet them by the time they had sauntered casually across the road to his house.

'Nipper, Eggy, always a pleasure,' he said, offering a loose handshake which both men declined. 'Friendly as ever I see, come on through.'

Nipper shook his head and raised the middle finger of his right hand as they followed Sniffler into the drawing room at the back of his house which doubled as an office. 'We haven't got much time S,' he said nonchalantly, 'We've got more people to see back in town, this is a really decent piece of work, there's plenty of interest.'

Sniffler licked his lips in anticipation as he watched Eggy Barnes place the container he was holding on the table and carefully lever the lid off. 'Well come on then,' he said impatiently, 'let's all sample the merchandise.'

'I'll pass if it's all the same to you,' said Nipper, producing a small sterling silver christening spoon from his jacket pocket which he handed to Eggy. 'It's a bit early for me, but my man here will join you for the quality control test.'

'You're getting too old for this racket son,' replied Sniffler, a patronising smirk forming across his sallow features. 'Come on Eggy, come on.'

Nipper resisted the urge to react, and remained impassive as Eggy Barnes scooped up a modest amount of powder and snorted it through his right nostril before handing the spoon to Sniffler who'd already decided to prescribe himself a more generous dose of Mordi's medicine.

'Fackin 'ell … that's gear ain't it!' exclaimed Sniffler, inarticulately proclaiming Eggy's immediate impressions of what they'd both sampled. 'It seems a lot purer than the usual merchandise … is it?'

Gotcha, thought Nipper to himself, everything really is tickety-fucking-boo. 'Only the best for you mate,' he said, measuring his reply carefully. 'Not much quality toot around at the moment, I could let you have another kilo of this if you're interested.'

'Interested,' replied Sniffler enthusiastically, the drug livening him up more than he anticipated. 'I'll take whatever you've got,' he said, handing the silver spoon back to Nipper.

'How much are you willing to pay?'

'The going rate.'

'Thirty large for both then.'

'Done!' agreed Sniffler, without hesitation.

Nipper checked his watch and waited while Sniffler resealed the container. 'Fifteen bags now, and fifteen later, I'll have to pick the rest of the work up this afternoon and meet you tonight or maybe you could send Riddler.'

'I'll do it myself.'

As Sniffler walked across to his desk, Nipper gave the thumbs up to Eggy and pointed at the door. 'Up to you mate,' he said, casting his eyes around the surprisingly well decorated room. 'I guess Kenny wont be involved though, not after what you did to him eh.'

'Oh you've heard then,' replied Sniffler smugly, opening the drawer of his desk as he continued to speak. 'The black nonce had it coming to him, someone with a bit of authority had to teach him some respect.'

Eggy, mind still racing from the effects of the gear, looked at Nipper trying to gauge whether or not he would have to intervene if his friends patience finally gave way in the face of Sniffler's pretentious arrogance, but he needn't have worried.

'Yeah. You're the man now Sniffler,' replied Nipper calmly. 'We're getting out of the game, it's too hardcore for us. Someone's gonna end up getting killed.'

The look on Sniffler's face was one of triumph. 'What's this then ... lost yer nerve av ya?' he sneered, as he handed Nipper an envelope containing £15,000.

'You could say that Sniffler,' replied Nipper, feeling the weight of the envelope and handing it to Eggy Barnes. 'But then you could say it's time for me to move on,' he continued, his voice a dreary monotone. 'Hysteria, Holly, all of it ... I don't need it anymore.'

'I cant say I blame ya. What ya gonna do then? Retire?'

Nipper shrugged his shoulders and resisted the urge to smile at a bemused looking Eggy Barnes. 'Who knows,' he said, winking at his adversary and pointing at container on the desk. 'I'll call you this afternoon to sort out the other half of that little lot. Right, come on Eggy. Let's get out of this farmyard.'

★ ★ ★ ★ ★

'I'll tell ya something mate,' said Eggy, opening Sniffler's envelope and emptying the contents onto his lap. 'That was quality. You should've gone to drama school. Where the fuck did you learn to act like that?'

'Hanging around with that silly bitch Holly my son,' replied Nipper, fiddling with the settings of the Range Rover's sat nav as he drew heavily on one of the Hamlet cigars he enjoyed occasionally. 'How was the gear?'

'Amazing!' exclaimed Eggy, carefully placing the money in the glove compartment and screwing the envelope into a tight ball. 'It seemed to have more bite for some reason than it did when we picked it up from Mr Sheen's.'

'Wait till you try the next lot then,' laughed Nipper, flooring the accelerator and sitting back in his seat as the car lurched forward. 'Mordi the magician, strikes again ha ha ... I'm gonna give him a bonus, in fact fuck it ... I'm gonna give him my bonus.'

'What about Kenny?'

'Yeah, we can buy his loyalty easily enough.'

Eggy looked out of the window, trying to find something of interest to focus on. He wanted to ask his best friend a lot of questions, but he wasn't sure where to start, things were getting complicated. 'You wanna be careful with him,' he said soberly.

'Queers cant keep their mouths shut about anything. He'll grass you to Holly, y'know she's got that fag hag hold on him.'

'Eg-fucking-zact-a-mundo,' replied Nipper patronisingly. 'So if I tell him something, and give him a carpet or two to keep his gob shut, he'll think its well important won't he.'

'He's got no option but to keep his gob shut at the moment,' joked Eggy. 'Maybe that cock Sniffler was right after all.'

Nipper smiled as he spoke, 'He didn't break his fingers to stop him sending a text message or writing shit down on a piece of paper though did he.'

Eggy turned the stereo on and tapped the touch-screen menu. 'Listen mate, I know that you know what you're doing, but I've lost the thread slightly,' he said, frowning as he realised that there were no CD's in the machine. 'I feel like I'm reading a book and someone's ripped out a few pages here and there.'

Nipper yawned, letting go of the steering wheel momentarily, stretching his arms out in front of him and interlocking his fingers. 'Fair point mate. Fair point,' he said, nodding in agreement as he thought about what he could explain and how. The pendulum of fortune was slowly swinging in his direction; his patience and tenacity would soon be rewarded, and those that had crossed him would wish they hadn't. In fact by the time they got around to making that wish, it would be too late.

'For a start,' said Eggy, with an increasing air of edgy impatience. 'There's this business you've got with Geezer Goodwin and that new club of his Mr Terry's, then the craic with this gear. We could've made just one drop, why make it complicated?

'Easy tiger,' replied Nipper coolly. 'That gear's nibbling at yer nerves.'

'Yeah well that's the idea isn't it, I've figured that part out.'

Fuck it, thought Nipper, what harm could it do? A sketchy outline would keep his mate happy. 'It's not that wild mate, honest it aint,' he said, scratching at the stubble on his chin. 'Geezer Goodwin came to me and Holly ages ago, wanting us to front a club for him. She got all pious about things and blanked the idea. The thing is, Geezer Goodwin aint the sort of bloke you blank, so I got involved on a consultancy basis just to keep him sweet. The interesting thing is though, he's bang on the money. If Holly hadn't finished it between us, I could've talked her round and got her back in. Beery Barlow, Sniffler, Steve Bruno and all that lot, they're so off the pace, they're a fucking embarrassment. Clubland is changing, we all know that. You've gotta move with the times and be in with the right people, all the right people.'

The pregnant pause that followed Nipper's revelation was broken by the usual jokes about requiring passports, visas and up to date inoculations as the Range Rover carried the men north of the River via Blackfriars Bridge, but it didn't take long for Eggy Barnes, curiosity aroused, to request further information.

'What about the gear then?' he asked, lighting up another Marlboro as he tried to digest the potential ramifications of what he'd already learnt.

'There's only so many punters in London mate.'

'Eh?'

'Okay, so Hysteria's the biggest club in town. The place is iconic. People only go elsewhere because they cant get in there. Mr Terry's, as you'll see, shits all over it from every angle. The trouble is it's new, and ...'

'And it's called Mr Terry's,' interrupted Eggy jovially.

'That's right,' nodded Sniffler. 'So the only way to make a change is ...'

'To get Hysteria shutdown so ...'

'Look we're here, Cloudsley Square,' announced Nipper, curtailing the question and answer session just as it had become confusing again for Eggy, who was trying to understand why selling good shit in a club rather than the usual knicker staining gear would result in Hysteria's closure.

'The blue door over there,' said Eggy, pointing across the road. 'Number 42 that's were Kenny's old dear lives, park up here.'

* * * * *

'Easy mate you'll break the fucking door down,' said Eggy, grabbing at Nipper's arm to prevent him knocking again. 'I'm sure his mum heard the first couple of raps.'

Nipper suddenly felt stressed. Explaining part of his game plan to Eggy had wound him up slightly and reminded him just how sore he still was about Holly. What goes around, comes around, he thought to himself. I'm not bitter like the Murphy's at all. The door opened as far as its security chain would allow and the frail voice of Kenny's mother informing would be thieves that she'd not hesitate in calling the police, was the hypnotists finger click that brought him back in the room.

'It's all right Madge, its Nipper and Eggy ... friends of Kenny,' announced Nipper directly. 'We've come to say hello, he told you we were coming didn't he?'

When the door eventually opened properly, it was Kenny and not his mother who was waiting to greet them. But this wasn't the Kenny that Nipper and Eggy were used to. In place of the charming, confident, gaily amusing, stylish and impossibly good looking man they knew stood someone who resembled a casualty of war. A bandaged nervous wreck with fear in his eyes and the worlds problems on his shoulders.

'Fuck me Kenny, that's a liability innit,' said Eggy grimacing at the thought of what might lie beneath the facial bandages. 'You aint gonna win any beauty contests for a while are you.'

'Don't listen to him,' said Nipper consolingly. 'He's an insensitive prick at the best of times. You gonna invite us in then?'

They followed Kenny into his mothers sitting room and watched in silence as he reached for the A4 foolscap pad and pen that was placed neatly in the centre of the small mahogany coffee table upon which was also a flier advertising Hysteria's 10th birthday party. The message he wrote was simple, humorous, and served to break the ice.

INTRODUCING EGGY BARNES, THE NEW PIN UP BOY FOR VASECTOMIES

'Very good Kenny,' said Nipper, winking at Eggy. 'I'll get to the point as we haven't got too much time to hang around. I've got a new project which I'd like your involvement in, Mr Terry's yeah.' He waited for Kenny to nod before continuing. 'Thatclub is having the best of everything, no expense spared, and that includes hiring the best staff. There's a long one here for you, a signing on fee. I want you to come on board and run the door. It's an important job, and you're the person I want to do it.'

'It shouldn't be too hard a decision to make after what happened last week,' added Eggy, pointing at the pen and paper.

BUT WHAT ABOUT HOLLY? WHAT IF SNIFFLER COMES AFTER ME? WHAT ABOUT MY BOAT? I WONT BE ABLE TO FACE PEOPLE FOR A COUPLE OF MONTHS UNTIL THE SCARS HEAL.

Nipper, head tilted to one side, was able to read what Kenny was writing in real time. 'Ha ha,' he laughed, clapping his hands as he did so. 'Don't be so vain, we can have a top plastic surgeon have a look at the milky bar's on your boat race. You can wear a mask. Phantom of the Opera, Silence of the Lambs, use your imagination. What's the alternative? Staying in? Camp Kenny doesn't do staying in. Holly will be okay about it, I'll speak to her, and as for Sniffler, that's all in hand. You've got nothing to worry about apart from being as gay as eight leprechauns doing a jig on your very own tombstone.'

I'LL THINK AB————

Nipper reached over and pulled the pad away from Kenny before he could finish what he was writing. 'Listen Ken … I love you a lot mate but I aint got time to fuck about. You're good at what you do and you will be looked after. Fuck me over the way you fucked Holly and Sniffler over that gear and I'll have you castrated. Be a good boy and you'll have the pleasure of working at the coolest club in the capital … so what's it to be?'

Kenny rubbed his chest nervously with his right hand before extending it to shake Nipper's and Eggy's in turn.

'Lovely Kenny,' said Nipper, putting his arm around his waist and blowing him a kiss. 'Now just be sure not to say anything just yet. We can keep in touch by text. We've gotta go now, pay a little visit to our friend Mordi who lives just up the road. Convenient that really aint it … now you stay there, we'll let ourselves out my old fruit.'

'So far so good,' said Eggy, as they left the house.

'Yes mate,' replied Nipper already thinking ahead. 'All good in the hood.'

15

DEALERS CHOICE

'Go on then mate, for fucks sake!' shouted Nipper shaking his fist at the driver of a large articulated lorry who had been hesitating at the junction in front of them. 'Wanker!' he yelled, braking hard to see if the driver reacted.

'Chill mate,' said Eggy calmly. 'He's just an old boy doing his job. Come on, it aint worth it, we're nearly at Mordi's anyway.'

'Yeah! Sorry mate. You're right,' replied Nipper, lighting a Marlboro and smiling. 'Got a lot on my plate at the moment as you well know.'

'Never as much as Fatboy Green though.'

'Very good mate ha ha.' Nipper had to laugh, even though everything was crystallising perfectly, he still found himself umming and arring over Holly. Would he have been as sore had she not finished their relationship just like that? What would he have done about Trixie had he still been with Holly when he'd met her again? You need a bit of fresh once in a while, and he'd always fancied her on the sly.

It was a mute point now since Trixie's 'Clothes for Heroes' global brand expansion was being bankrolled by Geezer Goodwin. They would have met anyway. Maybe he needed to break with the past completely. Plenty more fish in the sea eh ... but who wants to end up with a fish?

Sensing his friend was in a reflective mood, Eggy kept quiet and contemplated the meaning of life, his own life. There was plenty to do and precious little time to do it in. Chelsea, the craic and making money, that's what it was all about. You had to find the balance. Women were a pleasant distraction, allow them to get under your skin at your peril. If Nipper was getting tetchy over a couple of moody birds then that was his call, as far as Eggy was concerned they were all in it for themselves. How many times had it all come on top for a bloke because of crumpet? ... Exactly!

Take Mordi's niece Esther for example. Eggy had, and he was proud of it. But as they entered the old mans shop and he caught sight of her again there were no pangs of desire, no tugging of heartstrings, and no feelings of guilt whatsoever. He'd fucked her within an inch of her life earlier in the day when he'd come to pick up the consignment they'd just delivered to Sniffler.

'Just gonna drop the kids off at the pool while you finish that off,' he'd said surreptitiously, as Mordi had busied himself weighing out the preparation. The old goat never thought to question the amount of time he'd spent in the toilet, and as for Esther, that had all been done via eye contact. No romance, no candlelit dinners, no flowers. Just a quick knee trembler up against a cold toilet wall, fucking quality.

'How much is this treacle?' asked Eggy, nudging Nipper as he picked up a tube of vaginal lubricant and held it up in the air.

Esther frowned, pulling at the dark hairs on her arms and looking at the floor. '£3.75 sir,' she replied coyly. 'Was it just the one tube, or would you like a box?'

'Don't let him wind you up love,' said Nipper, waving at Mordi who was stood behind the preparation room hatch. 'It's just wishful thinking on his part.'

Eggy smiled, and as he did so Esther looked up and smiled also. Eggy knew that Esther knew that he'd kept his mouth shut about their little dalliance, and that was what it was all about. Nipper saying , 'she'd get it that Esther', when in fact she had already 'got it'.

'Boy's boys,' croaked Mordi, his eyes sparkling with a fierce intensity. 'Leave the virgin Esther alone. Come let us go upstairs and conclude our business.'

'Virgin,' chuckled Nipper, prodding Eggy as he followed him through to the back of the chemists. 'I wouldn't mind popping her hairy cherry. She looks like she's got a proper thatch.'

'Not half, I bet it looks like Davy Crockett's hat,' replied Eggy rubbing his crotch. 'I'd put money on it.'

Mordi looked agitated as he climbed up onto a small footstool and reached for the green plastic container that was nestling amongst some small brown medicine bottles on the top shelf of the huge stainless steel cupboard that dominated the rear of the prep room.

'If I were you, I'd put your money on this gear instead,' said Nipper, rubbing his hands together, a wry look forming on his face as he watched Mordi place the container on his workstation and carefully open it.

'What is it?' asked Eggy Barnes, his suspicions confirmed that Nipper was up to something.

'Crystal Meth cut with Atropine I'm afraid,' answered Mordi, his voice sounding distressed as he looked at the harmless looking powder in the container.

'Fuck me Mordi,' said Nipper, handing the chemist a roll of £50 notes. 'When did you develop a conscience?

'The day I decided to retire heh heh,' cackled Mordi, his mood lightening at the sight of big money.

'Retire,' joked Eggy. 'You love the filthy lucre too much, you wont retire.'

'Watch me.'

'We will ha ha,' replied Nipper, laughing raucously. 'You'll have more comebacks than Liberace and Frank Sinatra had put together.'

'One thing I don't understand though,' said Mordi, cocking his head to one side and twitching his nose as he flicked the roll of notes open in readiness for counting. 'The stuff that Eggy collected this morning, that was just the neat flake you brought over before you went to Moscow, what was the point of that?'

'Do what?' groaned Eggy, trying to figure out the latest twist in the tale.

'I'll tell you later,' replied Nipper, raising his eyes skywards as he walked over to Mordi and patted the old man on the right shoulder twice, the second time gripping it tightly and hooking his fingers into its joint which had loosened with age. 'Mordi, I don't pay you to ask questions like that,' he said, making the old man wince. 'Enough now, this jobs a good un,' he concluded, relaxing his hold and picking up the container. 'We'll crack on now.'

'Yes you must crack on,' said Mordi, clearly relieved that the deal was concluded and that the risk of personal injury had abated. 'Come, I will show you out through the backdoor.'

'Good enough,' replied Eggy, throwing a knowing smile at Esther as they walked through the shop and along the hall. 'I don't mind using the back door.' At the end of the day, fuck it, he thought to himself. Nipper could reveal as much or as little of his plan to him as he wanted to, that was his prerogative, but he had his own little secrets too.

★ ★ ★ ★ ★

'Mate, can you pull up at the top of St. John's Hill,' said Holly as the taxi she was a passenger in crawled through the rush hour traffic that seemed to be even more congested than it usually was around Clapham Junction.

She was feeling good about herself both inside and out, and as the cab drove slowly by Hysteria, she knew she was making the right decision. The driver, one of her regulars, had appeared surprised at her instructions, she normally arranged to be picked up and dropped off directly outside the club.

Looking out of the window at the huge neon Hysteria sign, already lit and dominating the field of vision with its garish blue and white glow, Holly felt dispassionate. Hysteria was a part of her past with Nipper, and even if she did decide to let him back in her life at some point, the time was right to move on.

Perhaps she should have been less judgemental about Geezer Goodwin and the opportunity he represented. Maybe she should have reeled in the cocaine fuelled arrogance that so irritated her when she saw it in others. Hindsight eh, what a wonderful thing, she thought as she tapped the cabbie on the shoulder and motioned him to stop at the junction with Spencer Road, opposite the bingo hall.

Holly walked down the hill into the face of a chill but refreshingly dry evening breeze which further reinvigorated her already buoyant spirit. Wearing a full length vintage Ungaro fox fur coat, she felt as confident as she looked, and she looked like a woman lavished with care. What a difference a few days can make, she thought to herself, catching her reflection in a shop window. Youthful vitality regained. Glossy hair, newly shorn a boyishly short length and dyed back to its natural black. Mascara and eye shadow perfectly applied to make the most of her attention getting aquamarine contact lenses. Full red lips quenched with colour. Sassiness redefined.

A shrill wolf whistle cut through the noise of the passing traffic drawing Holly's attention away from herself. She looked across the road and saw the human colossus that was Mad Max Chillman, Hysteria's head of security, waving at her.

'Looking good sugar,' he shouted at couldn't care less volume. 'Very good indeed!'

Holly watched as he strode across the road. Traffic stopped for Mad Max, he was one of those guys that commanded respect without having to try too hard and he'd proved to be an indispensable part of her team ever since his younger sibling Jack had recommended him to her. The girls loved him almost as much as they loved his superstar DJ brother, and there were plenty of ribald stories about the pair of them doubling up on the odd, willingly persistent, groupie now and then. Mmm thought Holly to herself, now that would be interesting.

'You look fantastic treacle,' he said, scooping her up with his large hands and holding her close. 'Feeling better now?'

'Yeah,' replied Holly, catching her breath as she remembered how nice it felt to be appreciated in this way. 'Feeling great ... really great,' she continued, planting a big smacker on the side of his face. Mad Max was 100% male. A walking contradiction, his meaty tattooed forearms and age defying muscled torso gave him menacing, stop at nothing sex appeal, whilst his close cropped curly grey hair and conservative attire afforded him a certain gravitas. You crossed him at your peril.

'Ready for tonight then?' he said, his deep baritone voice giving Holly butterflies in her stomach.

'Ready for anything,' she replied, following him into the club.

'Yeah. Me too,' added Mad Max, clicking his fingers in time with the old Soul Providers tune 'Rise' that was warbling from the stereo in the back office. 'I've gotta mind Sniffler when he goes to pick up some work later ... er from Nipper I think.'

'Good enough Max, be lucky.' Holly stopped in her tracks letting Max go on his way, he had things to do.

'Rise ... rise ... rise ... keep on rising,' sang Holly, two part harmonising with the stirring vocal. Four to the floor. Pure soulful house music, fucking quality, she thought to herself wondering if the associated chemical desire to powder her nose would kick in like it normally did at this sort of time on a Friday evening.

'Lets go to a place that you belong, give you strength to carry on. Open your heart set your mind at ease, live your life and you'll be free ...'

Holly danced and sang her way along the corridor to the office conscious of the fact that Sniffler was watching her from the its doorway. 'Come on Sniffler you cock. Bust some moves with me,' she shouted, unbuttoning her coat and raising her hands above her head.

'You're gonna rise, rise, rise ... keep on rising.'

'Check you out,' he replied, resisting the urge to move his feet. 'No bad side effects from the other day then obviously.'

'You know me,' said Holly, following Sniffler into the office and turning off the stereo.

'Oi, I was enjoying that.'

'So was I, couldn't you tell?'

Sniffler lit a Marlboro and offered one to Holly which she gratefully accepted.

'I didn't expect to see you back so soon,' he said, sitting down on the edge of the office desk and running his eye over her as she took her coat off.

'Were you looking forward to running the show on your own?' asked Holly, running the fingers of her free hand through her hair and smiling.

'Yeah maybe.'

'I'll get straight to the point Sniffler,' said Holly adroitly. 'Do you fancy buying out my share of the club?'

Sniffler smoked his cigarette to its filter and stubbed it out. This all sounded very familiar. A paranoid man, having heard what Nipper had said earlier on in the day about retiring, would have put two and two together and probably come up with seven. Ex lovers and business partners both separately sharing their intention to exit the game with him, on the same day. Bollocks, it just didn't add up.

'Come on S,' said Holly impatiently. 'It's not like you to be lost for words now is it?'

'No it aint,' replied Sniffler, contemplating another line of the seriously good coke he'd bought earlier in the day. 'It just seems strange,' he continued, stopping himself from revealing what Nipper had said. Maybe he could play both ends off against the middle here. It looked like the drugs business was his for the taking now, throw Hysteria in as well and that could be really interesting. Sniffler imagined how impressed his father would be when he told him about the deal he was brokering all off his own back. A bit if credit from his old man, now that really would be something to look forward to.

'What seems strange?'

'Er nothing … Why would you wanna sell me Hysteria now? The tenth anniversary party next Saturday is gonna generate loads of publicity, and Christmas is just around the corner innit.

'Yeah innit ha ha,' laughed Holly. 'I didn't mean you had to go and ask your old man for the money tomorrow you Muppet.'

'Very funny,' replied Sniffler. 'I aint that fick.'

'I know,' agreed Holly, rubbing an index finger under her nose and accentuating a sniff as she did so. 'You've gotta go and sort the gear out for next weekend now with Mad Max aintcha. You'd better get cracking.'

Sniffler looked at his watch, and then at the clock on the wall. Holly was right, he did need to get a move on. Ordinarily he would have displayed less haste, but the merchandise previously purchased was of such high quality that he'd already made plans for it, and if the balance proved to be of the same standard then he'd be stepping on it good and proper. Money for old rope and Sniffler as top boy. Fucking love it.

'Absolutely,' he agreed finally in an accent that was more Eton than East End. 'Your old man sold me some quality toot today, you must try some later.'

'Top quality, that'll be the day.'

'I'm serious. Riddler's been busy with the lottery tickets already, the punters will be loving it later I'm tellin ya.'

Holly was deep in sober thoughts as she watched Sniffler open the safe and pick up the money that would pay for the work. What exactly was Nipper up to? He always got that geriatric chemist Mordi to step on the gear. Caffeine, baby laxative, glucose. He didn't give a fuck, but he never left money on the table. Strange really, very strange.

'All in,' said Sniffler, putting on his heavy leather Nicole Farhi jacket and stuffing the cash into its inside pocket. 'I'll see ya later.'

'Yeah!' said Holly, winking as she patted Sniffler on the back. 'Give my regards to Nipper, tell him I'll call him soon.'

As Sniffler left the office, Holly thought about sampling the gear. Just a little live'ner, that wouldn't do any harm now would it? No, it was too early yet. The nauseous memory of her recent binge was still fresh in her mind, a mind that was becoming increasingly preoccupied with thoughts about Nipper.

★ ★ ★ ★ ★

'Here they come,' said Sniffler, tapping Mad Max Chillman on the thigh as he spotted Nipper and Eggy Barnes ambling down Penwith Road towards the Knife and Fork public house. 'Cocky facking cahnts eh … bleedin Chelsea for ya innit eh son,' he continued, drumming his fingers impatiently on the Cortina's steering wheel. 'They weren't givin' it that swagger on my manor this morning.'

Mad Max nodded but said nothing. The only thing he had in common with Sniffler was a hatred of Chelsea. Being a QPR fan he'd been bitterly disappointed when his younger brother had started following the Blues, and the fact that they were now bankrolled by a billionaire and looked like they were set to dominate the English game for the next few years stuck like a spiny little fishbone right in the back of his throat.

Sniffler was an arrogant racist twat. A coward who'd got a big kick from slicing up a defenceless brother. Cockney Red's ha, he probably didn't even know where Old Trafford was, at least Nipper and the rest of the Chelsea mob still went to as many games as they could, the same way he still had his season ticket at Loftus Road. Mad Max turned to face him, flexing his muscles as he did so. If it wasn't for Holly, he would have ripped the cunts head off a long time ago.

'Right then,' said Sniffler, shrugging his shoulders and jerking his neck forward several times as they watched Nipper and Eggy enter the pub. 'You take the cash and the car keys, go to the khazi and come straight back here after the exchange. I wanna have a few verbals with Nipper, it wont take long.'

'Right boss,' said Max, zipping up the roll necked Helmut Lang blouson jacket he was wearing and donning a beanie hat which he pulled down so it covered the tops of his ears. As he got out of the car, a thought crossed his mind. Why the fuck was he still doing this?

★ ★ ★ ★ ★

Considering it was Friday night, the Knife and Fork was virtually empty. Regulars who frequented the place were tiring of its dated décor and its rundown, grotty appearance. Even Eggy, who lived just around the corner, had stopped calling in there for a quick slurp on his way to the football.

The place was a washed up anonymous watering hole badly in need of a makeover, and as long as it remained that way Nipper was more than happy to conduct his clandestine drug deals in its grubby confines.

'Light and Lager?' enquired Nipper, as Sniffler entered the bar in the manner of some hotshot High Noon gunslinger. 'Where's Maxie Chillman then?'

'In the toilet. Same place as Eggy I expect,' replied Sniffler, accepting the offer of a drink, which was just as well because Ossie the landlord had already prised off the top of a light ale bottle and was busying himself with the task of pouring half a pint of Fosters into a pint glass. 'Same rate of pay for the overtime as usual, I've told him. That's right isn't it?' he continued cryptically, nodding at Ossie as he did so.

'Yeah, that's right,' agreed Nipper, finishing the Marlboro he was smoking and dropping it on the floor to his side. 'All easy,' he said, stubbing out the cigarette and motioning Ossie to open him another bottle of light ale.

Sniffler looked smugger than usual, and as far as he was concerned he had every right to. Some of the coke he'd bought earlier would be served up tonight, the rest he'd step on himself before making it available to the punters who'd be celebrating Hysteria's tenth anniversary the following weekend. Tonight's acquisition he'd allow Riddler and Mad Max to sort out, if it was of the same quality then they'd have no problems with it. Who needed Camp Kenny?

'You gonna talk to me then?' asked Nipper, lighting another cigarette. 'Or are you too busy thinking about how much cash yer gonna make now I've weighed in.'

'You aint the only rider that's weighed in,' replied Sniffler, unable to keep his own counsel as the prospect of combining the roles of nightclub owner and drug baron inflated his ego and loosened his tongue.

'Do what?'

'I'm buying Holly's share of Hysteria,' crowed Sniffler, slovenly slurping at his beer. 'She's had enough, same as you. She says it aint a conspiracy though.'

'Fuck me Sniffler! You're as bad as Kenny,' drawled Nipper, looking over towards the toilets as Eggy Barnes and Mad Max Chilman emerged, both looking synthetically re-energized. 'You just cant keep yer north and south shut.'

'Kenny's learnt his lesson.'

'Oh yeah, and who's gonna teach you yours then Sniffler?'

'All done,' interrupted Eggy, arriving at the bar just in time to prevent the fledgling verbal spat developing into something a little more serious.

'Good,' said Nipper, steadying his fraying temper by finishing his drink. 'Where's my old mate Maxie gone then?'

'Back to the car like what I instructed im,' said Sniffler, spoiling for the simmering argument to go on. 'A couple of L and L's for the boys Ossie,' he continued, his level of familiarity surprising even the landlord, 'and have one yerself.'

'Nah you're all right Sniffler,' replied Nipper, winking at Eggy and pointing at the door. 'I only drink with winners.'

'I am a winner, from a family of winners,' growled Sniffler, stepping back from the bar to face Eggy and Nipper. 'My old man runs London. Don't you forget that.'

'Yeah we won't,' replied Nipper smiling. 'Come on Eggy, lets go and spend some of that hard earned cash.'

'Too fucking right you won't,' countered Sniffler, as the two men brushed past him and headed for the door. ' Oi you wankers, don't take the piss out of me ... you cunts ... oi ... wait.

16

November 5th 2004

GEEZERS

'Toot toot said Charlie the train as he set off down the track, disappeared into the tunnel, and made Eggy Barnes smile again.' Nipper laughed as the words came to him whilst he watched Eggy snort his second line of sparkle. 'Nice innit,' he continued, patting him on the back as he traced his fingers through the cocaine residue remaining on the granite kitchen worktop.

'Very good mate,' replied Eggy, rubbing the bridge of his nose and sniffing. 'The same grade as the toot we outed to Sniffler this morning.'

Nipper chopped out two more chubby lines and glanced at his watch. 'Yeah spot on. You watch he'll have worked it all out for himself. The stuff he bought this morning he'll step on himself and hope to out it all next week at the big Hysteria party, and that moody gear he's just bought he'll knock out this weekend. He'll have had a little dabble by now and realised we've fucked about with it.'

'It aint dangerous is it? asked Eggy, as Nipper went nose down with his favourite Nepalese tooter. 'The sample I had in the Knife and Fork was lively enough in all fairness, a little bit trippy too if you know what I mean.'

'Nah mate. Mordi knows what he's doing,' replied Nipper nonchalantly, 'Anyone who does gear regularly will treat it with respect. Anyone who doesn't might feel a little sick. I reckon Claire might be busier than usual tomorrow night. Come on we need to baptise John.'

'Yeah, head off. I know,' laughed Eggy, helping himself to the second line. 'So let me get this right. Bad drugs at Hysteria tomorrow night might put a lot of people off the party next week ...'

'Yes mate,' interrupted Nipper, picking up his car keys. 'The best party next weekend is gonna be over at Mr Terry's where we are headed now, and that my blue brother will spell the end of the road for Hysteria and dear old Holly 'it's me or Chelsea' Philips.'

'Fuck me you really did take it personally didn't you mate.'

'Yeah maybe I did. But let me tell you something mate, when the shit hits the fan next week ... and it will believe me, I'll be on my way to Thailand for a chummy little holiday. Happy days.'

So that was the plan, thought Eggy as he switched the kitchen light off and set the alarm before following Nipper along the hall. 'Yeah but what about Sniffler?' he said, a potential flaw forming in his mind. 'If Hysteria had its license revoked temporarily then he could pick it up on the cheap from Holly. His dad would grease a few palms down at the Town Hall. The club would reopen, and he'd be a bigger nightmare than ever. Clubbers are a fickle bunch, even he could woo them back without too much trouble.'

'You're making a big assumption there,' replied Nipper, as they climbed into the Range Rover.'

'What's that then?'

'Sniffler might not be in a position to buy out Holly.'

★ ★ ★ ★ ★

The main room in Hysteria was absolutely banging, Holly wasn't sure about hard house, in fact she wasn't sure about a lot of the genres that had spun out from the original scene, it all seemed a bit pretentious now. Hard house, funky house, latino, breaks, garage, two step, trip hop, techno, acid jazz, chill out, ambient.

'I'm into house and garage now dad', she remembered saying to her old man, laughing at the memory of his reply. 'What, have you become an estate agent?' he'd said jokingly, forgetting his own roots, in the way older people tended to do.

The true sound of the underground, don't you believe it. In the same way that punk had imploded, the dance scene had fragmented, and promoters needed to be a lot more savvy in their marketing, whether they were trying to fill venues or sell mix CD's. Having a brand helped. Beery Barlow and Steve Bruno knew this. They'd overseen Holly engineer Hysteria into pole position, putting their hands in their pockets when it had been required but staying in the background, cognisant of the fact they didn't understand the scene.

She remembered a shopping trip back to her old haunt Kensington Market. Young kids selling roughly recorded DJ mix tapes with the Hysteria logo crudely emblazoned on the cassette box cover. What a great idea. DJ's like Chiller had made a fortune, helping catapult the Hysteria brand into stellar orbit. But you have to build and develop, keep it human, imaginative and seductive. Peoples tastes change, you have to keep one step ahead. After ten years, it was becoming a pain in the arse.

All these reasons and more confirmed back to Holly that she was making the right decision to get out at the top. They'd all understand, she'd go and see Kenny tomorrow, track down Beery and Bruno, firm things up with Sniffler and call a meeting next week. Plain and simple. Right now, the prospect of another sweaty night held no appeal for her whatsoever. I always knew I couldn't do this straight, she thought to herself, looking at her watch and contemplating what time it would be safe to leave the club early.

★ ★ ★ ★ ★

'Tell you what mate,' said Nipper, concentrating on his driving and keeping to the speed limit as he negotiated the Wandsworth one way system. 'I'll show you the ropes tonight, but tomorrow will be the proper craic. Geezer Goodwin's invited a lot of faces, and all our lot will be in the house. Hold on, ere have a look who this is from will ya.'

Nipper handed his mobile to Eggy as he turned onto York Road and made more use of the power that was available to him.

'It's from Trixie Fowler mate,' said Eggy, d'ya want me to read it out?'

'Yes mate,' replied Nipper lighting a Marlboro as he braked for the lights at the junction of Battersea Park Road and Latchmere Road.

'Hello babe. I'll be over first thing in the morning if that's okay. Kiss kiss kiss.'

'Lovely. I'll get to pour out my baby gravy before we go to the Everton game, this is turning out to be a pretty fine weekend.'

'That aint like you,' said Eggy, emphasising the look of surprise on his face as Nipper pulled over to the kerb and parked on the brow of the low hill just past the dogs home on Battersea Park Road. 'Since you split up with Holly, you've been having a good look every time we've been out. What if there's some decent fanny at Mr Terry's tonight and you pull?'

'I'm sure there will be,' said Nipper, slowing his speech as he looked out of the passenger door window. 'Trixie Fowler's money box is good enough though, and besides I've got another reason.'

Eggy frowned and shook his head. Here we go again, he thought to himself, admiring the view and resisting the temptation to ask further questions.

'Now that Mr Barnes is it,' announced Nipper. 'That does me that. Big Ben, the Houses of Parliament, Nelson's Column, yeah they're important landmarks steeped in

history and tradition, but that mate is London to me. Battersea Power Station.'

'Live'ner?' replied Eggy, nodding in agreement and reaching into the breast pocket of his jacket.

'Be rude not too.'

'Managers specials?'

'Definitely,' said Nipper, gazing lovingly at the rundown old building whilst Eggy chopped out two stout lines of coke on the Range Rover's raised central armrest. 'You know that building right, it looks fucking impressive from the outside, but lemme tell ya about how it used to look on the inside.'

'Go on mate, there you go,' interrupted Eggy, handing him a rolled up £20 note.

'In a minute mate, in a minute,' replied Nipper, slightly disappointed that his friend didn't share quite the same level of enthusiasm for the disused power station as he did. 'The control room was art deco and the turbine hall finished in Italian Marble. Sir Giles Gilbert Scott went to town when he was commissioned to design it, the place even had polished parquet floors and wrought iron staircases.'

'Like a stately home then,' said Eggy, as Nipper paused to snort a line of coke.

'I expect so,' he replied seconds later, not wanting to allow the taking of drugs to stem his flow of praise for the architect. 'Y'know he also designed the red telephone boxes, Waterloo Bridge and er Liverpool Cathedral.'

'Fuck me!' exclaimed Eggy, as Nipper clicked the 4x4's auto box into 'drive'. 'You should go on Mastermind.'

★ ★ ★ ★ ★

'Oi Oi treacle, rinsin' innit,' said Riddler Rowan, leaning into Holly and speaking wide mouthed, thereby giving her twice the opportunity to understand what he was saying. 'This gear that Sniffler brought back this evening, Mad Max reckoned it was a bit mum and dad. I think it's been fucked about with, so we aint sellin it yet.'

'It's all right Riddler,' chuckled Holly. 'I hear what you're saying, no need for me to lip read. 'What's being served up tonight then?'

'A bit of the stuff I had delivered this morning,' said Sniffler, his cheese-cake grin baring nicotine stained teeth that turned Holly's stomach.

'So what's the problem? she asked, her brow furrowed as she turned to face Riddler. 'Just step on it, and we'll knock it out tomorrow. Keep the good stuff for the big party next week. Come on lads, think about it, you'll need to be a bit more creative than this if you're gonna make a go of this place when I'm not around.'

Sniffler chewed his top lip, buying himself a little time as he reached for his cigarettes. He'd had other plans for the good stuff, but he knew he had to put things into perspective and look at the bigger picture. 'What d'ya reckon about this moody gear then Riddler? You're the expert.'

Riddler wrinkled his nose and thrust his hands into his pockets. 'I cant be sure, I'll take some home and test it later,' he said, shrugging his shoulders. 'I reckon there's crystal meth with it though.'

'Crystal what?' asked Sniffler, finally lighting up and throwing the packet to Riddler.

'Meth,' he replied, catching the packet. 'A bit of a do-it-yerself designer drug.' 'Do-it-yourself?' enquired Holly and Sniffler in unison.

Riddler sparked up and smiled. He liked the fact that he was everyone's friend. He had no beef with anyone, and even though he'd remained loyal to Holly, he knew that Nipper and all the other Chelsea lads still loved him. They'd had the craic in Moscow and they'd have it again tomorrow at the Bridge. The nightclubs, he could pick and mix. The life of a dealer, it wasn't a bad one.

'Well?' asked Holly impatiently, thinking about going home again.

'Oh yeah sorry,' said Riddler, blowing several large smoke rings before continuing. 'There's only three things in it really. Psuedoephidrine, which is the active ingredient in a lot of over the counter cold remedies like Sudafed for example. Iodine crystals that you can buy in tincture form which is normally used for treating horses hooves, and red Phosphorus which forms the basis of the strike pad on boxes of safety matches. To cook it up you'd need some methanol and some other shit. Cheap and nasty, anyone could make it without too much effort.'

'Interesting,' sighed Holly, tapping her heels on the floor and running her eye over Riddler. She didn't view him as a drug dealer. To her, dealers hung around inner city school gates at lunchtime. They inhabited the squalid world of fetid, piss stinking, rundown tower blocks and underground car parks whose floors were littered with used syringes. They were the ones responsible for the deaths of young kids.

Drugs in clubs, that was a lifestyle decision, and Riddler was there to make sure that the punters made an informed choice. 'So,' she continued, smiling as she spoke. 'If you see a bloke with a runny nose, smoking a fag and riding a lame horse, the chances are he's on this shit ha ha. But why would Nipper bother?'

'It's more profitable,' replied Riddler, flicking ash onto the floor and rubbing his feet across it. 'It's also quite a buzz, big on the faggot scene as you'd expect.'

'I'll get Kenny's opinion on that,' said Holly, walking across the office to pick up her coat. 'I'm seeing him first thing in the morning … right then Sniffler, you gonna gimme a lift home then?'

Sniffler looked at Holly, then at his watch and then at Riddler Rowan. Maybe he was going to get really lucky tonight. 'Course I will Holly,' he replied, rubbing his hands at the prospect of driving Holly home in his prized Ford Cortina.

'A lift that's all Sniffler,' said Holly, arching her eyebrows as she turned to give Riddler a kiss on both cheeks. 'Check the gear out anyway mate, and ticket up enough to sell tomorrow night. Bring it over to the flat on your way to the football, why not front Nipper about it whilst you're with him at the game. I'm sure it'll be all right, we can get Kenny to sell the rest. Sorted eh.'

'Sorted all right. You aint the boss for nothing eh,' gushed Riddler. Whilst his heart had skipped a couple of admiring beats as he'd listened to her logic, he wouldn't be asking Nipper any questions about anything, that wasn't his style. Two ears, one mouth, use them in that order.

Sniffler nodded begrudgingly. It wasn't in his nature to be patient, but if he played his cards right, Hysteria would be his soon. Nipper was already a rank and file has been and with Holly on her way, he'd be able to run things his way, make his mark, earn the plaudits, and with it the respect of people like Riddler Rowan and Mad Max Chilman. Easy.

★ ★ ★ ★ ★

'Shit, it's starting to fucking piss it down,' said Eggy, as he climbed out of the Range Rover. The icy windswept rain immediately levelled his high, and as he looked across the car park at the large puddles that were forming on its uneven tarmac surface, he wondered if he'd be able to make it to the clubs entrance before he turned cold turkey and was washed away, never to be seen again.

'Come on son,' said Nipper enthusiastically. 'Look Duncan Disorderly's on the door waiting to greet us.'

Eggy Barnes sprinted ahead of Nipper, determined not to get too much of a soaking. 'Duncan Disorderly!' he exclaimed breathlessly, 'I thought he was inside.'

'He was,' replied Nipper, catching his friend up by the time they'd reached the entrance.

'Always a pleasure to see you Mr Nipper,' said Duncan, opening the heavy steel door with effortless ease and showing both men into the clubs foyer.

'Nice one mate,' replied Nipper. 'This is Eggy Barnes, he's Chelsea. You might remember him from back in the day, although he had longer hair then.'

'I remember the name,' said Duncan extending a heavily tattooed hand. 'He was with you when you done Old Bill up at West Ham in the mid '80s.'

'Yeah that's right.'

'Nice work that.'

'Yeah thanks.' Fucking hell, thought Eggy. Here was one of the real old school. His mind was drawn back to his formative years as a Chelsea fan. Born in the Shed, the same as Nipper, Duncan Disorderly was as much a boyhood hero as Peter Osgood and Alan Hudson. A true terrace legend. 'You goin to the game tomorrow Duncan?'

'I haven't been to game in years,' he replied jokingly, his granite features cracking into a broad smile. 'I've been banned from every football ground in England indefinitely. If I so much as fart within a mile of one, plod would have me back inside so quick my big flat feet wouldn't touch the ground … now you lads have a good evening.'

Eggy nodded and winked at Duncan Disorderly, his mind desperately tried to recall why he had been incarcerated, but was soon sidetracked by the sight of three bottle blonde hostesses kitted out in risqué green devil outfits complete with three foot long forked tails who were patrolling the lobby area with mischievous intent written all over their heavily made up faces.

'Come on son, we just need to sign in,' said Nipper, as they followed one of the hostesses through to the lavish looking reception area.

'It aint that busy,' observed Eggy, watching as Nipper exchanged his name and address for a bar coded white rubber bracelet given him by a dark haired, androgynous looking receptionist dressed as an angel who then proceeded to photograph him with a webcam.

'It will be,' replied Nipper, blowing a kiss at the angel and smiling. 'Trust me.'

'Welcome to Mr Terry's gentlemen,' said one of the green devils, wiggling her backside suggestively. 'Follow me.' she continued, leading them through a wrought iron archway into a tunnel covered with a rich purple velour fabric and lit with a myriad of tiny ultra violet rope lights.

'I could follow that arse all night,' said Eggy, suddenly imagining he was about to enter some enchanted fairy kingdom, populated by elves, pixies and delectable green devils who loved being taken roughly from behind.

The tunnel opened out into a clean, open, warehouse-style space which comprised of a large dancefloor flanked by a catwalk on one side and a long bar on the other. TV screens were embedded into every flat surface including the floor, and the complicated light show dazzled and deceived the eyes with its clever use of lasers and mirrors. 'Fuck me!' exclaimed Eggy. 'This place is amazing.'

'I know it is mate,' replied Nipper cockily. 'I designed it.'

★ ★ ★ ★ ★

'C'mon mate, pay attention,' said Holly, wiping condensation away from the windscreen with the back of her hand. 'I wanna get home in one piece.'

Sniffler had failed to notice that the lights were red at the junction of Lavender Hill and Latchmere Road and a late attempt to brake had sent the Cortina aquaplaning perilously along the greasy surface of the road.

'Sorry darlin, it's the rain,' he replied, shrugging his shoulders and dropping down through the gears carefully as they approached Queenstown Road.

Holly tried to refocus her mind on her plans to sell Hysteria, but a combination of Sniffler's driving and a nagging concern over what Nipper might be up to made it difficult. As they turned into Battersea Park Road her eyes were drawn to the familiar site of the power station which further served to stir things up. The gloomy foreboding chimneys looked the same by day or night, come rain or shine. Some things never changed. Maybe that's why Nipper identified with the building.

'Mr Terry's,' sneered Sniffler, 'Waste of time and money.'

'Maybe,' replied Holly not caring. She knew that Sniffler was itching to get back to Hysteria and liven himself up. She could sense his irritability growing by the minuteand was eternally grateful to God that she'd made it through the day without succumbing to the temptation herself.

'Nipper's in with that Geezer Goodwin,' said Sniffler, pulling into Elm Quay and dropping his left hand onto Holly's thigh. 'You wanna watch that.'

'And you wanna watch that,' replied Holly, slapping at his hand and frowning. 'I recommend you drive with due care and attention on your way back to the club boy.'

Holly smiled at Sniffler as she got out of his car. It was a friendly smile, what did she care about the dopey fucker anymore? Disregarding the rain, she watched Sniffler U turn the Cortina and zip back out onto the deserted main road. Silly wanker, she thought to herself. Mind you, at least he was going back to something ... a club full of people. Whereas she was going back to an empty flat. Empty excepting Jezebel.

'Three messages eh Jezzy,' said Holly, getting her priorities in order after she'd entered the flat. Feed the cat, a cup of tea, check the answering machine. 'Right let's see who they're from.'

'Hi Holly, it's Claire. Hope you're safe. Good girl. See you tomorrow.'

'Hi Holly. Mr Sheen here. Why haven't you called me?'

'Yeah hi Holly. it's me Nipper. Long time no parlez. Why don't you pop round tomorrow before I go to the game. I wanna chat to you about about a few things. Gimme a call.'

Holly's heart jumped at the sound of his voice. She replayed the message several times, judging from the background noise he must be in a late bar or a club somewhere. Mr Terry's perhaps. Keying 1471 into the handset, confirmed to her that Nipper had made the call using his mobile phone. Resisting temptation had been the order of the day, she wasn't going to come over all keen now. 'Wait until the morning cherub.'

★ ★ ★ ★ ★

Geezer Goodwin had presence. If he walked into a room crowded with talkative people the chatter would soon abate. An urbane and sophisticated operator in the Square Mile, he wielded power, authority and influence. A cabal of insider traders had enabled him to manipulate share prices during the dotcom boom, and the profits had been ploughed back into a diverse range of legitimate national and international projects.

What set him apart from his business rivals was a genuine flair with people; he kept his finger on the pulse by winning the trust of and rewarding those who kept him abreast of the latest lifestyle marketing opportunities. Owning a nightclub he'd viewed as the icing on a cake already rich in ingredients; acquiring the old Adrenalin Village site had been the first step, a chance meeting with Davy Truelove had resulted in the second.

Goodwin had been amazed at Holly Philips' reticence to get involved, she'd been the one that Truelove had said was fiercely ambitious, the girl with the club know-how, but Johnny Nipper hadn't disappointed him. Far from it, in fact he'd been a revelation, providing sound advice right across the piece, including highlighting those people who could threaten his planned dominance of the UK club scene. Mr Terry's was the blueprint for a national franchise, and Nipper had swiftly manoeuvred himself into pole position to run it.

'Mr Goodwin, let me introduce you to a very good friend of mine, Edward Barnes.' The formal manner of Nipper's introduction surprised Eggy, who was about to go down the well worn 'but everyone call's me Eggy' route, before his friend added, 'Middle name Egbert, known to one and all as Eggy.'

'Eggy, very good,' said Geezer, a sincere smile forming on his craggy suntanned face. 'I don't like people who use their Christian names, it shows a lack character.'

Cocaine cockiness often got the better of Eggy Barnes, but he felt comfortable in the current company, and he wasn't going to pass up on the opportunity to ascertain the origins of Goodwin's nom de plume. 'Geezer,' he said, scratching the side of his chin and running his eye over the bespoke herringbone Boateng suit that Goodwin was wearing. 'How did you come by that without stating the obvious?... er by that I mean you are a geezer.'

Geezer Goodwin's eyes narrowed slightly, he didn't mind a joke, Eggy was clearly a funny guy, but familiarity this early on could be taken as contemptuous. If the lad wasn't such a pal of Nipper's he'd have put him down with an acerbic one liner, but fuck it, at the end of the day he'd had the bottle to ask, and front like that deserved an answer. 'I used to play the bass in a Black Sabbath covers band,' he replied poker faced, wondering if that would mean anything to Eggy.

'Blimey!' exclaimed Eggy. 'What, like that Geezer Butler geezer?'

'That's the fella.'

'That's amazing.'

'It's more interesting than being called Terrence, Terry or Tel.'

'Do you still play?'

'Don't be fucking silly,' answered Geezer laughing. 'I packed up hard rocking the first time I saw the Stranglers at the Hope and Anchor.

'Jesus wept,' interjected Nipper, I'd probably have been at that gig. I saw 'em play there loads of times.'

'*Christ has told his mother?*' growled Geezer, dropping his cool for a moment as he jerked his neck forward and threw a shape with his brand new air guitar.

'*Christ has told her not to bother,*' continued Nipper, joining in enthusiastically, his minds eye picturing the original Stranglers main-man Hugh Cornwell at the peak of his venomous vocal power, spitting out the lyrics and cranking out the chords on that battered old Fender Telecaster he used to play.

'Cos he's high above the city,' sneered Eggy, feeling left out.

'He's high above the ground ... he's just hanging around ...'

'Fucking classic,' said Geezer, regaining his composure, relieved that no-one else had witnessed his momentary lapse of reason.

'Yeah,' agreed Nipper, almost overcome by sentimentality. 'An old mate of ours used to always used to put that on the jukebox of a drinker we used to use back in the day.'

'Let's go and have a drink in the VIP lounge,' suggested Geezer, putting his arms around both men's shoulders. 'We can have a nice chat about the old times. I cant fucking stand this dance music shit if I'm honest.'

Fuck me, thought Nipper, as they walked through the club. Geezer Goodwin used to be a punk. He'd already decided to keep Holly's name out of any discussion that might follow. Geezer would want to know more, and he wanted her kept out of any kind of equation that his benefactor might care to formulate. He didn't have to worry about Eggy, because they hadn't known him back then.

'It's a small world isn't it,' said Geezer, pulling Nipper to one side as they walked through the VIP room doors. 'Let's keep it that way eh son.'

'Of course Geezer,' replied Nipper, slightly taken aback by the insinuation. 'I don't share any information about my business dealings with you.'

Geezer Goodwin cocked his head back slightly as he looked Nipper squarely in the eyes. 'I'm sure you wouldn't, but I know you lads have penchant for the sparkle, that rubbish combined with a few beers loosens tongues. Remember the old adage son, careless talk costs lives. There's a lot happening tonight, if you know what I mean.'

The knockabout humour and friendly demeanour Geezer Goodwin had displayed a few minutes previously was suddenly less evident. The thin veneer of tolerance masked a malevolent 'fuck me about at your peril' streak, and Nipper was already patently aware that the man didn't trade in veiled threats. Without regret or remorse, he removed barriers with ruthless efficiency.

'You can trust me,' said Nipper, fronting out the situation confidently.

'I know I can,' replied Geezer, looking at his watch and smiling as they made their way over to join Eggy at the bar. 'We're on the right track Nipper, and the obstacle train is just about to be derailed.'

17

DEADLY DEL'S TREBLE TOP

Silly cunt, thought Sniffler, drumming his fingers on the steering wheel nervously as he drove cautiously along Battersea Park Road. The rain, sheeting down in torrents, had made driving conditions hazardous and the Cortina's old fashioned windscreen wipers were proving increasingly ineffective against the deluge. Visibility was poor.

'Maybe you should've tried it on with her son,' he said to himself, fidgeting with the demister settings and braking gently as he approached the junction with Falcon Road. 'If she'd stood for it, It would've saved me the grief of driving back in this fucking poxy weather ... what the fack-in-fack-facking hell ... CAHNT!'

The Cortina had been struck from behind, the impact sending it skidding sideways into the nearside kerb. 'CAHNT!' cursed Sniffler, powerless to react as the momentum caused by the crash catapulted him forward towards the windscreen. The loose racing harness he was wearing restrained his body but jack-knifed his head against the dashboard, instantaneous whiplash bouncing him back into the door pillar causing his elbows to buckle as he maintained a white knuckle grip on the steering wheel.

'CAHNNNNT ... FACKIN CAHNNNNT!' he yelled, wide eyed with shock as the cars engine stalled and its electrics fizzed, popped, and shorted out.

Any pain he may have felt as a result of the bruising injuries sustained in the accident were immediately anaesthetised by the combination of rage and adrenalin that reactively surged through his body.

Within a matter of seconds Sniffler had freed himself from the harness and instinctively reached into the glove compartment for the telescopic truncheon he kept there to cater for such eventualities. Hauling himself out of the passenger door that had swung open and wrenched itself away from its hinges, he was ready for action.

'Look what you've done to me fackin motor you cahnt!' he screamed lividly, oblivious to the wind and rain and the absence of anyone willing to take responsibility for the debacle. 'You're gonna pay for this scum cunt.'

Flicking open the steel sprung truncheon and raising it above his head, he ran towards the navy blue BMW that had pulled up a couple of car lengths in front of the wreck. 'Do you know who I am you facking cahhhhnt!'

The car looked familiar, the paintwork, the privacy glass and the six spoke alloys. He'd seen one like it before but he couldn't be sure where, but in the heat of the moment Sniffler was in no mood to play detective, he wanted swift retribution.

'WANKER!' he shouted, smashing the ball end of the truncheon against the drivers window, the glass shattering instantaneously. 'Let's have you then.'

Sniffler opened the door, readying himself to strike the driver. But despite the fact its engine was still idling, the car was empty.

Wiping the rain away from his face, he reached in, removed the keys from the ignition and walked around to look at the front of the vehicle. No questions, this was the car that had struck his. The damage was minimal, but the bumper had been pushed up and the distinctive radiator grill was fractured across the middle. 'Hit and run? Fucking clowns. You're meant to fuck off in the car, not on foot.'

Sniffler's head began to throb as he trudged back to the Cortina. 'What the fuck am I meant to do now?' he said, pushing his fingers against his right temple and grimacing at the pain this caused him. 'Call Old Bill? Fuck that, fucking cunts!'

'D'ya need some help mate?' said a helpful sounding voice.

Sniffler spun round on his heels, he'd just begun to wonder if the commotion might have woken anyone, maybe someone had witnessed what had happened. 'Yes mate,' he replied, rubbing his face again, screwing up his eyes as he tried to focus on the face of the good Samaritan stood under the bus shelter on the opposite side of the road. 'Some cunt's just driven into the back of me and fucked off.'

'Some cunt eh!' said a different voice, this time from behind.

Sniffler felt a prod in his back. As he turned his head, the owner of the second voice caught him a glancing blow on the point of his chin with the butt end of a sawn off shotgun.

'What the … ?'

The reverse strike by his unknown assailant knocked him unconscious to the ground.

'Right bro,' said Jamie Black, lowering the hood of his raincoat. 'Let's get this chav in the motor and fuck off before we wake the street up.'

'Yes mate,' replied Leighton, kicking the prone figure of Sniffler in the ribs hard enough to determine whether he had regained consciousness or not. 'He's got a nasty gash on the side of his head there look,' he continued, as he bent down, grabbed at Sniffler's feet and dragged him over to the BMW.

'Probably needs stitching ha ha,' said Jamie, opening the boot and helping his twin brother to bundle Sniffler unceremoniously into it.

'He wont have to worry about that where he's going,' replied Leighton, looking up and down the street. 'Shame about the motor though, that's a write off.'

★ ★ ★ ★ ★

Del Goss was a consummate professional with a reputation for being callously efficient. Every job he undertook was planned with meticulous detail and carried out precisely as instructed by the person who had contracted him.

A military man with the prerequisite nebulous background, it was widely believed that he had served with the French Foreign Legion, although no-one could be sure. Goss wasn't the type of person that was idly gossiped about, indeed when his name cropped up in conversations, it was whispered for fear that the man, known in certain quarters as Deadly Del, might somehow be listening.

The universal nature of organised crime in the 21st century meant that his was a truly global business. Recently, his work had taken him as far a field as Japan and Chile. Abroad, he would dispatch his victims at long range with a snipers rifle, death would be instantaneous, there would always be a body, but no clues for the police to follow up on.

Here in London, he could indulge the psychopathic whims of his paymasters. Everything had a price, all that was required was patience and a little imagination. The failure rate was zero, if you somehow found out that your card had been marked by Del Goss, suicide would be a better option than the fate that would befall you at his hands.

Doogie Black's scrap metal yard in Merton was a discreet enough location for Del Goss to use as and when he required a venue that offered a diverse range of facilities. Tucked away at the end of an alley just off Haydon's Road, it was the perfect place to conclude a deal and dispose of the evidence. Its proximity to St George's hospital and Lambeth Cemetery was an amusing irrelevance.

Doogie Black had been Del's mentor, providing him with contracts and contacts. Doogies boys Leighton and Jamie were like brothers to him. Trusted, well paid accomplices, who viewed it as an honour and a privilege to work with a friend of their fathers, tonight they were helping him rid Geezer Goodwin of three of his business rivals.

★ ★ ★ ★ ★

Del Goss walked across the yard and cursed as the rain swirled around its narrow confines like a mini typhoon picking up leaves and rubbish and hurling them sodden against anything and everything in its path. Fuck this, he thought to himself, as much as he loved working in London, he just couldn't handle the weather at this time of the year.

'Right lads?' he said in a low voice, tapping the workshops steel roller shutter door three times and waiting for the reply.

'Yes Del.'

As he pushed the button to engage the mechanism which opened the door, his mind drifted momentarily. The house in Santa Eularia, the smell of mimosa floating on the dry warm air, Layla lying on the bed touching herself, waiting for him to come home. Maybe I should just do seasonal work, he thought, chuckling to himself as he checked the time on the oversize Italian Navy divers watch that he always wore for work.

The Panerai Luminor Marina watch had been a gift from Doogie Black. 44mm across the face, with a distinctive protective clasp across the crown, he wore it with a heavy duty vulcanised rubber strap. The watch was robust, practical, and more importantly, easy to clean. Popularised in certain men's style bibles and normally the preserve of Premiership footballers and Gangsta Rapper's, it was Deadly Del's one a-la-mode concession.

'All easy?' he asked, as he watched Leighton and Jamie drag Sniffler Barlow's still unconscious body across the steel rimmed threshold into the workshop.

'Piece of piss,' replied Jamie, looking up and smiling. 'The cunt had no idea what was going on, right up until the split second before I knocked him out.'

'He was going mental about his car,' said Leighton, placing Sniffler in the recovery position adjacent to the rusting chassis of an E-Type Jaguar that was being stripped down for restoration.

'In all fairness you could see why,' added Jamie, patting the Jag and nodding. 'He must've done a bundle on that Cortina, it looked the bollocks.'

Del's normally impassive features fractured into a broad grin, and his cold, basalt black eyes twinkled with humour as he walked over to where the twins were stood. 'Looked, is about right eh. That motor could be your next project.'

'Nah,' replied Jamie, sighing sorrowfully before continuing to speak. 'It's gonna take some time to bring this baby back to its former glory. We owe it to our old man Doogie, as much as we owe it to ourselves.

'Fair point,' agreed Del, buttoning up the front of his overalls and bending down to retie his shoelaces.

At the time of Doogie Black's conviction, the police had sequestrated a number of properties and cars which were alleged to have been purchased with the proceeds of his crimes. A decade later, an inside man had tipped Jamie off about a forthcoming government auction, and more specifically about one particular lot, a distressed looking black E Type Jaguar which bore the registration mark DOO 81E. For a small consideration, he'd acquired the Jag on the Black twins behalf, and their mission now was to have it in showroom condition by the time Doogie was released. It was slow, painstaking work, but with their father still only half way through his sentence, time was on their side.

'Cup of tea Del?' asked Leighton, walking over to the vending machine by the workshops office.

'I'll have a sip of yours son,' replied Del, as he always did. 'It's time to crack on, it's getting late.'

Del gratefully accepted the plastic cup, cradling it with both hands, absorbing the heat and blowing on its steaming hot contents before gingerly taking a couple of sips and handing it back to Leighton. There was an element of theatrical routine about the way Del worked which wasn't lost on the twins who winked at each other and smiled.

'Well well,' said Del Goss, noticing that Sniffler was showing the first twitching signs of regaining consciousness. 'There are gonna be a few puzzled people when this little lot fail to turn up for school next week. Right then, let's just double check the class register eh.'

Jamie Black rubbed his hands together in anticipation, the expectant look on his face was one akin to that of a young boy who'd managed to sneak into a certificate 18 film at his local fleapit.

'Barlow senior, Barlow junior and Bruno,' announced Del Goss proudly. 'All present and correct.'

A couple of metres away from the prone figure of Sniffler, Beery Barlow and Steve Bruno were sat on a couple of high backed dining chairs which were positioned precariously close to the edge of the workshops inspection pit. Feet bound, hands cuffed behind their backs, mouths gagged by gaffer tape, you could almost smell their fear as Del Goss made his way over to them.

* * * * *

'What the fack is this all abahhht?' croaked Sniffler as he came round. Turning his head sideways to look at his captors, he had yet to realise that his predicament was shared and not solitary. 'Who the fack are ya? Answer me.'

His terse question was met with a stony silence, and as he tried to get to his feet he almost fainted as the insane throbbing pain in his head doubled in intensity. 'Listen … d'ya fackin' know who yer dealin' wiv? Yer makin' a big fackin' mistake,' he shouted, dropping to his knees and flexing the muscles in his arms in a bid to loosen the cord that Leighton Black had expertly bound his hands behind his back with.

'Well now Stevie Barlow, that's just where you're wrong,' replied Del Goss, walking around the side of the E Type so that Sniffler could see him. 'Y'see I know exactly who I'm dealing with, and I'm pretty certain I'm not making any mistake whatsoever,' he continued, folding his arms and cocking his head to one side as he spoke. 'Jamie wheel the Clarke 900 over, and bring the Paslode with you while you're at it.'

Thick crimson blood oozed once more from the open wound on the side of Sniffler's head, it ran into his eyes, blurred his vision and enraged him further. 'Cahhnt! Who put ya up to this? If ya take me out you'll 'av my old man's firm to deal wiv' they'll find ya and kill ya. What is it ya want? Fackin' cash? I've got bundles. Whatever you want eh … name it.'

Del nodded at Leighton Black and motioned him to reposition Sniffler Barlow so that he was facing his two fellow captives. He then took a handkerchief from his pocket, soaked it in the turpentine substitute which was in a bucket by his feet, and walked over to him. 'Well well Stevie now there's a coincidence,' he said sarcastically, bending down to wipe the blood away from Sniffler's eyes. 'Y'see it seems to me that I've been given your old man's firm to deal with myself.'

Sniffler flinched at the smell and yelped in pain as Del cleaned his face and then held the hankie against the wound to staunch the flow of blood. 'Fackin fack!' he screamed repeatedly, as he recognised the familiar face of his father and that of Steve Bruno.

'Jamie, hand me the Paslode, I'm getting bored now,' said Del, throwing the hankie on the floor as he stood up.

'Fack … cahnt … me Dad, Steve Bruno,' whimpered Sniffler. 'Please, what the facks this abaht?' he pleaded, terror now modulating his voice as he continued to buck on the floor in a futile attempt to free himself.

As Jamie Black handed the Paslode gas powered nail gun to Del, Steve Bruno raised his head and tried to communicate. Rolling his frightened eyes and nodding at Sniffler, the words he wanted to say remained trapped in his mouth by the gaffer tape and all that could be heard was a muted, unintelligible moaning sound.

Del wasn't exactly sure what Steve Bruno had done to warrant a contract being taken out on him, nor did he care really. A contract was a contract, and whilst no-one deserved to have their life terminated early, most of Del's victims probably knew they had it coming to them. With a conscience like a great white shark, sympathy was the most underused word in his vocabulary. He never felt sorry for anyone although it did sadden him sometimes to see how weak the human spirit could be, and how easily hecould break it.

'Have a look at this Mr Bruno,' said Del, holding the Paslode out in front of him in the manner of Dirty Harry Callaghan. 'This nail gun requires no compressor, as you can see it's very mobile, you can use it anywhere,' he continued, revelling in the sheer terror he could see in Steve Bruno's imploring eyes. 'It fires 64 millimetre hardened T nails, and although its main use is for fastening wood to masonry, I believe that it could be equally effective when used for other purposes.'

Bathed in perspiration, Steve Bruno began to cry and squeal, rocking his head back he tried to overbalance the chair he was secured to, but it was of little use.

'Well now let me ask you a question. Do you feel lucky punk?'

'Fackin psycho!' yelled Sniffler, drowning out Steve Bruno's desperate grunts.

'Shut it shit for brains, or you'll get the first nail in your bollocks,' growled Del, angered by the interruption.

Sniffler closed his eyes and shivered, the adrenalin rush had abated, he felt pain, he felt fear, and as he lay on the cold damp concrete floor the stark realisation that he was about to die caused him to retch and lapse in and out of consciousness.

'Time's up Mr Bruno,' said Del Goss, as he gently squeezed the trigger. The Paslode hissed as the compressed gas discharged its deadly cargo. The nail entered Steve Bruno's face through his left cheek and exited just below his right ear ricocheting off the floor and embedding itself in the wooden perimeter of the inspection pit. Blood haemorrhaged from the wound, arcing through the air and showering Sniffler who had curled up into the foetus position and was muttering to himself.

'That's nailed it,' chuckled Del, as he fired three more nails at Bruno's head in quick succession. The first tore through the soft tissue of his left eye, mashed his brain, and penetrated the rear of his skull; he was already dead before the last two nails hit him.

Jamie Black covered his eyes and nose, the bloody sight and smell of Bruno, who'd soiled his pants as he died was gory and grotesque in the extreme even for a man like him who prided himself on his strong constitution.

'No one likes to see that eh,' said Leighton giggling. 'Least of all Jamie. Too much for you bruv? Y'know if you can't handle this kind of work you could always get a job down at McDonalds, they're always looking for people.'

Jamie smiled as he watched Del Goss push Steve Bruno's body into the inspection pit. He tried to think of a witty riposte, but nothing came to mind. Instead he imagined that Guy Ritchie or Quentin Tarantino might suddenly walk across the workshop floor, clapper board in hand, and yell, 'cut!' This was no film though, that was real claret on the floor, and Del Goss was about to increase the body count.

'I aint wasting nails on this old cunt,' said Del, lifting his right foot and placing it on Beery Barlow's chest. Barlow shrugged his shoulders in what looked like a 'fuck you' gesture as Goss applied sufficient pressure to over-balance the chair to which he was shackled causing it to topple backwards into the inspection pit.

There was a sickening thud as Barlow's skull cracked against the floor and fractured, dark red blood rapidly forming a lava-like halo around his motionless head.

'Two down, one to go,' said Jamie, wheeling over the Clarke Jumpstart 900 over to where Sniffler was lying in a pool of Steve Bruno's congealing blood.

'This cunt is a bit of a bully apparently,' said Del Goss, kneeling across Sniffler's body so that he couldn't move whilst Leighton Black removed his shoes and socks. 'He picks on defenceless queers.'

'Where's my dad?' asked Sniffler, shaking his head as the icy cold water Jamie Black had just poured onto his bare feet brought him round. This time his vision was impaired. As he opened his eyes the images he saw were flickering, distorted ones. Horizontal hold, vertical hold. Please adjust. Squinting, he managed to focus on the large crocodile clamps that were pinching each of his ankles. 'What the fack ... ARGHHH!'

Leighton Black had flicked the switch of the portable boost starter he was holding sending 400 amps of current along the Clarke's heavy duty cables, into the crocodile clamps attached to Sniffler whose body arched as the circuit was completed.

'Sorry, I didn't quite catch what you said then son,' said Del Goss, holding his right hand up.

'Please … please … I've … I've got money er eh huh huh huh,' sobbed Sniffler racked with pain, each of his joints feeling like they were about to burst open like overripe fruit.

'You've got fuck all son,' replied Del caustically. 'Your Dad was potless … done all his dough in Geezer Goodwin's casino. It's no use gambling if you don't win. Your cash is all tied up in Percy. That aint no use to me. The only way you could make any money would be if you had tonight's winning lottery numbers … and you aint even bought a ticket.'

'Please!' whimpered Sniffler.

'Please,' mimicked Del. 'Not so big now are you … better luck in the next life sunbeam,' he said, lowering his right hand, the cue for Leighton Black to switch the Clarke on again. 'Leave it on for a couple of minutes this time sonny.'

★ ★ ★ ★ ★

'It's sorted Nipper,' said Geezer, motioning the barman to pour him another glass of Jameson's as he put his mobile phone back into his pocket.

'Sorted?' asked Nipper stifling a yawn. Tiredness had caught up with him since he'd had to lay off the cocaine. Eggy Barnes had long since departed with a coffee skinned Brixton beauty, leaving him to pander to Geezer Goodwin's whims and ego.

'Beery Barlow, his Muppet son, and that Steve Bruno,' replied Geezer, swirling the Irish whisky around in front of his eyes. 'All taken care of. Now we just need your little plan to work tonight and we're home and dry,' he said, knocking back the Jameson's in one gulp once he had finished speaking.

This was fucking serious shit, thought Nipper, holding his tongue, resisting the urge to ask any further questions. Were the Barlow's and Steve Bruno that big a threat? Surely not. Maybe Geezer was just making a point. Put that could've been done just as effectively without hiring a psychopathic mercenary like Deadly Del.

'You never have to worry about a body turning up when he tops people here in the Smoke,' said Geezer, rolling up the sleeves of his shirt and resting his elbows on the bar.

'Go on,' said Nipper, realising that Geezer was probably feeding him this information to ensure that if he might be contemplating any kind of side bet he'd think twice about it.

'He lobs the bodies in the inspection pit at Doogie Grey's old workshop, and torches em,' continued Geezer, looking Nipper in the eyes as he spoke. 'Scatters the ashes on Wimbledon Common by all accounts, I wonder what the Womble's would make of that? Ha ha ha.'

Nipper frowned. He'd heard these stories about Deadly Del before. But it had been just pub talk with the lads. Hearing the same story from Geezer Goodwin was different, it was no longer an urban myth, it was reality.

'He carries everything out to the letter, fucking loves it,' added Geezer, smiling as he sensed he had Nipper's undivided attention. 'Remember Fireball Freddie? The bloke who used to torch motors on request for insurance purposes.'

'Yeah, I remember Freddie,' replied Nipper, lighting a Marlboro and shaking his head. 'He vanished a couple of years ago.'

'In a puff of smoke ha ha,' laughed Geezer. 'I told him he'd have to pack it in after I bought out Old Street Insurance. But he didn't. A mans gotta protect his interests, so I had Deadly Del give Freddie a bit of his own medicine. He doused him in four star, pushed him into the pit and dropped a match on him. Whoosh! Fireball Freddie lived up to his own name. Apparently as he burned, he'd repeatedly tried to scramble out of the pit but Del kept stamping on his fingers. What a way to go eh.'

'Point taken Geezer,' said Nipper, looking at his watch and rolling his eyes in frustration. 'Don't worry I wont try and fuck you over.'

'I know you wont son.'

'Listen I'd better get off. There's a lot going on later. I could do with a decent kip.'

'You do that boy.'

Johnny Nipper winced at the firmness of Geezer Goodwin's parting handshake. With new friends like this, who the fuck needed enemies? he thought to himself as he made his way out of the VIP room. Trixie Fowler, Holly Philips, Everton at home, the demise of Hysteria, a holiday in Thailand, Geezer's lolly. I'm the man from Dundee ... I'm fucking caked.

18

HELL HATH NO FURY ...

'I aint seen him treacle,' said Riddler, nervously fidgeting with the keys to the office safe. 'He never come back last night, after he dropped you off. I've tried his mobile, and his home number ... nothing.'

Holly held the beads of her Jet necklace up to her mouth, chewing on them as she ruminated. 'Strange that,' she replied eventually. 'I'll tell you what though. The way that maniac drives, it wouldn't surprise me if he'd crashed. The weather was as shabby as you like when he dropped me off.'

'That'd be a shame wouldn't it,' said Riddler, opening the safe and checking the contents. 'Nah, he aint touched nothing here. That moody nose is still there.'

'Do me favour and ring round a few hospitals. You never know, try Old Bill first as well, there can't be too many of those old Ford Concertina's kicking around.'

'Cortina's.'

'Yeah, whatever.'

Holly looked at her watch and gathered her thoughts as Riddler called the police. She hadn't been able to get hold of anyone. Beery, Steve Bruno, Sniffler, all of them on voicemail. It was a Saturday morning, but that was no excuse. All she wanted to do was to set up a meeting to discuss her future involvement with Hysteria. There was no mad rush, but now she'd made her mind up, she just wanted everything sorted out.

The moody crystal meth gear, she'd speak to Nipper about. She'd take a couple of ounces with her. Whatever he was up to, she'd find out, a blow job would take care of that. Camp Kenny could fill her in on the rest of the detail later. His text messages had been quite specific. 'Any luck?' she enquired, looking up at Riddler as she split the seal on the Tupperware container.

'Yeah, sort of,' replied a perplexed looking Riddler. 'The police 'ave a record of the car. It 'ad been shunted into a skip on Battersea Park Road just up the road from your drum. The car aint been reported nicked or nuffink, and they've already checked with all the local 'orspitals.'

'What about Claire?' suggested Holly, estimating weight by sight as she scooped up the suspect coke into a zip-lock plastic bag.

'Already checked with Claire.'

'Strange innit.'

'Yeah, innit.'

★ ★ ★ ★ ★

'Easy tiger,' breathed Trixie Fowler huskily. 'Mmm ... well no need to ask if you're pleased to see me then,' she said, grinding her crotch into Nipper's groin as she reciprocated his fervent kisses and pushed him against the kitchen wall.

'Good to see you again honey, and so soon,' replied Nipper, intoxicated by the musky scent of Trixie's perfume. 'You ... are so fucking horny,' he continued, dropping down to his knees and pushing up her skirt, circling and gripping her buttocks as he did so.

'Watch the dress darling,' sighed Trixie, as Nipper pulled the cheeks of her arse apart and began kissing her thighs. 'It's a Diane Von Furstenberg number oh ah,' she said, moaning as his snaking tongue reached the gusset of her thong and he chewed on her sex through the flimsy material.

'Really!' exclaimed Nipper, pulling his head out from under the skirt. 'I thought it was by Dries Van Noten.'

'Ha Ha, very funny,' replied Trixie sarcastically. 'Let's cut the haute couture chat and get down to the hot thrusting action. I want your cock inside me now.'

Trixie moved quickly. Dropping down to her knees, she rocked Nipper backwards, tugged down his boxer shorts and forced herself onto his willingly erect penis. 'Come on you dirty bastard fuck me hard,' she hissed, adopting the squat position, her gym honed thighs making light work of the task.

'You fuck me babe, you fuck me,' encouraged Nipper, mesmerised by Trixie whose face was a contorted mask of libidinous lust. He watched as she closed her eyes, tightened her grip, moistened and moaned, and he was right there with her seconds later when she let out a banshee-like wail as the intensity of her orgasm caused her to lose control of her bladder.

'Blimey,' said Nipper, recovering his composure as he held Trixie in a lovers embrace. 'I've experienced a few things, but never anything like that.'

'Female ejaculation, water-sports … Who the fucks that?' asked Trixie, interrupting herself as the doorbell rang. 'Oh look at the state of my dress!' she exclaimed, as Nipper extricated himself from their clinch, pulled up his piss soaked boxer shorts, picked up his dressing gown and made his way hurriedly to the door.

★ ★ ★ ★ ★

'Come on Max, answer your fucking phone!' said Holly impatiently, stabbing at the doorbell with her Gucci gloved index finger as she spoke, her irritability exacerbated by the fact that she'd been unable to resist the temptation of sampling Nipper's moody merchandise.

Riddler was right. The buzz from the crystal meth, if that's what it was, was an altogether different proposition to normal sparkle. It was harder and shorter, the comedown was bumpy, and all in all it had left her feeling short changed and wanting more. Too late now, she thought to herself, reaching for the doorbell again as Max's phone rang through to voicemail. With Sniffler still on the missing list, she was keen to find out if he'd mentioned anything to Max when they'd made the pick up. Full of his own self importance, Sniffler loved boasting, and Max was just the sort of person he loved to talk down to. Maybe he'd know something.

'Nipper, Nipper wake up,' said Holly, keeping her finger pressed on the doorbell and looking across the street at his immaculately clean Range Rover. He had to be in, she reasoned, he never went anywhere without that thing. Finally she heard the sound of footsteps approaching down the hall, and as the key turned in the five lever mortise lock and the door opened, the butterflies that had been gathering in her stomach all morning finally took flight.

'Hello N N Nipper,' she stammered nervously. 'I thought you were gonna leave me out here on the doorstep.'

'Hey doll face,' he said, tying the cord of his dressing gown into a bow and smiling as he gave her a peck on the cheek. 'Please come in, er lemme go and throw some clothes on. D'ya fancy a brew?'

'Tea's good,' replied Holly, frowning as she followed him into the kitchen, disappointed that the greeting had been so formal having half hoped that he would have scooped her up in his brawny arms, taken her upstairs and ravished her.

Nipper grinned cheesily at Holly as he filled the kettle, narrowing his eyes and looking her up and down, arousing her curiosity with his jittery behaviour, not really knowing what to say or do. The uneasy silence was broken as Holly's phone, now buried at the bottom of her pastel blue Juicy Couture satchel, began to ring.

'Take the call,' said Nipper, brushing past Holly and winking at her but avoiding eye contact. 'I'm gonna get dressed, I'll be back down in a couple of minutes.'

Holly answered the phone. It was Max, he didn't know anything that she didn't, but told her that he'd check with his brother before he went to the football. Fucking football, she thought, shaking her head. Why were these blokes so obsessed with it?

'You want one too?' she shouted, as the kettle boiled. But there was no answer. She scanned the kitchen looking for clues, as she made herself a cup of tea. Clues for what though? The place was immaculate just as it always was. Nipper had retained the services of the cleaner that Holly had hired when she'd lived there, and as she walked through to the living room and sat herself down in the classic Charles Eames reclining chair that she'd bought when they'd first moved in, she began to wonder why she'd ever left.

What a lovely room. Its high ceiling created a feeling of space, and the wax polished Swedish hardwood floor looked almost too beautiful to walk upon. The large Max Alto sofa, with its bright scatter cushions still sat under the bay window just as it always had and the curvaceous Arcolight that swooped gracefully up from behind it helped to balance out its sharp edges. The only thing that was new was a huge Panasonic plasma TV that had been mounted on the wall above the Acantha fireplace. Holly thought it looked hideous.

'Hi Mikki,' said a familiar sounding female voice. 'Nipper said you were downstairs, what a lovely surprise.'

'Ouch!' yelped a startled Holly as she leapt to her feet and spilt scalding hot tea on her arm. 'Trixie Fowler! What on earth are you doing here? I thought you lived in New York.'

'I used to,' replied Trixie calmly, standing in the doorway, a smug look of satisfaction on her newly made up face. 'Moved back to London, well Brighton actually when Geezer Goodwin commissioned me to work for him ... that's how I bumped into Nipper.'

Prepared for just about any eventuality apart from one like this, Holly could feel the fine downy hairs on the back of her neck standing on end as she bent down and placed the dripping mug on the B&B Italia coffee table that had been a gift from her late father.

'Really!' exclaimed Holly caustically, her stomach knotting in anger as she flexed her fingers and regulated her breathing, trying desperately hard not to fly into a jealous rage.

Trixie was unfazed, but slightly taken aback by Holly's confrontational attitude. 'Yeah, I heard about you two splitting up. I must say I was surprised, but hey you must've had your reasons cos Nipper's still a blinding bloke.'

Unflappable she may have been, but Trixie Fowler wasn't stupid, and neither was Holly Philips. Both women probably heard the penny drop at precisely the same moment.

Of course it all made perfect sense now to Holly. The invitation to visit, the insistence that it was this morning, Nipper the control freak playing both ends off against the middle. He didn't care for women like Trixie Fowler. In all the years they'd known her he'd viewed her as a shallow soulless creature who'd lacked the courage to keep Pete Philips' drug habit in check. How different might things have been if her brother had been loved by a strong woman.

'Yeah he's blinding all right,' sneered Holly sarcastically, opening her bag again and rummaging around for her cigarettes. 'He's blindingly obvious.'

Trixie ran her hands through her hair and shook her head. 'Maybe,' she said nonchalantly. 'D'ya think he thought he'd be able to make you jealous if you came over and found me here?'

'Let's ask him then,' replied Holly, tossing her bag onto the sofa and lighting a Marlboro. 'Oi Nipper, get your hairy arse downstairs now,' she said, raising her voice sufficiently for it to be heard in every part of the house.

Nipper gripped Trixie's waist as he entered the room, causing her to emit a girly squeak that only served to fan the flames of rage that had just been ignited and were beginning to burn brightly in the depths of Holly's soul.

'Hello girls,' he said calculatingly, wondering just how far he had pushed his boat out.

'Wanker!' shouted Holly, casting her eye over Nipper's apparel. That pale blue Katharine Hamnett padrino shirt he was wearing, the one she'd bought him for his Birthday, what a stitch up. 'You evil conniving bastard!' she yelled, pacing in measured steps across the room, drawing deep on her Marlboro one last time before dropping it on the floor and stubbing it out with an exaggerated twisting motion of her right foot. The pointed tips of her brand new Christian Louboutin shoes were made for such drama, fuck the Swedish hardwood floor.

'Behave Holly,' said Nipper calmly. 'It's not fair on Trixie, she aint done nothing to deserve this.'

'Oh yeah,' replied Holly, squaring up to Trixie and Nipper, eyes widening, pupils dilating as she readied herself for a fight. 'So what's she doing here then?'

'Fucking hell Nipper, I'm outta here,' said Trixie, her pseudo mid Atlantic drawl antagonising Holly still further. 'You've set this up you cock,' she added, clapping her hands as she edged herself backwards out of the room.

'You've got it all wrong hon,' interjected Nipper, trying to placate Holly as he began to realise that the script for the show was being rewritten.

'Why? ... Why?' she screamed , her black eyes burning like coals, the volcanic rage smouldering inside her ready to erupt. 'Bastard!' she yelled, her right hand forming itself into a tight fist which she threw forcibly in the direction of Nipper's face.

'For fuck's sake calm down doll face ,' said Nipper, raising his right arm to deflect the blow and pushing her away.

'Don't call me doll face you bastard,' growled Holly gutturally, her face contorted with rage. 'I know what you're up to you fucker, and it aint gonna work.'

'Whatever,' replied Nipper, folding his arms and standing in front of a bemused looking Trixie Fowler. 'What are you gonna do about it now?'

'What am I gonna do?

'Yeah, what are you gonna do? Hysteria's finished. The Barlow's are finished, Steve Bruno is finished, we're finished, you saw to that. It's over doll face, believe me.'

The callousness of Nipper's words cut through Holly like a craftsman's knife through a humble piece of balsa wood crumpling her spirit and crushing her heart. But she'd half expected it, the events of the past 24 hours had confirmed to her that she'd been right all along.

'You're just a lowlife, scumbag drug dealer,' she hissed, walking back over to the coffee table and picking up her half drunk cup of tea. 'Geezer Goodwin aint no mug, he'll wise up. You think I'm finished? Ha! You bastard, think again.'

'Right,' said Trixie pushing Nipper away from her. 'I've seen enough.'

'No you aint you silly bitch,' said Holly, drawing her arm back and launching the cup at the TV. 'You aint seen nothing yet.'

The front door slammed shut, with Trixie on the outside, at the very moment the cup smashed into the plasma screen. The impact shattered the glass showering the floor with a zillion shards which refracted the light like a meteor shower as they cascaded across the floor.

'Mental bitch!' exclaimed Nipper, resisting the overwhelming urge to knock Holly spark out. 'You're gonna fuckin' pay for that now,' he continued, grappling with her flailing arms, trying to protect himself from her razor sharp nails as she fought like a cornered rat, spitting, biting and gouging, losing the plot completely.

'Get off me!' she shrieked, scrabbling over the slithers of glass, her mind now focused on exiting the scene.

Nipper bundled Holly through the living room door wrestling her along the hallway. 'Get the fuck out of my house you maniac!' he yelled, propelling her towards the solid oak front door like a rugby player in a ruck and maul. 'You'll be sorry for this,' he added, slapping her across her tear streaked face repeatedly until she collapsed exhausted on the floor.

Summoning her last reserves of strength, Holly got to her feet. The temptation to find a way to maim and kill subsided as she suddenly remembered the crystal meth. 'You win you fucking bastard, again you win,' she mewled convincingly, struggling to regain a modicum of composure. 'Just gimme my handbag, and I'm out of your life forever,' she cried melodramatically, her mascara streaked face resembling her to some freakish bastard offspring of an unholy union between '70s rock icon Alice Cooper and '90s Birds of a Feather harridan Dorien Green.

★ ★ ★ ★ ★

'Tiago oh oh oh oh … Tiago oh oh oh oh … He comes from Portugal, he hates the Arsenal.'

'They've closed our midfield right down, aint they,' observed Fatboy Green, licking the mustard residue of the hotdog he'd just consumed from his fingers. 'Come on Chelsea! You can do it in Europe, now lets do the Scousers.'

'Oh here he is, the international fun city playboy,' said Eggy, standing up to applaud the arrival of Nipper. 'That Trixie Fowler, keeping you busy was she?'

'Don't mate,' replied Nipper, shaking hands with Eggy and Fatboy as he took his seat. 'I've had a stinker.'

'She aint that bad,' said Fatboy, laughing at his own joke and failing to see why Nipper didn't find it funny.

'Leave it out Fatty,' replied Nipper scowling. 'Fucking women, I've had enough of em for one day.'

'Oooh hark at him!' continued Fatboy camply.

Just as Nipper was about to lose his temper, Arjen Robben flummoxed Everton defender Weir and volleyed the ball from the edge of the penalty area. Everyone got to their feet, gasping and cursing in amazement as goalie Nigel Martyn acrobatically kept the ball out of the net.

'Unlucky son!' shouted Nipper, relaxing slightly. 'Sorry mate,' he said, turning to Fatboy and apologising. 'It's all come on top this morning. Holly turned up and was less impressed than I thought she would be about me and Trixie.'

'What did you expect?' asked Eggy, turning up the collar of his jacket. 'You must've known she'd get pissed off.'

'Yeah, but it was Trixie that got pissed off and fucked off out of it.'

'What about Holly?'

'She smashed my fucking plasma TV.'

'Do what?'

'I'm telling you. She threw a fucking mug of rosy at it.'

'What did you do?'

'Threw her out into the street.'

'Nice,' said Fatboy, who'd reserved comment on the situation until now. 'Still it could've been worse mate,' he added, a jocular look of mischief forming on his pudding shaped face.

'How?' enquired Nipper and Eggy simultaneously.

'It could've been me,' said Fatboy, his face reddening with mirth as he burst out laughing.

Nipper chuckled, he had to because it was funny. 'Very good,' he said, getting to his feet again as the referee blew for half-time. 'You coming down Mr Terry's later then? I might need you to pull me a new bird.'

'You wont need him mate,' said Eggy, wiggling the middle two fingers of his right hand. 'That place is crawling with crumpet, I kept having to remind myself last night when you was talking to Geezer. All them girls who were in the VIP area will be in tonight, we can have a proper bubble.'

'Better make sure you don't go ugly early then,' said Fatboy, lighting up a cigarette.

'They don't let ugly birds in mate,' replied Eggy.

'Or fat blokes,' added Nipper, checking his phone for missed calls and text messages of which there were neither.

★ ★ ★ ★ ★

'I've come to apologise,' said Holly sympathetically, putting her arm around Kenny's shoulder as she sat next to him on the tired looking old sofa in his mums living room. 'I was a bit harsh when I came to see you at Claire's just after this happened,' she added, pointing at the dressing on his face.

Kenny nodded, picked up the pad of paper that was lying on the coffee table and placed it on his lap. He loved Holly, in his eyes she could do no wrong. If she wanted to talk, then he was a willing listener.

'You might've heard a few stories going around about me finishing with Hysteria,' she said calmly, her natural composure reinstated after the drama of the morning. 'In all fairness, there was some truth in it. But a few things have changed, Nipper for a start.' Holly paused momentarily, lighting a Marlboro, waiting to see if her mentioning Nipper would provoke a reaction, but it didn't. 'Last night he sold Sniffler some of this gear which Riddler reckons is part crystal meth.

Holly opened her satchel and took out the plastic bag containing the suspect drug. 'Here check it out for yourself,' she said, handing the bag to Kenny. 'I've had a toot myself, it's too hardcore.'

Kenny opened the bag carefully and scooped out a small amount of the powder with the elongated nail of his little finger. He looked at it for a moment before holding his nail up to his right nostril and snorting the powder. After sniffing several times he shook his head and picked up the notepad and the pen that Holly had handed him and began to write.

METH DEFINITELY PLUS SOMETHING ELSE. TOO MUCH OF THIS STUFF COULD MAKE YOU ILL

'That's what I thought,' said Holly, sitting back in the sofa and relaxing. 'So Nipper sells Sniffler this gear in the knowledge that it will probably be pushed to my punters. One or two of 'em have a funny turn, and before I know it I'm in trouble. Just the sort of publicity I need what with the big 10th birthday bash next weekend.'

I CAN SEE WHY YOU MIGHT BE THINKING THAT. WHAT DID SNIFFLER SAY ABOUT IT?

'Dunno,' replied Holly, sitting up again, and stubbing out her cigarette. 'He's vanished into the ether, and so's his old man for that matter.'

ODD THAT. YOU KNOW NIPPER HAS OFFERED ME A JOB AT MR TERRY'S?

'He's offered everyone a job at Mr Terry's,' sneered Holly, her vexed mood returning as she remembered Trixie Fowler telling her how she too was part of Geezer Goodwin's burgeoning business empire. 'Let me tell you what he stage managed this morning sweetness, and then you tell me if you wanna work for him, or you wanna stay with me.'

Even if he'd been able to speak, Camp Kenny would have been rendered speechless by Holly's bitter tale of woe. She knew she'd be the talk of the town just as soon as the bandages came off, but also that the positive publicity would be overwhelming.

THAT IS SO SAD. WHAT A BASTARD. I'M SO SORRY

'Don't be,' said Holly, pointing at the crystal meth. 'Do you wanna help me out of this situation darling?'

COURSE I WILL

'Just imagine if this stuff turned up at Mr Terry's tonight.'
FANCY THAT
'Can you organise it?'
CAN I HAVE MY OLD JOB BACK?
'Yes of course you can.'
I'LL GET ONTO IT RIGHT AWAY

★ ★ ★ ★ ★

'Baba one, baba two, baba three, Babayaro … Baba four, baba five, baba six, Babayaro. Baba seven, baba eight, baba nine Babayaro … ohhhh Babayaro.'

'I still like singing that song,' said Fatboy Green, remaining standing as everyone else around him sat down.

'Sidarrrrn Fatboy,' brayed the crowd, applauding as he obliged.

'If we win this we go top,' said Eggy, stamping his Timberland clad feet on the concrete floor in a bid to reinvigorate his circulation.

'That's a big if,' replied Nipper, his mind back on the game. 'Looks like this is heading for a draw. Anyway the Arse are bound to do Palace later so they'll go back on top.'

Nipper was glad he'd made it to the match. He'd thought about blanking it, but fuck it why? Over a couple of moody birds? Nah. Eggy was right, they'd have the pick of the bunch tonight, a nice bit of fresh, a tasty young bird, not an old dog with a bite as bad as its bark. And while he was enjoying himself, Hysteria would be flushing itself down the toilet along with that mad bitch Holly. 'It's me or Chelsea'. Yeah right, fuck off.

'Go on Eidur … go on son,' said Fatboy, reaching across and grabbing the sleeve of Nipper's jacket as Eidur Gudjohnsen turned brilliantly and floated an inch perfect pass to Robben.

'We're on here!' shouted Eggy expectantly, as the Dutchman advanced on the Everton goal.

'Yes!'

Robben broke free from the shirt-pulling Weir and lobbed the keeper. It was a another sublime goal from a player whose form in Moscow earlier in the week had convinced supporters that he might be the final piece in Abramovich's expensive jigsaw puzzle.

'Top of the league, we're havin a laugh. Top of the league, we're havin a laugh.'

19

There were a lot of glitter skinned, enthusiastically drunk disco dollies loitering by the entrance to the VIP area by the time Nipper arrived. He'd driven past Hysteria a couple of times in the last hour or so to try and gauge what was going on, but it looked like business as usual.

The thought had crossed his mind that Riddler Rowan might have sussed the gear he'd sold to Sniffler. If he had, Nipper reasoned that he'd probably look to corner a piece of the work himself and step on it a little. Riddler was always bang on the money when it came to drugs, but Geezer Goodwin knew his form and that had precluded him from becoming a part of the new enterprise.

'Hello mate. All right?' said Davy Truelove, tapping Nipper on the shoulder. 'Shaping up to be a good night again. All the usual suspects are in, plus a few more.'

'Yeah not bad son.'

'Good result tonight for you lot.'

'You what?'

'Arsenal … they only drew at Palace. You're top of the league good and proper my son.'

Nipper grinned and gave Davy the thumbs up. 'Which other suspects are here besides the usual ones?' he asked, intrigued by what he'd just been told.

'Camp Kenny, he was here,' replied Davy, clicking his fingers as he tried to attract the attention of a passing waitress. 'Trixie Fowler, she's here, fawning all over Geezer like a Hollywood wannabe on a directors casting couch.'

'Camp Kenny?'

'Yeah,' said Davy, pointing at the VIP room. 'He was with your mate Fatboy in there for a while. Dunno what they were up to but there was a lot of sign language going on.'

'Where is he now?'

'Dunno mate, who am I his keeper?'

Nipper screwed up his face as he lit the cigarette Davy Truelove had just offered him. Probably nothing, he thought to himself, checking his mobile for messages again. 'Just wondered that's all,' he said, mentally undressing the silicone enhanced waitress now stood in front of them.

'She'd get it,' said Davy, as the girl took their drinks order and left.

'Definitely,' agreed Nipper, catching sight of Trixie Fowler out of the corner of his eye. 'So Trixie and Geezer mate. What's the story there?'

'Geezer fancies her like mad,' replied Davy, surprised by Nipper's inquisitiveness. 'That's why he's bankrolling her. She's never shown any interest in him before tonight. It's amazing.'

'Fucking slag!'

'You what?'

'Nah ... nothing mate.'

Never one for a conspiracy theory, Nipper was starting to feel a little paranoid as he adjourned the discussion and made his way into the toilet. A little live'ner was required, that would calm the nerves, he wasn't used to these feelings that were starting to knot in his stomach.

* * * * *

'Hello Davy, Nipper,' said Geezer Goodwin, patting Davy Truelove on his face and winking at him. 'Sorry to interrupt, but I need to have a little chat with young Johnny here,' he continued, his patronising demeanour agitating Nipper slightly. 'Come on, its too noisy out here. Follow me.'

'Is there a problem Geezer?' asked Nipper several minutes later, as he stood like an errant schoolboy in the corner of Geezer Goodwin's office frowning and trying to suppress the cocaine high that was encouraging him to blurt out his words rather than speak normally.

'There will be if that fat clown friend of yours Danny Green doesn't calm down,' replied Geezer, raising his eyebrows disdainfully. 'He's taking liberties in the VIP room. Off his tits on nose I've no doubt. Have a word can you.'

Fucking prick, thought Nipper, shaking his head. 'Yeah, I'll have a word.'

'Oh and another thing,' said Geezer, pulling Nipper in close so he could whisper in his ear despite the fact that their was nobody else in the office. 'Can you get me a couple of viagra?'

'What now?'

'Yes mate now,' confirmed Geezer Goodwin, puffing his chest out proudly. 'I reckon I'm on a promise tonight.'

'No problem,' replied Nipper, steadying himself as he came to terms with not one, but two situations that were all of his own doing. Fatboy Green, was Fatboy Green, he'd have a word with the lairy sod. Eggy had probably let him loose on the Percy too early. Trixie Fowler? Yeah well, he'd just have to put that one down to experience. She'd mentioned that Geezer had chatted her up on several occasions, but she'd said she'd always dismissed him as moneybags chancer who wasn't her type.

Nipper wracked his brain trying to think of any information he might have unwittingly imparted to Trixie during the course of their liaisons. Just what I need, he thought to himself, another mad bird on my case.

'What the fuck is that?' said Geezer, startled by the sudden high pitched shrill of the clubs intruder alarm which had been triggered just as they were about to leave his office.

Geezer picked up the office phone. ' What's happening? … Where? … Right shut it down. Keep 'em there and get the paramedics. Oh and switch this fucking alarm off its worse than the fucking music, and that's bad enough.'

Nipper couldn't stop himself grinning at Geezer's parting shot at the clubs head of security, but the way he slammed the phone back into its cradle, and the look of intent on his face as he turned to confront him wiped the smirk off his face immediately.

'Right, you with me … the VIP area now,' he growled, bristling with rage as he bowled out of the office and began jogging along the crowded corridor.

As Nipper followed, he noticed there was a serious commotion going on at the entrance to the ladies toilets. An aerated Duncan Disorderly and two of his security colleagues were trying to placate three distressed girls who were shouting and screaming at them.

'What the fuck's going on?' he asked, finally catching up with Geezer at the entrance to the VIP room.

Geezer had spotted Davy Truelove and Trixie Fowler amongst a large group of people who were gathered by the bar. 'I don't fucking know,' he replied tersely. 'But I think we're about to find out.'

'Oh no fuck it,' cursed Nipper, as he saw the familiar figure of Fatboy Green lying prone on the floor. Eggy Barnes was knelt beside him mopping his brow with a napkin, a look of despair on his face.

'Right everybody out of here now please,' shouted Geezer, his rasping voice clearly audible above the music.

'You heard the man,' shouted Nipper, barging his way through the crowd of onlookers. 'Please leave now.'

'He's fucking dead mate,' sobbed Eggy, as Nipper bent over him.

'He cant be.'

'He fucking is. Look at him.'

Fatboy Green lay perfectly still. His face was a blotchy yellow colour, his lips blue and his open eyes were gazing vacantly at the ceiling. A milky white fluid flecked with blood oozed from his nostrils and vomit was dripping from the corner of his mouth.

'The paramedics will be here in a minute,' said Nipper, looking back across the room at Geezer Goodwin who was talking to Davy Truelove. 'He'll be all right.'

'He's dead,' repeated Eggy sombrely, stifling his tears as he got to his feet. 'He had a fucking massive heart attack right in front of me. He's dead all right.'

'What the fuck's been going on mate?' asked Nipper, disregarding what his friend had just said and craving a cigarette as he tried to remain calm. 'Geezer had just pulled me to one side not five minutes ago and told me to come up here and speak to Fatboy because he was upsetting a few people.'

'Listen mate,' whispered Eggy, wiping his eyes and hushing his voice as the paramedics arrived. 'It's the gear innit. Camp Kenny was here earlier, he served up a few tickets and then left. I've had a dabble myself, it's that fucking moody stuff that Mordi cooked up which you sold to Sniffler last night, I'm sure of it.'

'That aint possible,' replied Nipper, shrugging his shoulders as he watched the medical team vainly attempt to revive Fatboy. 'The only way that could happen ...'

Both men were distracted by the arrival of a further paramedic team carrying a stretcher and two police officers. Mentally, Nipper was rapidly working his way through all the permutations. If it was the gear that had been meant for Hysteria, then how had Camp Kenny got hold of it? Holly? Oh fuck it.

'What drugs had your friend been taking?' asked one of the policemen, shaking his head at his colleague who was talking to Geezer Goodwin.

'Er dunno,' replied Eggy nervously. 'Maybe a little coke.'

'Was he a regular user?'

'Dunno.'

'Look mate, your friend is dead,' said the policeman in a monotone voice that finally registered the dreaded truth. 'The post mortem will tell us everything we need to know, so it's up to you what you tell me. It aint gonna bring him back.'

'What do you want him to say?' asked Nipper flippantly, immediately regretting his decision to speak.

The policeman stood upright and removed his hat. The officious 'now listen here sonny' arrogance that Nipper had so despised and riled against as a young man was writ large across his bearded pock marked face. Fucking Old Bill, he thought, realising that politeness would be a wise alternative to the surly attitude he was currently displaying.

'Okay, can we start with your friends name please,' said the policeman lackadaisically, his laissez faire manner startling Nipper who was expecting a tirade of text book nonsense.

The policeman took notes and his colleague spoke into his two-way radio as Nipper and Eggy confirmed Fatboy's, name, address and age. They were both surprised by how little else they actually knew about their friend. Family, relatives, next of kin, call them what you will, they just didn't have a clue. Fatboy Green had always kept his life private, even when they'd been at school together. Suddenly it dawned on Nipper that in 30 odd years he'd never once been to his house. Wife? Girlfriend? Place of work? Shit, they didn't even know what he did for a living these days.

Creeping paranoia filled Nipper with fear as he tried unsuccessfully to catch Geezer Goodwin's eye. Too many people were in the know. Trixie, Holly, Riddler Rowan, Mordi, Camp Kenny, Eggy Barnes, they all knew enough between them to piece together the whole story from start to finish. He'd be all right though. Surely no one would say anything. Everybody had been wading knee deep through shit for years, he was just being stupid.

Fatboy Green had just been unlucky. 'A heart attack waiting to happen', that would be the coroners verdict. The post mortem would show that his artery's were clogged with the fat of all that greasy over-fried food he used to hurl down his neck. The cocaine? Purely recreational, they'd all warned him about the risks, about his high blood pressure, but Danny never listened, never had, and sadly never would.

As additional police arrived, people began leaving the club, among them was Davy Truelove. He'd already promised Geezer Goodwin that he'd find out more about what had happened and the background to it, even if that meant compromising old friendships. Geezer wanted answers, and he wanted them quickly.

★ ★ ★ ★ ★

Nipper hadn't slept properly since the weekend. At face value it didn't look like he had too much to worry about. The police were currently treating Fatboy's death as misadventure. Drugs had been a mitigating factor, but since several other kids had wound up in hospital with hypertension and breathing difficulties as a result of snorting moody gear at Mr Terry's that night, the whole episode was being written off as an unfortunate case of clubber's folly.

Deep down, he knew that Mordi had fucked up again, just like he had done all those years ago with the Red Playboy pills. Maybe it was a good job he was retiring, otherwise someone might retire him. Crystal meth had been a bad proposition, crystal meth mixed with Atropine was just asking for trouble if the mix wasn't right. Over do it, and the initial exciting effect of the drug could rapidly lead to hallucinations and delirium. If your central nervous system or heart wasn't up to the job, coma and death could result.

Geezer Goodwin was keeping his own counsel. He knew that Nipper was flying to Thailand today and that he'd planned to be away until just after Christmas. It was a trip that had been in the diary for a couple of months. Why then did he refuse to return any of his calls? Trepidation and mistrust stalked Nipper, he just couldn't get the thought out of his mind that someone might talk. Information would be passed on that would result in Geezer placing a call to Del Goss. It wouldn't matter where he was then, Deadly Del would find him.

It was for this reason that first thing on Monday morning Nipper had made his way over to the Indian High Commission and purchased a six month visa that would permit him to travel to Goa. It was a simple plan that he'd kept to himself which hadn't been difficult because even his best friend Eggy was now avoiding him. Fuck em all, he thought, rubbing his eyes and switching on the portable TV on his bedside table.

'Good morning, I'm Chris Bottrell. It's 7am on Friday the 12th of November 2004 and here is the news in London today. Police last night confirmed that a rogue batch of contaminated cocaine, sold in a top London nightclub last weekend, was responsible for the death of one man and the hospitalisation of at least fourteen other people.

Danny Green, 44, from Stoneleigh, Surrey, had been with a group of friends at Mr Terry's, a Battersea nightclub owned by London based businessman Geezer Goodwin, when he'd complained of feeling unwell and suffered a fatal heart attack.

Reporting restrictions have now been lifted on the case and a police spokesman has confirmed that analysis of cocaine found on the deceased's person showed that it had been cut with crystal methamphetamine and Atropine, which in its natural form is better known as Belladonna or Deadly Nightshade. A large quantity of the drug is also believed to have been subsequently found on the club premises.

Police are now treating Mr Green's death as murder and are keen to speak to anyone who was at the club on Saturday night and may have seen anything suspicious. The number to call if you have any information is displayed on your TV screen now and will be repeated at the end of this bulletin. All calls will be treated in the strictest confidence. In the meantime the club has had its license suspended until further notice. Other news now and ...'

Dazed by what he had just heard, Nipper switched off the TV and looked at his watch. His flight wasn't for ten hours yet, Gatwick now rather than Heathrow. The sooner he left town the better he thought, picking up his passport and travel documents and putting them in his jacket pocket.

He'd walk down to the railway station at Clapham Junction and board the Gatwick Express, the anonymity of public transport would be his safe-guard. With his money readily accessible via several internet based bank accounts Nipper ascertained that he didn't really have anything to worry about. Boredom? Forget it. Who in their right mind would miss anything about freezing cold England eh?

★ ★ ★ ★ ★

'Any news?' asked Eggy Barnes, shaking hands with Max Chilman and Riddler Rowan as he finally found them in the upstairs bar at Hysteria.

'Fuck all mate,' replied Max, ordering three bottles of Peroni. 'Old Bill interviewed me about Sniffler, it seems that Holly was the last person to see him. Beery has also disappeared, as has Steve Bruno.'

'Did they ask you anything about Fatboy?'

'Nothing. Nothing at all.'

'Same here,' said Riddler Rowan, shuffling his feet and swigging his beer.

Eggy Barnes stubbed out the cigarette he'd been smoking and shook his head. 'Old Bill haven't released his body yet,' he said, pausing as he looked over the balcony and spotted Holly walking towards the DJ booth. 'We can't even plan his funeral.'

'I'm gutted about Fatboy,' replied Riddler frowning. 'I feel somehow responsible.'

Eggy knew Riddler was being sincere, it was the first time he'd heard him string a few sentences together without resorting to rhyming slang. 'It aint your fault mate, it would have happened sooner or later anyway, we all know that.'

'Kenny's in pieces about it,' added Max, waving at his brother who had just entered the club and was being mobbed by the crowd as he made his way across the dancefloor. 'Right, I'm gonna have to get to work lads,' he continued, finishing his beer and chinking his bottle against Eggy's and Riddler's. 'Later yeah.'

'Did you hear from Nipper before he left?' asked Riddler, leaning on the balcony they had just walked across to, his eyes scanning the club to see what his boys were up to.

'Sort of,' replied Eggy, tapping his feet against the balustrade in time with the music. 'He said Old Bill had quizzed him about Fatboy, but they'd been more interested about his involvement with Geezer Goodwin.'

'How much does he know?'

'Dunno mate, he's played his cards pretty close to his chest these last few months.'

'How long d'ya reckon he'll stay in Thailand for?

'Dunno that either.'

'He'll be gutted about missing out on watching the Blues.'

'Not half, we were fucking awesome against Fulham today.'

'Nice touch bringing Holly to the game.'

'Yeah, well you know. I've been a shoulder to cry on for her over Fatboy. They went back years.'

'A shoulder eh,' laughed Riddler, as Chiller faded the music and they watched Holly climb on stage to the sound of rapturous applause. 'You aint lost the magic son.'

'Ten years at the top … ten years of Hysteria,' announced Chiller over the clubs public address system. 'Ladies and gentlemen show your appreciation for the Queen of Clubs … Miss Holly Philips.'

'In every nightclub across the nation. She's the life of the party, she's a real sensation. She's got style, y'all she's got class, she can groove it slow or move it fast …'

'That's right mate,' replied Eggy, hands above his head.

'In the early evenin' through the midnight hour, she keeps swingin', she's got super power …'

'Nice one!' exclaimed Riddler, punching the air as Chiller pumped up the volume and rocked the house.

'She's the queen of clubs. She's the queen of clubs.'

April 30th 2005

HAVE YOU EVER SEEN CHELSEA WIN THE LEAGUE?

'You are my Chelsea, my only Chelsea. You make me happy when skies are grey ...'

This is it, thought Nipper, cradling his motorcycle helmet in his left arm as he scrutinised the ticket he was just about to pay £300 for.

'It's kosher mate,' said the tout, whisking the ticket out of Nipper's right hand and stepping back onto the pavement.

'It better had be for a fucking carpet,' replied Nipper, handing the tout his helmet and reaching into the back pocket of his jeans. 'I've travelled a long way to see this match.'

The tout rocked back and forth on his heels impatiently as Nipper counted out fifteen dog eared £20 notes. 'Come on mate,' he said impatiently, 'I haven't got all day.'

Six months ago, Nipper would have whacked the tout for speaking to him like that. But that was six months ago. Then he'd looked like a man in his prime. Razor haired, sharp dressed, clean shaven, lean and mean; respect had been easy to come by. The scumbag wouldn't have contemplated addressing him like that back then.

Respect. What's that? he thought, saying nothing as he handed the tout the money and pocketed the ticket. Admiration, high opinion, deference, reverence, esteem? Bollocks, it was all about pride.

'Travelled far then?' asked the tout, handing Nipper back his helmet and looking at the brand new Yamaha Fazer motorbike he was sat astride.

'About 4,800 miles,' snapped Nipper mordantly, donning the helmet and revving the bikes 600cc engine aggressively.

'Hope its worth it mate,' replied the puzzled looking tout, as Nipper engaged first gear, relaxed his grip on the clutch and opened up the throttle.

'It will be!' shouted Nipper, smoking the Yamaha's back tyre as he screeched away from the kerb.

'Flash Cockney wanker!' bellowed the tout, waving his hand in front of his face as the acrid smell of burning rubber filled his nostrils.

The bike, which belonged to an airline steward friend of Chopper Lewis', was far more powerful and agile than the antiquated Enfield that Nipper was used to riding around Goa's dusty tracks on and the short, mainly motorway journey that he'd embarked on an hour or so previously from Manchester airport had given him insufficient time to master its nuances.

The temptation to return 'home' to watch the Blues win the title had proved too much for Nipper who'd grown tired of watching 'live' feeds of their games at the Cave. The more he'd thought about it, the more he'd realised that if he was to live out his life as a paranoid exile in Goa he'd need one last Chelsea fix, and what better shot in the arm could there be than watching them win the title at Bolton?

Too much time in the company of Chopper Lewis had darkened Nipper's obsession about the consequences of his actions. Drink and drugs had dulled his senses when he'd needed them to, but the nagging doubt was always there at the back of his mind. What if? What if? What if? It was the not knowing that was torturing his soul.

With the help of the internet, he'd ascertained that Hysteria was still thriving, Mr Terry's also. Geezer Goodwin had announced himself as a major patron of a new charity that had been set up to tackle inner city deprivation, and Riddler Rowan had been the subject of a three part BBC documentary chronicling the life of a 'reformed' drug dealer. 'Reformed!' What the fuck was going on?

As he swooped down the hill and Bolton's futuristic new Reebok Stadium loomed into view, Nipper's thoughts reverted back to football. Chelsea vs Bolton, Bolton vs Chelsea. There'd always been something in that fixture. The game at the Bridge almost 30 years ago when he'd stood on the Shed terrace, a carefree young punk with a safety pin attitude to match. The crucial victory at Bolton's dilapidated old Burnden Park ground back in 1983 when relegation to the old Third Division had been staved off by a whisker, and the away defeat back in '96 when Matthew Harding had been killed returning home from the game.

'... *you'll never know dear, how much I love you, so please don't take my Chelsea away la la la la la uhh!*'

* * * * *

'Nice ground innit,' said Holly, standing on her seat and shading her eyes as the late afternoon sun beamed through the clouds breaking above the far end of the stadium. 'Are you lot gonna sing that song that Fatboy Green invented again, the one that goes along with the 'Only Fools and Horses' tune?'

'Maybe,' replied Eggy, patting Holly's backside and winking at Chiller who was mouthing 'I getcha' at him. 'Come on the Chels, let's 'av it!'

The 5.15pm start had been late enough to ensure that all of Chelsea's vociferous travelling support fortunate enough to have tickets for the match were ensconced in the Reebok's South stand. As referee Steve Dunn blew his whistle to initiate proceedings and Bolton kicked off, Eggy Barnes looked around him.

Everyone was here, Chiller, Riddler, Jamie and Leighton Black, Duncan Disorderly, Fuck Off Colin, Belfast Billy, Ronny Cutlass, even Topper Townsend who'd apparently chartered a private jet to fly up for the game.

All the faces, young and old. The only absentees were Chopper Lewis, Fatboy Green and Johnny Nipper. Chopper would probably be watching the match in some ramshackle bar in Goa, whilst Fatboy and Nipper, the poor fuckers, would be hoping that God had paid his Sky subscription this month.

Within the scene no one had been blamed for Fatboy's death. That could have come at any time, anyone of them could have given him the line that arrested his heart. The police had scaled down their investigation within a matter of weeks, and Fatboy Green was now just another Home Office statistic whose loss had been sadly mourned by his friends and the Chelsea faithful.

Nipper? Now there was a cautionary tale. Eggy knew more than most, but hadn't breathed a word to anyone, not even Holly Philips. The rumour, propagated by Davy Truelove, had whipped around London like an empty crisp packet in a gale. The Barlow's, Steve Bruno and Johnny Nipper had been working together over a period of time, their objective being to rinse money out of Geezer Goodwin's assets.

Beery Barlow had apparently mortgaged his gambling debts and used the credit to fund the purchase of a huge quantity of high grade cocaine. The cocaine had been stepped on several times thereby increasing its value six-fold. A small batch of the consignment had been purposefully contaminated, the intention had been to create mayhem at Mr Terry's and a select number of other establishments, bizarrely including Hysteria, in which Geezer Goodwin had a vested interest.

Local authority's and the police would have revoked licenses, and the

resale value of the leases on the properties affected would have been deci-
mated. In due course Steve Bruno would have then bought up the leases
for a nominal amount and returned them back to operating status, where-
upon they would have been sold at a vast profit. Geezer Goodwin's good
name in the City would have been indelibly tarnished paving the way for
Beery Barlow to ease himself back into the Square Mile.

When the roof fell in on the plan, the unscrupulous team had no choice
but to leave the country. Thailand was the chosen destination. This had
been corroborated by the discovery that Nipper had rented a villa in the
coastal resort of Phuket. He'd also booked a flight from Heathrow to
Bangkok, although the ticket had never been used.

Whilst this seemed strange, the assumption made was that the four men
had travelled by rail and boat in order to keep a low profile. The Boxing
Day tsunami that ravaged Phuket obliterated the villa, its deadly waves
swept it away leaving just the foundations to mark the spot where it had
originally stood. With the local death toll in the thousands, many bodies,
including those of the Barlow gang, had never been recovered.

The story was preposterously plausible. Even Eggy had to admit that
he'd sometimes wondered about the dark cloak of secrecy that Nipper had
wrapped around himself up in during the last couple of years. What the
fuck had he really been up to?

'Go on Eggy, start the song,' said Holly, distracting him as she became
frustrated with Chelsea's inability to break down a resolute Bolton side,
spurred on by the majority of a near 28,000 crowd who were determined
to spoil the party.

'Okay, Okay,' he replied, waiting patiently for a break in play to lull the
crowd and dampen the electric atmosphere. He needed those in the know
around him to participate if Fatboy's chant was to be given a proper
airing.

With a only a couple of minutes of the first half remaining, Bolton striker
Kevin Davies appeared to elbow John Terry in the face. The Chelsea
captain went down like a sack of potatoes and the referee halted play to
allow physio Mike Banks onto the pitch to administer the magic sponge.

'Ready lads?' shouted Eggy, clenching his fist as Chiller started tra la la-
ing out the opening bars of the much loved sitcoms theme tune.

*He stuck a Veron in his pocket, he nicked Glen Johnson from West Ham.
'Cos if you want the best ones , and you don't ask questions, then Roman he's
your man. 'Cos where the money comes from is a mystery, is it from the drugs or
the oil industry? So come on Chelsea chuck your celery 'cos we are the famous
CFC ... la la la la la, la la la la la.*

★ ★ ★ ★ ★

Sitting on his hands in amongst the Bolton fans congregated in the adjacent stand, Nipper had picked up on the chant immediately. He was close enough to the Chelsea supporters to be able to pick out many familiar faces including those of Eggy Barnes and Holly Philips.

Holly Philips! What was she doing here? he asked himself, biting the knuckle of his right index finger in angst, and what was she doing with Eggy Barnes?

Half-time came and went, but Nipper's mind wasn't on the game. Intense turbulent thoughts were spinning around his head like clothes in a washing machine, their meanings fuzzy like the vestments colours, running into one another until everything appeared drab and grey.

He imagined himself walking down to the front of the stand and speaking to one of the stewards. 'Listen mate, I'm Chelsea, you couldn't let us in the section there with the rest of my mates?' Everyone would be shocked to see him, shocked but happy. The prodigal son returning home. Holly would burst into tears, proclaiming undying love as she flung her arms around him.

Alternatively he would wait until the end of the game and then walk into the Chelsea end. Punches and kicks would rain down on him as he was recognised. The spiteful coward who's actions resulted in the death of a friend, a man who'd crossed the line and betrayed the trust of those around him.

Maybe he should've stayed away altogether and remained in Goa. Chopper would be up at the Cave, sitting at his usual table nursing a cold Kingfisher and singing the new songs he'd taught him.

Maybe not.

'Go on Frankie, Go on my son!' he shouted, leaping to his feet and forgetting where he was as Drogba flicked the ball onto Lampard who shimmied his way into the Bolton box and rifled the ball into the net. 'Yes!'

Fortunately Nipper wasn't alone, around him others were also on their feet. Jumping and screaming, all of them watching as Lampard ran towards the Chelsea fans gathered behind the goal to celebrate.

'*Super, super Frank … super, super Frank. Super, super Frank … super Frankie Lampard.*'

★ ★ ★ ★ ★

'Fucking brilliant!' shouted Riddler Rowan, clapping his hands above his head and joining in the chant.

'*We are the famous, the famous Chelsea.*'

'How long's left?' asked Chiller, looking across at the small pocket of

Chelsea fans in the nearby Bolton section who were now surrounded by stewards.

'About a-quarter-of-an-hour,' replied Eggy, standing up as Lampard latched onto a Makalele pass in the centre circle and sprinted towards them.

Chiller could've sworn he'd recognised one of the Chelsea supporters in the next stand. He couldn't quite put his finger on it. The hair was too long and curly, the skin too dark and tanned, it couldn't be who he thought it was. Or could it?

'Go on Frankie!' urged the crowd, snapping Chiller's attention back to the game. 'Go on son!' he shouted, as Lampard dribbled the ball around Jaaskelainen in the Bolton goal and coolly slotted it into the net. 'GOAL!'

Have you ever seen Chelsea win the league? Yes we have. Have you ever seen Chelsea win the league? Have you ever seen Chelsea, ever seen Chelsea, ever seen Chelsea win the league? Yes we have!

The blue and white party had started. By the time the referee had blown the final whistle, the majority of the home supporters had drifted away, their ears ringing with chants in praise of the new champions.

'Thanks for this,' said Holly, embracing Eggy as they watched the Chelsea players form a line and run towards them, diving on the grass in a display of unbridled joy that matched the scenes of celebration when the team had won the FA Cup at Wembley back in '97. Who would've guessed that I'd end up here today watching Chelsea, squired by Eggy Barnes of all people? she thought as she applauded the players who were deservedly basking in the adulation afforded them by their devoted supporters.

'Fucking brilliant eh,' replied Eggy, punching the air as the words to another of Fatboy's terrace anthems formed in his mind.

Knees up mother Brown, knees up mother Brown. Under the table you must go eee aye eee aye eee aye oh. If I catch you bending, I'll saw your legs right off, knees up knees up, don't you get a breeze up, knees up mother Brown. Oh my what a rotten song, sing, what a rotten song, sing, what a rotten song. Oh my what a rotten song, and what a rotten singer too ooh ooh. Chelsea ... Chelsea ... Chelsea!

★ ★ ★ ★ ★

Nipper had seen enough. As he watched the jubilant scenes of triumph, an incandescent loneliness swathed his soul which made him shiver. He felt uncomfortable and unanchored. Goosebumps of uncertainty crept across his flesh as he rolled down the sleeves of his denim jacket and picked up his helmet. It was time to return home.

'Let's go fucking mental, lets go fucking mental … la la la la, la la la la!'

The chant reverberating around the stadium was clearly audible in the car park as Nipper walked over to his motorbike.

He didn't have to go mental, he already was. The thought made him smile as he gunned the engine and looked over his shoulder one last time. 'Have I ever seen Chelsea win the league? Yes I have,' he shouted, twisting the throttle and enjoying the surge of adrenalin as he accelerated away from the ground.

Nipper didn't see the blue BMW veer across the slip road as he braked on the approach to the Mansell Road roundabout. The car caught him broadside and sent him catapulting through the air like a rag doll, headfirst into the path of an oncoming bus.

In the blood dimmed blur of the next few seconds, his fractured memory tried to put a name to the face of the hit-and-run driver who'd smiled at him as he'd sped past. Del Goss? That man never missed a trick. But how could he have known?

One more question left unanswered. But what did it matter now? Because by the time his crumpled body had slumped to the tarmac, Johnny Nipper was dead.

ABOUT THE AUTHOR

On completing his education, London born Mark turned down the opportunity to train for the priesthood, opting instead to travel the world. On returning home he immersed himself in the burgeoning dance music scene and its pharmacological subculture, funding a hedonistic lifestyle with a variety of jobs, including, baker, DJ, seismologist, piano tuner, and most recently, mobile phone salesman. Mark Worrall is the author of the cult Chelsea terrace classic *Over Land and Sea* and writes a popular weekly column, *The View from Gate 17,* for the influential *cfc.net* website.

ALSO BY MARK WORRALL
OVER LAND AND SEA